"One cannot work in the modern healthcare space and not be confronted with ethical issues and situations, regardless of your clinical role. However, as the demands of modern healthcare have grown regarding patient access, clinician productivity, and the explosion of digital technology for both the acquisition and storage of clinical data, recognizing and addressing these ethical issues and situations is more challenging than ever before. And moreover, there is less available time, both real and perceived by clinicians, to really think through these scenarios – that will continue to confront them through their coming years of practice. This book helps to address and frame the major ethical dilemmas and situations that both individuals and healthcare organizations now face in the twenty-first century. The reader is guided through the major topics and subtopics of the most relevant ethical considerations with concrete and relatable examples. One cannot help but be impressed with the depth and breadth of the book as well as Lisa's ability to impart the information in ways I've not seen it presented before. This is a wonderful resource for clinicians of all specialties at any stage in their career – an enlightening read to be sure."

Brian M. Parker, M.D., *Chief Quality & Learning Officer, Allegheny Health Network, Pittsburgh, Pennsylvania*

"Traditional ethics discussions tend to be esoteric in nature. The reality for those of us who are responsible and accountable for organizations is that we understand that virtually all decisions lay in the gray. Very rarely do we find ourselves with the luxury of deciding between clear black and white options thus the importance of a reality based view on Organizational Ethics is critically important. The author's opening example of a primary care physician talking to her mother in context of what is important to her sets the stage for a well thought-out examination of how human or stakeholder decision making must be influenced by life. These are not trivial discussions in healthcare and they have only been amplified by the pandemic and the need for disparate stakeholders to come together in service of humanity."

David Holmberg *(President and CEO of Highmark Health, One of the Largest Integrated Healthcare Systems in the United States).*

"There has been a longstanding need for a new approach to organizational ethics in healthcare that goes beyond the typical focus on an institution's mission, vision, and values. This book provides such a pivotal evolution by explaining the ethical accountability of organizational leadership to stakeholder communities in healthcare. The extraordinarily insightful discussion of moral agency is based on decades of the author's experience in very large health corporations. The argument adopts in an imaginative manner the well-tested approach of stakeholder theory. And, highlighting the need for empathetic engagement, an ethics of care model perceptively emphasizes the interconnectedness and dignity of human relationships. Also, ethical considerations about confidentiality and privacy of stakeholder groups are incisive and astute, especially given the increasing impact of big data in healthcare. Furthermore, the illuminating analysis of distinct stakeholder communities shrewdly selects critically vulnerable populations: pediatrics, older adults, and persons with disabilities. The masterly account is intellectually refreshing and profoundly challenging."

Gerard Magill, *(Vernon F. Gallagher Chair & Professor at the Center for Global Health Ethics, Duquesne University)*

Stakeholders and Ethics in Healthcare

This ground-breaking book uses organizational ethics and stakeholder theory to explore the ethical accountability of leadership in healthcare organizations to their distinct vulnerable stakeholder communities.

The book begins with a discussion of the moral agency of healthcare organizations and introduces stakeholder theory. It then looks at key ethical challenges in relation to the confidentiality and privacy of healthcare data, before turning to child health and interventions around issues such as obesity, maltreatment, and parenting. The book ends by focusing on ethics of care in relation to older people and people with disabilities.

An insightful contribution to thinking about ethics for contemporary healthcare management and leadership, this interdisciplinary book is of interest to readers with a background in healthcare, business and management, law, bioethics, and theology.

Lisa A. Martinelli, PhD, JD, MA is a bioethicist, educator, and attorney. With more than two decades of experience as a healthcare executive, she is currently the president of Lead with Ethics, LLC focusing on organizational and clinical ethics, data ethics, and decision support. She is a vigorous advocate for persons with disabilities, particularly children with special needs, and dedicates much of her time to creating and advancing social programs to enhance the quality of their lives.

Routledge Studies in Health and Social Welfare

Stakeholders and Ethics in Healthcare

Ethical Accountability for Organizations

Lisa A. Martinelli

Routledge
Taylor & Francis Group

LONDON AND NEW YORK

First published 2022
by Routledge
4 Park Square, Milton Park, Abingdon, Oxon OX14 4RN

and by Routledge
605 Third Avenue, New York, NY 10158

Routledge is an imprint of the Taylor & Francis Group, an informa business

© 2022 Lisa A. Martinelli

British Library Cataloguing-in-Publication Data
A catalogue record for this book is available from the British Library

Library of Congress Cataloging-in-Publication Data
Names: Martinelli, Lisa A., author.
Title: Stakeholders and ethics in healthcare: ethical accountability for
organizations / Lisa A. Martinelli.
Description: Milton Park, Abingdon, Oxon; New York,
NY: Routledge, 2023. | Series: Routledge studies in health and social
welfare | Includes bibliographical references and index. |
Identifiers: LCCN 2021044875 (print) |
LCCN 2021044876 (ebook) | ISBN 9781032135823 (hardback) |
ISBN 9781032214498 (paperback) | ISBN 9781003229957 (ebook)
Subjects: LCSH: Medical care. | Medical ethics. | Leadership. |
Management. Classification: LCC RA427 .M297 2023 (print) |
LCC RA427 (ebook) | DDC 174.2--dc23/eng/20211116
LC record available at https://lccn.loc.gov/2021044875
LC ebook record available at https://lccn.loc.gov/2021044876

ISBN: 978-1-032-13582-3 (hbk)
ISBN: 978-1-032-21449-8 (pbk)
ISBN: 978-1-003-22995-7 (ebk)

DOI: 10.4324/9781003229957

Typeset in Goudy
by KnowledgeWorks Global Ltd.

I dedicate this book to my mother, Dolores.
She continues to inspire all that I do.

Contents

Acknowledgments

I am most grateful to my husband, David. Thank you for putting so very much of our life on hold, one chapter at a time. Thank you for tiptoeing through the house, explaining why invitations were declined, altered, or cancelled and for always supporting this book with patience and love.

1 Introduction

What Matters Most

I recall with high-definition clarity, the moment, 7 years ago, that forever changed my understanding of healthcare. After more than two decades working for and with esteemed healthcare systems, opining, designing, and implementing important strategies against complex roadmaps and regulatory compliance mandates, it took the simplest of realities to open my eyes to the true meaning of *care*. What happened in less than ten minutes redefined in perpetuity how I would approach my work, my community, and those who mean the most to me.

Seated on his stool, he scooted toward her using the heels of his shoes. And when he was positioned in front of her, with his back to my sister and me, my mother's primary care physician placed his hand on top of hers. He met her gaze with a twinkle, leaned in, and gently asked, "Mrs. Martinelli, when you think about your life and the things that you wish for, what do you think about? Is there something that you want, or something that worries you? What matters most to you, Mrs. Martinelli?"

While caring for my mother and watching her health decline over years, I grew accustomed to the watery stare she offered me when struggling to process information. She would search my face for clues to the answer, or the right word before offering a response. It's what I expected when I heard her doctor's line of questioning. But this time the expression she wore was different. Perhaps the fact that she harbored a not-so-secret crush on her physician played a role in her renewed attentiveness. Or perhaps it was because what mattered to my mother wasn't the same thing that mattered to me, and it was easy for her to process *his* questions. Perhaps for once, she was not concerned about my reaction to her answer. She wasn't worried about her A1c levels, her latest brain or bone scans, the forbidden candy bar she enjoyed in private, or whether she had showered. She did not care whether she had forgotten to take her hydrochlorothiazide, knew which day of the week it was, or could name the current President of the United States. No, those were the things I fretted over as her caregiver daughter. For my 83-year-old mother, answering the question of what mattered most to her was easy. Without removing her eyes from his, from her unencumbered hand she pointed a finger toward my sister and me and said, "That they're okay."

It took a long time for me to recover from the impact of her answer, and in some ways I still have not, as it has profoundly shaped my work as an ethicist. During

DOI: 10.4324/9781003229957-1

the years that I spent consulting legions of specialists, therapists, and social workers searching for their opinions of what was best for her, I never once seriously considered what *she* wanted. Rather, my idea of caring for an older parent was to ensure that she received what she *needed* according to medical models: the best medical treatments available, assurances that her long-term care needs were met according to a medical assessment, and a safe environment. So focused on her physical well-being, I was somewhat blind to her humanity. However, her geriatrician's desire to understand what it meant to be Mrs. Martinelli illuminated for me that what mattered to my mother – the simplicity of what she valued most – was what she needed to flourish with dignity throughout the remainder of her life.

Like so many people, my mother's age, her environment, and long list of comorbidities rendered her vulnerable. And in those few moments with her doctor, I came to understand that her vulnerability was compounded by the fact that much of the control she once had over her life had been entrusted to others, including to me. And in partly failing to recognize the values that mattered most to her and how they differed from ours, those of us with decision-making authority were unwittingly hindering her ability to flourish. In contrast, my mother's geriatrician momentarily set aside concern for her physical condition and allowed her humanness to speak. He gave her a voice, and asked permission to enter her world to better understand how his decisions could cohabitate with her to best align with her values. As a primary *care* healthcare professional, he understood that his moral duty to her, and to my family, went beyond medical treatment. He was ethically accountable to ensure that his best clinical judgment included respect for her dignity and values.

That serendipitous, yet routine wellness exam changed the course of my mother's goals of care plan, and was an inflection point in my work. To be sure, the array of patients whose conditions, social contexts, and unique personal narratives define what matters most to them is practically infinite. Therefore, it became crystal clear to me that my mother represented a mere microcosm of the universe of vulnerable healthcare constituents whose dignity and ability to flourish depended upon the moral decisions and actions of healthcare leadership.

Ethical decision-making, as a cornerstone of accountable healthcare leadership, requires awareness and understanding of the communities of stakeholders served and the expectations and values of those constituents. Through planned happenstance, I began to relate the value conflict my mother experienced to other groups of vulnerable individuals who encounter similar barriers to flourishing in healthcare. I saw the nexus between the matters I confronted as healthcare lawyer and privacy advocate, and the stakeholder value conflicts that arise from the use of patient data. Because of my relationship with the disability community, and decades of ministry to families and children with special needs, I linked the negative impact that disability biases and value conflicts can have on quality of care and human dignity for these individuals. Accordingly, I adopted stakeholder theory as an approach to organizational ethics that heeds to the rights, values, and interests of individuals, or groups, who could be affected by the organization's decisions.[1]

This theory is applicable to many other stakeholder communities in health-care and should inspire work with other vulnerable populations. However, in this book, I highlight vulnerable stakeholder communities across the life continuum whose dependency and dignity are most typically subordinate to the decisions of healthcare leadership: certain pediatric populations, the aged, and persons with disabilities. Respect for human dignity and enabling all its stakeholder communities to flourish are quintessential moral obligations of ethically accountable healthcare leadership. This book focuses on those obligations.

Overview of Contents

There is much written on organizational ethics in healthcare. Most of the literature addresses the organization's moral duty to adhere to its mission, vision, and values through ethical decision-making considering its competing interests. There is nothing in the literature, however, which directly links organizational ethics and stakeholder theory to the ethical accountability of leadership to their distinct stakeholder communities in healthcare. This book confronts this gap by addressing how moral agency guides an organization's decisions and actions for the common good of constituent needs, particularly vulnerable communities of stakeholders.

Addressing this gap is important. The contemporary healthcare organization (HCO) in the United States is complex and is comprised of intricately inter-dependent systems of stakeholders with varied needs and interests. Traditional stakeholder theory espouses corporate responsibility and strategy by managing for the interests of the organization's stakeholders. Because of this, stakeholder theory is a promising model for creating and maximizing value and opportunities in healthcare. Accordingly, literature on healthcare management increasingly includes applications of stakeholder theory to specific care settings. Further, the present research and literature on ethically accountable leadership focuses on singular stakeholder concerns that are internal and external to the organization. However, healthcare is no longer binary. Ethical accountability of leadership demands that moral agency and the preservation of the organization's integrity is necessary not merely for its own benefit but for the benefit of the communities it serves.

This analysis examines the highly complex anatomy of contemporary health-care organizations whose constituent parts are interdependent and shaped by corporate leadership. The ethical accountability of leadership includes both individual and institutional moral agency. This combined approach to moral agency, illustrated by the metaphor of an organization's moral soul, guides an organization's ethical decisions for the common good of its stakeholders. Hence, this book integrates moral agency and the ethical accountability of organizational leadership to communities of stakeholders in healthcare. The arguments for organizational accountability are presented in a centrifugal fashion, expanding outward as the chapters develop. The arguments are developed in the following way.

Chapter 2 provides the foundation for the broader discussion concerning the ethical obligation for leadership accountability to community stakeholders in healthcare by first articulating an understanding of moral agency. It bifurcates organizational moral agency into two broad components, *individual* and *institutional* agency. Individuals and institutions are expected to support the core values, culture, and structure that define the organizational ethics of the HCO. And, just as the human body cannot depend solely on the form of anatomy to achieve health, it is also the case that it takes more than the form and structure of an HCO to survive and thrive in an era of unprecedented change. It requires the exposition of moral integrity and the virtue of its leadership. That is, it requires soul. This chapter then illustrates the unification of individual and institutional moral agents, and their ethical decision-making through the HCO's moral soul. This chapter reveals, through a specific use case, how deficiencies in governance, unaccountable leadership, stakeholder abandonment, and uncritical decision-making can permit and even cause an HCO to lose its moral soul.

The potential for corporations lacking soul and moral accountability to do real harm to people necessitates checks on an organization's decision-making power. It also bespeaks of the need to shift the managerial mindset from the shareholder to other alternative constituents who possess a stake in the company. The birth of stakeholder theory is the epicenter of that mindset shift and is discussed in the remainder of this chapter.

An organization's stakeholder is "any group or individual who can affect or is affected by the achievement of the organization's objectives."[2] Many stakeholder expectations are tied to social norms, and many are fundamental expectations that are not unique to healthcare but exist as a central aspect of human dignity. To that end, the human desire to flourish and respect for human dignity also include a person's inherent moral and legal right in preserving that which is unique and personal to them – the confidentiality and privacy of their most intimate thoughts and facts.

Secrets live in the recesses of every person and define aspects of selfhood that intentionally remain hidden to preserve that which is uniquely human and different.[3] Healthcare organizations are keepers of patient secrets, and the duty of confidentiality in those secrets is the cornerstone of trust in healthcare. Chapter 3 examines the ethics of secrecy, and concepts of confidentiality and privacy (which are often mistakenly conflated but are not synonymous) as significant stakeholder concerns. These concerns and value conflicts transcend all communities of care, and are in most cases, agnostic to the patient's healthcare condition. And since they are intrinsically tied to humanness, this book treats these stakeholder concerns for confidentiality and privacy as a separate stakeholder community of interests. This chapter thoroughly explores both concepts and explains their differences.

Patient data is the lifeblood of the contemporary HCO as it holds the key to unlocking crucial medical advances. Diverse organizations compete to consume and use as much patient data as possible to advance their interests, or those of their constituents, oftentimes at the expense of preserving confidentiality and privacy. The proliferation of digital information, the ubiquity of the big data phenomenon, and the emergence of artificial intelligence, machine learning, and algorithmic decision-making not only drive desirable healthcare innovation, but they also endanger patient autonomy and give rise to value conflicts. In demonstrating how accountable healthcare leaders must consider the moral rights of their normative stakeholders vis-à-vis their secrets, this chapter concludes with an exposition of data ethics and ethical data review that has at its heart a better respect for human dignity,[4] and value-based, principled data decision-making.

Ethical accountability to stakeholders in healthcare requires a moral commitment from an HCO to the common good, and to the sustained well-being of the communities they serve. Providing for the common good is both an expectation of members of society, and a duty of those who are empowered. Since healthcare is a common good of a moral and civil society,[5] the duty to provide for the common good requires the HCO to disrupt the status quo and provide opportunities for the good of at-risk stakeholders to flourish, especially the most vulnerable amongst them. The remainder of this book illustrates the healthcare organization's ethical accountability to certain normative stakeholder groups who are the most vulnerable across the life continuum. Chapter 4 centers on children and their attendant vulnerability. It begins by examining the moral obligation to promote children in ethical clinical and social research studies, and to expand their participation.[6] Particularly, it looks at vulnerable pediatric communities: children and adolescents with HIV, abused and maltreated children, and those with cognitive disabilities.

The remainder of this chapter examines the ethical strategies for mitigating and preventing the adverse effects of obesity on children. Pediatric obesity is a public health threat. Moreover, it is widely understood and accepted that untreated obesity-related medical conditions will threaten the life of a child, and the adult they will become, if they are sufficiently severe. This is particularly the case when the conditions are in the later stages of deterioration.

While the long-term medical consequences of pediatric obesity are well-recognized, the less obvious but highly destructive and indelible consequences of pediatric obesity, and clearly the most pervasive one in Western societies, are its psychosocial costs.[7] This chapter examines the psychosocial and physiological effects of pediatric obesity, particularly considering Western culture's high value on thinness. To that end, it discusses the moral duty of ethically accountable healthcare leadership to protect these vulnerable children who cannot yet protect themselves and explores ethical intervention strategies.

Chapter 5 explores the far end of the life-continuum through the lens of the aged and the oldest old. It begins by examining their contextual vulnerability vis-à-vis ageism biases as well as their unique health needs. It then discusses the public policy trends for addressing these needs as well as different theories confronting age-based rationing of care. This chapter then presents justification for revised public policy to address long-term informal healthcare needs. This argument is examined from the perspective of the ethics of care model which builds upon the dependency of human relationships and the interconnectedness[8] of people rather than focusing on their separateness. This chapter then provides examples of how caregiver and provider advocacy support person-focused, long-term care that embraces dignity and flourishing by understanding what matters most to the older adult.

According to the World Health Organization, disability is part of the human condition.[9] As concern for the human condition is the central focus of health-care, promoting the dignity of persons with disabilities is a moral duty of the ethically accountable healthcare organization. The remainder of this chapter discusses the healthcare organization's obligation to enhance the lives of those with disabilities by creating enabling environments through which they can flourish.

Understanding human disability entails understanding the relationship between disability, human dignity, what it means to be human, to flourish, and to have a good life. This book explores that through relevant evolutionary and religious interpretations of the human condition. And it further investigates the ethics of improving the human condition through genetic intervention. The moral imperative for ethically accountable healthcare leaders to this stakeholder community asserts the need to create enabling opportunities that eliminate barriers to flourish, reverse ableism biases, and impart a culture of disability ethics.

Conclusion

Respect for human dignity and providing for the common good of society generally, and normative stakeholder communities specifically, are moral imperatives of ethically accountable health care organizations and their leadership. This moral mandate unfolds throughout this book by examining the value conflicts and needs of vulnerable and fragile stakeholder populations across the life continuum. It examines vulnerability through the lens of specific stakeholder theories to better understand and mitigate a variety of contextual harms, threats to dignity, and barriers to human flourishing. This work illustrates how the ethical accountability of organizational leadership is made manifest through the health-care organization's moral soul, and its contribution to enriching of the lives of the stakeholders it serves.

Notes

1. Patricia H. Werhane, "The Healthcare Organization, Business, Ethics and Stakeholder Theory," in *Managerial Ethics in Healthcare. A New Perspective*, ed. Gary L. Filerman, Ann E. Mills and Paul M. Schyve. (Chicago, IL: Health Administration Press, 2014), 83.
2. R. Edward Freeman, *Strategic Management. A Stakeholder Approach*, (New York: Cambridge University Press, 2010), 46.
3. Paul W. Mosher and Jeffrey Berman, *Confidentiality and Its Discontents. Dilemmas of Privacy in Psychotherapy*, (New York, NY: Fordham University Press, 2015), 1.
4. Giovanni Buttarelli, "Towards a New Digital Ethics, Data, Dignity and Technology." Paper Presented at the European Data Protection Supervisor (EDPS), Brussels, Belgium. (September 11, 2015): 12.

5. David M. Gallagher, "The Common Good." In *Catholic Health Care Ethics. A Manue for Practitioners*. (Philadelphia, PA: The National Catholic Bioethics Center, 2009). 29.
6. Rosamond Rhodes, "When Is Participation in Research a Moral Duty?" in *The Journal of Law, Medicine & Ethics* 45 (2017), 322.
7. Shireen Arani, "State Intervention in the Cases of Obesity-Related Medical Neglect." 82 B.U.L. Rev. 888–889. (2002); Tim Lobstein, Louise A. Baur, and Rachel Jackson-Leach, "The Childhood Obesity Epidemic." In *Preventing Childhood Obesity: Evidence, Policy and Practice*. ed. Elizabeth Waters, et al. (West Sussex, UK: Blackwell Publishing, Ltd., 2010), 3–5.
8. Martha B. Holstein, Jennifer A. Parks, and Mark H. Waymack, *Ethics, Aging and Society: The Critical Turn*, (New York, NY: Springer Publishing Company, 2011), 104.
9. World Health Organization, *World Report on Disability*, 2011, 3.

2 Organizational Moral Agency

Introduction

The human body is organized into interdependent and complex levels of form and function.[1] Human anatomy's rich composite of chemicals, cells tissues, and organs are precisely amalgamated to form organ systems that contribute to and enable bodily functions.[2] When form and function are in equilibrium, a body experiences a state of good health. *Homeostasis* – the body's ability to maintain equilibrium despite exposure to constant internal and external changes – depends upon its ability to respond to changes that affect form and function. Alerted to those changes, interdependent response mechanisms implicate all accountable organ systems of the body to restore and ensure proper form and function. Just as occurs with the body through which modern medicine is delivered, the health-care organization (HCO) similarly seeks to maintain order among its diverse stakeholders to achieve organizational homeostasis. When internal and external influences threaten form and function, the survival of the organization and the health of its stakeholders depend upon its ability to maintain homeostasis. Maintaining order depends upon the ethical accountability of leadership to its constituent stakeholder parts.

This chapter opens with an understanding of moral agency as the cornerstone of ethical accountability and decision-making to support a common morality. It presents a portrait of common morality and its framework including a snapshot of ethical norms, principles, rules and theories, and contemporary views espoused by renowned bioethicists Beauchamp and Childress, as well as Gert, Culver, and Clouser. The discussion bifurcates organizational moral agency into individual and institutional components and illustrates how their unification and ethical decision-making can innervate and preserve the HCO's moral soul. The discussion adopts the theological concept of soul in religious discourse, such as occurs in the Roman Catholic tradition, and further develops the metaphor of soul in healthcare as that which enables the intimate relationships generated throughout the health-care experience.[3] This chapter then examines the case of the notorious bankruptcy of a large HCO (the Allegheny Health, Education, and Research Foundation) to illustrate what happens when leaders are dispossessed of their moral agency, lack discernment, forfeit their soul, and act morally irresponsibly.

DOI: 10.4324/9781003229957-2

Because HCO decisions implicate more than shareholder interests, this section concludes with a brief introduction to stakeholder theory. As an approach to organizational ethics that heeds to the rights and interests of individuals or groups who interact with the HCO, this section examines the moral obligations to these groups as articulated through normative stakeholder theory. Specifically, it presents stakeholder theory through the lens of dominant theories which are based upon stakeholder relationships, the ethics of care,[4] stakeholder fairness,[5] and stewardship.

Common Morality and Moral Agency

Morality concerns the norms surrounding human behavior which are good and right and are so universally shared that they can cement a stable, predictable social framework. It includes measures of conduct, standards such as moral/ethical norms and beliefs, principles, rules, and theories. Some aspects of morality are so embedded into the social fabric that the norms they dictate are said to form a *common morality* shared and recognized by all moral persons across different cultures. These include standard norms such as "do not kill" and "tell the truth"; and moral character traits such as integrity, fidelity, and kindness.[6]

Some moral norms prescribe rules, obligations, and duties to reduce or prevent harm, others are created to increase the good, or provide relief to those who are harmed by a particular situation or encounter. Moral principles and rules are norms of obligation; that is, they create standards of action required of all people who subscribe to common morality. According to Beauchamp and Childress, the principles of autonomy, beneficence, nonmaleficence, and justice provide the basis for specific rules and for moral reasoning and apply to all persons committed to morality.[7] Autonomy refers to the freedom to decide for oneself, beneficence imposes an action to do good, nonmaleficence calls for refraining from harmful actions, and the principle of justice refers to that which is fair, equitable, and appropriate in light of what is owed to others.[8] For Beauchamp and Childress, these principles of morality rely upon substantive, authoritative, and procedural rules to help shape moral conduct.

Gert, Culver, and Clouser, in contrast, dispense with principles and their cascading rules. They propose instead, that there are ten highly comprehensible general moral rules that govern all right conduct. Five are designed to prevent direct harm: do not kill; do not cause pain; do not disable; do not deprive of freedom; and do not deprive of pleasure. And five moral rules prevent likely harm: do not deceive; keep your promise; do not cheat; obey the law; and do your duty.[9] These rules establish rights and obligations for actors and decision-makers. Gert refers to those to whom these moral rules apply as moral agents.[10] Those moral actors, and the rules and principles with which they work, must fit within a set of societal beliefs, or in the case of an HCO, its organizational beliefs, and decision-making processes. Those beliefs and processes establish a basis for common morality and associated moral action. Moral agents are expected to choose right actions on behalf of themselves and the HCO. The arguments for moral agency presented in this book are impartial to either the principled, or the moral rules approach. What matters most is that moral agents conduct themselves according to what is good.

Individual Agency

An institution cannot act on its own. It requires decision-makers and actors to help define its mission and purpose, and then act and perform in accordance with it, while supporting critical values and norms. These moral agents, who are both internal and external to the organization, are responsible for building and binding together a trusted organization. In short, an ethical healthcare organization is only as sound as the decisions and actions of those who create and support it, and who are also encouraged and equipped to make ethical choices according to prescribed ethical principles.[11]

The mission, values, and principles of ethics define the moral standards and illustrate the moral identity of the entity. Employees and other members of the workforce are an organization's agents and reflect that identity. They are the face of the organization's mission, identity, and culture, and are the embodiment of its values. As moral agents, they are responsible for executing on its mission and they step into the shoes of the organization every time they act within the scope of their role – and quite often, even when they are not acting officially.

Individual roles within the HCO are tied to the norms and standards that define expectations; for example, the qualities of an outstanding assistant, a respected leader, and an effective and strategic-thinking CEO. The presumed standards constitute the notion of role morality and the individuals performing in accordance with these moral standards help to establish and sustain the ethical organization. Actions that fail to meet these standards, as well as the persons attributed to those actions are said to be immoral.[12] To satisfy these moral standards, and in the execution of their duties, individual moral agents acting on behalf of the HCO indisputably must be persons of unwavering integrity and character who are adept at collaboration. Honesty, integrity, and truthfulness are but a few examples of moral character traits, and represent virtues indelibly engraved in common morality.

Although the United States has long been recognized as the source and summit of some of the finest and most advanced forms of medicine in the world, it cannot claim to be the original architect of morality in medicine. That distinction rests with the ancient Romans and Greeks from as far back as the fifth century, BCE as evidenced in the moral precepts of the Hippocratic Oath and other codes promulgated during this era.[13] These ancient codes were proclamations dedicated to achieving what was considered the end or goal of medicine – the good of the patient. And was the duty of the physician to achieve that good.[14] Medical ethics began as descriptive, in this sense: someone was a physician; therefore, it was known how they would act, and what they would do.[15]

The physician-centric precepts of these early codes became embedded in Western medicine. The notion of what was ethically right relied upon the character, duty, and the social ethics of the physician. *Character* addressed the inherent good qualities of one who heals; *duty* set forth the obligations of the good physician "to benefit the sick and do them no harm."[16] These were often reinforced in the form of oaths and codes, however they also existed in the moral beliefs and divine commands present in Judeo-Christian tradition. For example, the respect for life imposes a moral duty not to end a life. Finally, *social ethics* is the idea that the physician assumes responsibility for the entire profession through their behavior in the community. The American Medical Association, for more than a century, modeled the code of medical ethics as synonymous for rules of professional conduct, physician integrity, and social responsibility.[17]

From the early twentieth century, solo practitioners were the model of medical integrity. They were indoctrinated with notions of what to do on behalf of their patient from professors, colleagues, and trusted mentors. Rarely was their ethical judgment called into question. But, as science and medical technologies reshaped the practice of medicine, they also influenced the doctor's conscience. The patient-centered mindset of what constituted the good became distorted. Medical interventions provided or directed by machines competed with the physician's duty to her patient. The physician, who once saw her healing art inextricably tied to the good of her patient, was forced to share that relationship with science and technology.[18] Technology began to diagnose. This transformation of medicine and the evolution of the contemporary healthcare organization influenced the shift away from descriptive nature of ethics to more of a normative approach. And since an HCO is comprised of more than physicians, these transformations influenced a broad swath of moral agents, including regulators and administrators.

Aside from the standards attributed to their roles, individuals also have personal values that act as guiding principles in their lives.[19] People subscribe to their own unique beliefs and standards. Personal values are reflected in individual attitudes and are most often rooted in experiential as well as cultural influences. For the most part, an organization's values are similarly shaped by its tradition, culture, and the collective personalities of its leaders, which may not be aligned to the personal values of its individual agents. Good leadership must be able to articulate those values and strive to ensure a degree of congruence with individual values.[20]

A variety of individuals come together to build and sustain a morally accountable HCO. As moral agents, nearly all the professionals are expected to adhere to prescribed standards and codes of conduct unique to those disciplines, while upholding the virtues of common morality. The moral agency ascribed to the HCO requires it to cohabitate with its professional, clinical, and business professionals and integrate their normative ethical duties and values into the HCO mission.[21] Despite efforts to do so, dissonance between individual stakeholder, organizational values, and moral agents is oftentimes inevitable. Value dissonance upsets homeostasis. Diversity of interests and divergent methods for reacting to competing internal and external influences further enable conflicts to emerge, distrust to ensue, and the perpetuation of a negative ethical climate.[22] Ethical discernment and decision-making can resolve and even forestall value conflicts.

Institutional Agency and Decision-Making

Although it cannot act independent of its agents, nor can it be a moral *individual*, an organization does act through the collective decision-making of its moral agents. And while it cannot have a motive in the same way a person does, an institution is evaluated and adjudged to be moral or immoral according to the decisions, intentions, and actions of its moral agents.[23] Group actions and decisions are often so inextricably intertwined that it may be impossible to separate the individually identifiable actions from the moral agency of the institution itself. And it may be the case that a decision is made individually but executed collectively as a group. Nevertheless, when an organization acts upon decisions as part of a positive ethical culture and climate, self-interest is minimized, trust is imbedded internally and externally, and it is deemed to be a moral institution.[24]

The notion of culture implies that certain norms, habits, and beliefs are shared identities which reflect an organization's most important values, and its good governance and character. An organization's culture includes rituals, narratives, and assumptions, and even power struggles that constitute a way of life for constituents that is formed of shared behaviors and norms.[25] Organizations with robust cultures can transfer their identities onto new members to acculturate them into the values system of the organization. Culture and organizational identity are most often demonstrated through an organization's programs, policies, and procedures. Additionally, leaders within the organization are the most important antecedent of ethical organizational identity.[26] Their practices reflect both their individual and institutional moral agency.

To that end, moral and political philosopher Alasdair MacIntyre argued that good management and good judgment are based in part on *practices* – the collective human activity of seeking of moral excellence – that relies upon moral reasoning, not merely emotivism. *Emotivism*, according to MacIntyre, is the notion that moral judgments are mere expressions preferences, feelings, or emotions and because preferences are subjective and can be manipulated, they breed moral uncertainty.[27] Moral agents who act collectively in furtherance of the missions and values must be cautioned against organizational emotivism and should instead rely on sound moral reasoning. G. Moore contends that emotivism can be minimized when organizations establish a power-balance method of decision-making oversight to ensure that views and desires of some are not privileged and preferred over the preferences of others.[28]

Reliance on unique facts and circumstances that are often intermingled with emotions and other conflicting, life-altering factors is one of the complicating hallmarks of decision-making in contemporary healthcare. The amorphous and frequently ad hoc nature of healthcare decisions underscores the need for methods of systematic and morally justified decision-making. Without a systematic framework, many decisions are subject to allegations of arbitrariness. They may fail to consider or even ignore the values held by the stakeholders served. Values-based decision-making is an organizational challenge. For example, physicians endeavor to first do no harm to their patients while secondarily complying with medical necessity proscriptions and insurance coverage constraints. Nursing staff who advocate on behalf of the patient's best interest face moral choices when those perceived interests conflict with physician orders, or institutional barriers. And HCO leadership seeking to fill demographic gaps in care by increasing market penetration through potentially anti-competitive means all represent conflicts of commitment and interests, which present challenges to moral agency.[29] Reconciling these conflicts requires a moral decision-making process that recognizes the values and virtues espoused in the constituents' positions, identifies value conflicts, deliberates and decides, and creates opportunities to promote those decisions throughout the organization.

Virtue and Moral Soul

Moral agents' decisions and actions should be in harmony with the organization's moral identity and remain synonymous with its character and espoused virtues. Although secular and theological references to virtue and the state of being virtuous differ in terms of their origins and ultimate goals,[30] their commonly understood meanings, reflective of the desire for good, are similar. For simplicity and continuity, this text adopts the meanings promulgated by the Roman Catholic tradition insofar as that tradition is widely recognized in religious discourse.

Human virtues are attitudes and dispositions that guide conduct and actions according to sound reasoning and make it possible to live a good and a moral life. A virtuous person seeks to perform only good actions and to use reason to achieve good.[31] Virtues such as prudence and practical wisdom provide direction for the moral agent to know what is good. Similarly, an organization's virtuous character, which ought to be the core of the organization's self-concept, allow it to recognize the good when it is present.[32] Virtuosity requires human effort and disposition to maintain what is good. And the human body and mind, in concert, deliberating what is good rely upon its *soul* to animate and bring to life the decision-making.

Because much of human reasoning often confronts abstract and indiscrete information, good reasoning typically requires the imposition of artificial boundaries and illustrations to help make sense of human experiences. It is often easier to comprehend what something is like or unlike, than to understand what it is. As such, human thought seeks clarity from *ontological* metaphors – images that associate human experience in terms of familiar nonhuman entities or things.[33] Frequently, ontological metaphors will characterize a nonhuman object as a person or as having human traits. Difficult concepts such as motivations, characteristics, and emotions are often described through *personification* which imputes human qualities and traits to nonhuman things.[34] The soul is such an ontological metaphor representing the unifying and holistic web of connectedness in an organization.[35]

In both the secular and the spiritual sense, the *soul* depicts the essence of a person. The metaphor of the soul identifies the energy which gives life, manifests virtuous character, and expresses the dynamism of human reasoning. Moral agents are fueled by their soul. The soul represents the union of spirit and body, reflecting that two-fold constitution of humans. Since the integrated HCO is a unified system of people, things, and processes, the soul of an HCO represents spirit and body to preserve cohesion of its mission, values, and virtuous character.[36]

As a human characteristic, understanding the theological union of body and soul is helpful to understand the soul of an HCO, and the gravity of the consequences when the soul is compromised. According to the Roman Catholic tradition the spirit and body together form one unique human possessing a soul that is individual and immortal.[37] The soul is a unique attribute of humanness and is the lived manifestation of spirituality in an individual and represents the good in an organization through the actions and decisions of its moral agents.[38] Just as the mortal soul is a unity with the body, so are the souls of moral agents a unity with the organization. The leaders and governance bodies of organizations must look within their own souls and reflect upon and activate their moral virtues to make just and prudent decisions. William O'Brien aptly contends that maintaining soul and managing morally is difficult for most organizations because moral excellence requires commitments that often contrast with society's inclinations and habits as well as its own. Managing morally demands more than mere compliance with law and conformance with principles. Maintaining soul requires a vigorous and authentic commitment to moral truths. Leaders who seek self-satisfaction only or an emphasis on looking good over and above being good jeopardize the soul of the HCO.[39]

Organizational Leadership and Ethical Decision-Making

According to Margaret Benefiels' work on spiritual leadership in organizations, *mission discernment* is a reflective decision-making process designed to stimulate discussion amongst decision-makers enabling them to identify and report reasons for or against a particular course of action in relation to corporate values and mission. The process involves sifting through individual and collective experiences to know which choices will best support the ethical mission of an organization.[40] This continual process ensures that appropriate business and clinical analyses are elevated and prioritized considering the mission and core values.

Discernment does not merely help determine what to do; rather, mission discernment embraces the core values of what matters to the organization in every decision. It requires trust and openness among the organization's moral agents and presupposes that decision-makers and leaders hold the mission and values of the organization at the center of their leadership. Discernment demands the avoidance of temptation to make important decisions too quickly, or with underdeveloped information. When leadership is called to make decisions on behalf of the organization, the expectation is that they will provide strategic solutions to a variety of different problems. In so doing, they often must wrestle with conflicting values among stakeholders as well as find courage to render unpopular decisions. They are called to examine the collective conscience of the organization.[41] Discernment is the process of deliberating what is good and allowing the moral agents' soul to guide the ethical decision. However, when the soul is lost to conflict or vice, then the process of ethical decision-making, like the body that is separated from the soul, may already be dead.

Enabling Conflicts of Interest, Complicity, and Principles of Cooperation

Standards of role morality apply throughout the HCO. However, moral agents holding leadership roles, particularly members of boards of directors, are held to a higher level of fiduciary duty.[42] Conflicts arise when decision-makers are confronted with personal or financial incentives to act in ways that breach their fiduciary duty and normative standards. Acting on these incentives compromises their best judgment, integrity – their soul. Many conflicts of interest in healthcare involve financial incentives attributed to physicians;[43] however high-level decision-makers such as executive management and board participants are often targets of external influence.[44] Conflicts of interest can be eliminated by removing the incentive or inducement; however, conflicts of conscience originate from the ontological wiring of the actor and are impossible to eliminate unless the offending situation is materially altered.

Conflicts of conscience result from the inability to act in ways that are faithful to an individual's conscience and moral convictions. Since healthcare organizations have moral identities, and since their morality is adjudged according to the actions of its agents, the agents' consciences will impact the organization's moral identity. Moreover, the organization's collective conscience is inextricably tied to its mission and vision and cannot be separated from its moral agency. Conflicts between diverse agents and stakeholders within the healthcare organizations are nearly inevitable and render collective moral choices particularly challenging. Reconciling conflicts of conscience requires a moral decision-making process that provides a systematic approach to ethical problem solving acknowledging moral sensitivity, judgment, motivation, and character.[45] The process must recognize the values espoused by the constituents' consciences and create opportunities to discern the value of those positions vis-à-vis the organization's ethical identity.

Decision-making and moral reasoning are further jeopardized when conflicted moral agents compartmentalize decisions and issues insulating them from the rest of the organization. The failure to disclose individual conflicts eclipses discernment, collective reflection, and moral agency, thus, minimizing individual accountability and enabling loss of soul.[46] Because it lacks transparency, compartmentalizing conflicts may obstruct mission discernment. Without the ability to identify and report reasons for or against a particular course of actions, the rational decision-making process is woefully incomplete.[47] The presence of a genuine conflict of interest or conscience may explain an agent's desire to circumvent the decision-making process, even at the expense of the organization's soul.

An organization can also lose its soul when the decision-making is vested in one dominant leader. Role transference frequently occurs whenever there is a tightness binding the behavior and desires of top-management to the ultimate decisions of the organization. The actor, who is most frequently (but not exclusively) the CEO, represents the organization's public face and is assumed to also reflect its moral identity, and to exercise moral authority on behalf of all the organization. The danger of transference is that lower-level managers and frontline employees abdicate their moral duties – by default – and begin to think and act as if moral agency is not their responsibility. It is as if members of the workforce engage in a form of follow-the-leader.[48] This phenomenon can affect the organization's reputation and public image such that the image of the agent is the perceived image of the organization. In its most extreme, the mission and values of the organization are surreptitiously replaced with the values and virtues of one dominant leader which may conflict with the moral identity of the organization. Role transference may further endanger the organization's soul if narcissistic behavior pervades decision-making.

Since organizations are assemblages of individuals, they adopt an organizational self-esteem often imparted from senior leadership. Senior leadership personalities that exhibit extreme love of self, compartmentalization, and disclaiming awareness of their faults are considered narcissistic. In their work on organizational narcissism Grant and McGhee contend that narcissistic tendencies found in organizational culture are associated primarily with corporate governance. Since the board is responsible for the moral or immoral identity of the organization, they aptly hold that the character of the directors and the way exercise judgment in choosing the CEO is directly linked to the organizational culture of narcissism.[49] Extreme narcissism prevents an organization from acting properly because it lacks a moral identity; it cannot act virtuously. It is morally flawed. As a result, organizations can project a narcissistic rather than moral identity.[50] An organization can react and respond to issues with ego-defense mechanisms just as people do to protect and preserve the organization's image rather than its moral soul. Narcissistic leadership creates a fertile environment for scandal, corruption, and complicity with wrongdoing.

When an organization, through its agents, succumbs to conflicts of conscience, behaves objectionably, and breaches its fiduciary duty to promote its mission and values, it often involves cooperation with someone or something else.[51] However, not all acts of cooperation involve wrongdoing or objectionable conduct. Consider the image offered by Linda and James Henry of the high-flying geese who fly in perfect v-formation following the lead geese – a position that continually changes. They share a vision, trust, support of one another and a shared leadership to achieve a common end.[52] Cooperation involves compromise. The image of the geese invokes compromise of the rotating role lead geese – each taking their turn. Christopher Kutz similarly describes group cooperation as individuals who are suitably combined acting upon participatory intentions to achieve jointly intentional actions.[53] According to Kutz, participation in an act renders an actor accountable for the outcome and acts attributable to the group, as well as to the other participating members. Just like high-flying geese, group identity is explained in terms of individual participatory intentions.[54]

Cooperation can also involve the compromise of morality when individuals or institutions cooperate in the wrongdoing of another for the purpose of achieving some end. The consequences of cooperation are Janus-like – the identical act can result in either licit or illicit cooperation, with culpability being the determinative factor of wrongdoing.[55] Both the principle of cooperation and the complicity principle advanced by Kutz teach that accountability for what others do, and the harm associated with wrongdoings, turn on the intentions of the participant.[56] Plainly, anyone who knowingly participates in a bad act, or influences the particular outcome, is accountable for their role in that act. This is so, even if their contribution to the outcome is slight relative to the collective involvement of the group. Repeated acts of cooperation are assaults against the soul of the organization. The epic bankruptcy of the Allegheny Health, Education, and Research Foundation demonstrates such an assault.

The Sold Soul: The Allegheny Health Education and Research Foundation

Established in 1983, the Allegheny Health, Education, and Research Foundation (AHERF) was one of Pennsylvania's most prestigious hospital systems. It consisted of Hahnemann University of the Health Sciences and the Medical College of Pennsylvania in Philadelphia and merged with Allegheny General Hospital (AGH), a research and teaching hospital in Pittsburgh.[57] Under the leadership of its president and CEO, who was appointed in 1986, the period between 1990 and 1997 marked unprecedented expansion and organizational growth. By 1997, the Allegheny Health System had the distinction of being the first and largest statewide nonprofit integrated health system in the Commonwealth of Pennsylvania.

The HCO was initially inspired by a mission to expand its alliance with medical schools to enhance medical education in Pennsylvania. This included preserving the richness of medical education legacy in the Philadelphia region of Pennsylvania. AHERF's original mission proclaimed widely "to learn, to teach, to heal the sick, and to conserve health."[58] However, this mission was more akin to aggressive expansion through unprecedented mergers and consolidations. Almost immediately after the CEO took the reins, the HCO was goaded into expansion by the prominence and dominance of its rival competitor – The University of Pittsburgh Medical Center Health System (UPMC). The refusal of UPMC to partner with AHERF in 1983 fueled AHERF's longstanding desire to increase the size of its market footprint,[59] coupled with leadership's professional ambitions.

The CEO single-handedly spearheaded and orchestrated rapid and expansive hospital and ambulatory care acquisitions. By 1997, the HCO swelled to include 14 hospitals, 310 primary care physicians in the Philadelphia region, and 136 in Pittsburgh. They were purchased at remarkably high prices during a bidding war with competitors to enlarge its physician network. These physicians and their practices were acquired without adequate negotiation, due diligence, and prudent assessment of the value and worth of the entities. The deals were the result of leadership mandates to AHERF's chief operating officer to put together deals together as fast as possible.[60]

The chief operating officer was offered an incentive commission of $15,000 for every physician contract signed, and for every deal that was closed quickly, creating numerous conflicts of interest. Physicians and their practices were courted with excessive compensation packages that included salary, percentage of revenues generated through care delivery, and grossly inflated asset purchase prices. Compensation packages were often in the millions of dollars. Transactions were consummated without any long and short-range projections for performance or return on investment. Moreover, the physicians' employment contracts did not provide AHERF with post-acquisition oversight rights to monitor productivity and did not anticipate that physicians might refer patients outside of AHERF's geographic proximity. The absence of mission discernment, due diligence, and poorly calculated assumptions created unprecedented financial distress.

Losses mounted. Hospitals and physician practices purchased without adequate due diligence, asset valuation, or planning eventually drained cash and reserves from the healthy parent entity. AHERF purchased hospitals that had little to no cash flow, and it was forced to service the debt it bought with cash transfers between healthy facilities to compensate for underperforming professional and facility providers. To make conditions worse, secretive cash transfers between entities violated bond agreements, and raids on hospital endowments and enormous debt amassed from the acquisitions. Debts were created and cancelled without any consideration to the creditor. Losses became astronomical – ballooning from $41 million in 1996 to $61 million in 1997.[61]

Clinicians and research faculty were lured by large salaries as well as the promise of new labs and staff – incentives that are considered delicacies among physicians who are engaged in research. Additionally, associating with clinical and research faculty was a necessity for AHERF to compete with UPMC. But also, and possibly more important, it meant funding from the National Institute of Health (NIH); an avenue for enriching the cash-strapped organization. Anxiety and discontent slowly bubbled up from physicians and their practices, as many of the promises made during their recruitment and affiliation were broken. Promises were made by AHERF executives; many of whom knew at the time they were made that the growing financial problems would most likely preclude fulfilling them. Physicians, however, accepted the offers and promises without full knowledge of the impending financial implosion.[62]

AHERF's governance structure provided a very week undercurrent to support and oversee the explosive growth, mounting debt, and other decision-making activity within the organization. The organization was notable for having an enormous parent board consisting of between 20–25 members. It also had ten different boards responsible for oversight of 55 different subsidiaries and diversified businesses. The board compositions did not provide any director overlap such that directors on one board had little or no understanding or insight into what was occurring elsewhere in the enterprise.[63] This resulted in decisions made in a vacuum without line of sight into their overall impact.

The ability to achieve efficiencies, eliminate redundancies, and provide access to quality, cost-effective healthcare requires insight into the horizontal *and* vertical dimensions of each entity within the integrated structure. AHERF did not govern transparently; rather it operated under the command and control of the CEO.[64] As economic shortfalls spread throughout each of the merged facilities, mere survival became a priority, and depended upon the ability to subsidize one another rather than achieve efficiencies of scale. Instead of enjoying market dominance, which was one of its intended goals, AHERF's hospitals were unable to make capital expenditures and improvements and placed themselves at a competitive disadvantage in Philadelphia and Pittsburgh markets. Significant budget and expenditure cuts ensued in October 1997. More than 1200 employees lost their jobs. Faculty and staff were forced to take a 20% salary reduction, and care delivery budgets were slashed. Budgets were so thin, that antiquated and deteriorating equipment was not replaced. Patient safety concerns abounded. Access to critical medical supplies dwindled. Some operating rooms did not even have intravenous tubing.[65] During this same period of dire cutbacks and substandard care, the top five senior executives received salary increases.

The corporate bylaws gave AHERF authority to engage in intra-company transfers of money without parent/donor consent, which meant that money could be moved around by senior management without consent of the board. The absence of oversight checks and balances enabled and facilitated financial conflicts of interest and illicit cooperation. For example, five members of the AHERF board were executives of a major bank – a creditor of AHERF. In 1998, crumbling under the weight of suffocating debts, the CEO unilaterally ordered the repayment of an $89 million loan to the bank without board discussion, or board approval.[66] AHERF subsequently filed for Chapter 11 bankruptcy protection on July 21, 1998. At the time that the final decree and settlement was reached in 2003, the $1.6 billion dollar death of AHERF represented the largest not-for-profit healthcare bankruptcy in the United States.[67]

A Soul Restored: A Post-Mortem Analysis

The notorious collapse of AHERF set into motion a series of investigations, civil suits, settlements, and criminal indictments spanning the five-year period between 1998 and 2003. The cumulative results of various investigations revealed a host of individual and institutional moral deficiencies. In addition, imprudent decision-making and immoral actions that failed to consider and discern consequences and experiences that support the ethical mission of the organization cost AHERF its soul. Without discernment, no heed was paid to the needs of AHERF's internal and external stakeholders.

Not a vestige of AHERF's original mission to learn, to teach, and to heal the sick could be found in its decisions. Little concern for stakeholder interests existed. Conflicts of interest eclipsed moral agency, and complicity circumvented virtuous behavior. Additionally, AHERF's system of governance was so adulterated that its original values and mission statement were subsumed into the individual mission and motives of leadership. The motives of leadership and AHERF were so tightly aligned that it was difficult to distinguish whether there was a person representing an organization, or an organization living through the leader.

Everyone was enriched, except the wide swath of stakeholders who were harmed. This included the patients who suffered from a crippled delivery model, and the practitioners, clinicians, and members of the AHERF workforce who were financially impacted and ignored, and the various external communities it was to serve. While the AHERF bankruptcy discharged debt and nominally recognized creditors, it was impossible to make whole everyone impacted by this moral and financial cataclysm.

To restore its soul, an ethically accountable HCO must rely on the collective actions of its moral agents to demonstrate the intent to be reconciled with the communities it may have harmed. Such effort can be reflected in the exemplary conduct and integrity of its moral agents serving as organizational ambassadors within the community.[68] Since role transference can tightly link an actor to the organization's persona such that the organization adopts negative characteristics, it can also adopt and project positive ones; importantly, those that represent missions of healing and virtue.[69] Because moral agents are visible and tangible representatives of the HCO's values and purpose, role transference can be used to the positive advantage of the organization that seeks to rebuild or reinforce trust.

Further, moral agents can reunite with the HCO's soul through a morally rational and systematic decision-making process that includes consideration of the needs and interests of its various stakeholders. In this way, moral agents will place the best interest of the HCO and its stakeholders ahead of their own self-interest and preferences.[70] Rational and systematic decision-making builds trust and restored integrity between and amongst its agents and stakeholders.[71] The process of moral decision-making includes listening to the needs of the communities of stakeholders served by the organization. Done well, moral decision-making imbeds the trust of internal and external constituents within the organization.[72]

Nevertheless, the lure of conflicts of interest and conflicts of conscience can never be fully eliminated because persons, in their humanity, think, act, and share space in a world that is influenced by their own self-interest. As such, restoring soul and maintaining homeostasis necessitates a return to the principles of professionalism, acknowledgment of stakeholder interests, and compliance with normative standards of conduct that shape organizational ethics and guide moral agency.[73]

The consequences of AHERF's fall reflected the interdependency of an HCO and its stakeholders. The community relied upon the trustees of the foundation to guard its charitable assets. The trustees relied upon the auditors to validate the finances, and the auditors relied upon AHERF's executives, including the CEO, chief financial officer, and lawyers. The employees relied upon leadership to do the right things. And patients and their caregivers trusted their healthcare professionals to uphold their moral and legal obligations to them.

Stakeholder Theory and Normative Constituencies

Goodpaster and Matthews hold that rational and respectful decision-makers notice and care about whether the consequences of their actions lead to indignities and offenses toward others.[74] For the healthcare decision-maker, the stakes are even higher. Unlike other industries where the consequences of decisions most notably affect products, services, and profitability, decisions within an HCO can have direct impact on the length and quality of vulnerable human life.[75] Forestalling adverse consequences requires that decision-makers understand and consider the values and interests of others in their actions and choices.

Appreciating the consequences of decisions is made more difficult by the fact that healthcare is morally and ethically complicated.[76] The interdependence of healthcare and the wide range of constituent values and interests present challenges to even the soundest discernment process. Consider also that the tightly controlled corporate environment which typically characterizes an HCO can stifle ethical decision-making.[77] Decisions are often made in select committees, or by individuals who are insulated from the rest of the organization. In addition, issues and dilemmas affecting moral decision-making can result from pressures that, as Weiss advances are exerted at personal, organizational, industrial, as well as social levels. The AHERF case study exemplifies the extreme effect of such pressures on decision-making and the downstream impact on its stakeholders. The remainder of this chapter examines the organization's obligations to its stakeholders through the lens of stakeholder theory, according to notable theorists, to help frame arguments advanced throughout the rest of this book.

Normative Stakeholder Theory

Organizational homeostasis relies upon the systematic ability of the organization to respond to unanticipated sudden or gradual threats to its stability and health. Determining the appropriate course of action often demands making choices that benefit some to the detriment of others. The traditional capitalistic view of corporate decision-making placed shareholder interests at the center of such decision-making, with the managerial mindset of placing profit and returns ahead of all other considerations. This ubiquitous mindset generated the perception that the corporation was a corrupt and shameless construct lacking in good will and gratitude. Possessing unchecked power and resilient to shame or punishment, the corporation was soulless.[78]

The potential for corporations lacking moral accountability to do real harm to people necessitated checks on their power. It also bespoke of the need to shift the managerial mindset from the shareholder to other alternative constituents possessing a stake in the company. The birth of stakeholder theory was the epicenter of that shift. Broadly stated, stakeholder theory is an approach to organizational ethics that heeds the rights and interests of individuals or groups who interact with and could be affected by the organization's decisions.[79] Freeman is credited with developing stakeholder theory to underscore and draw attention to the way that managers and other individuals act and the consequences of those actions, based upon ethical principles. The most striking feature of stakeholder theory is that it demonstrates ways in which organizations can exercise social responsibility through moral management without contradicting the framework of a moral capitalistic economy.[80] Like the discernment process for ethical decision-making that reflects upon those who may be affected by decisions, stakeholder theory applies moral theory and considerations of right behavior to management decisions.

Over the past 30 years since Freeman unleashed his groundbreaking theory, a variety of modified stakeholder theories have emerged: each with its own set of assumptions and claims. Despite its appeal, the consequences of its popularity as well as the vigorous critiques of it have, in many ways, muddled and obfuscated its utility. For example, with at least fifty-five recognized definitions, there is much theoretical debate simply surrounding the definition of *stakeholder* itself.[81] For clarity, Freeman holds what is widely recognized as the seminal definition of stakeholder, and will unless otherwise stated, is the position adopted throughout this book. An organization's stakeholder is, "any group or individual who can affect or is affected by the achievement of the organization's objectives."[82]

Understanding what it means to have a stake in a matter is rather uncomplicated. Determining who is entitled to such a claim and identifying those who are responsible to the holder of those claims is less obvious. Methods of identifying stakeholders and determining the organization's duty to them is often an exercise in moral classification. The following discussion illustrates the ethical obligations of leaders to, and the moral classification of stakeholder's according to Phillips' theory of normative and derivative stakeholders.

According to Phillips, the organizational universe is not structured according to legitimate stakeholders, and non-stakeholders. It is, however, partitioned in the first instance by normative stakeholders. *Normative stakeholders* are those individuals and groups of individuals to whom the organization has a direct moral obligation to attend to their well-being.[83] They are the beneficiaries and objects for which the organization is managed – they give the organization purpose. They are not recognized according to their proximity and situs to the organization. That is, they are not uniquely internal or external to the company. Rather, they are descriptive of their relevance and presence as customers, patients, employees, local communities, suppliers, or financiers and lenders.[84] In its broadest sense, normative stakeholder theories seek to alter corporate behavior according to what *ought* to be done to achieve good. They consider what *should* be done to meet the needs, interests, and claims of the organization's stakeholders according to certain moral norms.

Just as the human body is affected by external influencers that create disruption as well as equipoise, so it is that an HCO can be influenced by derivative stakeholders. *Derivative stakeholders* are groups who can either sow seeds of discord, or create benefit to the company by virtue of their passions, such as activists, the media, and competitors.[85] Although the organization has no direct moral obligation to advance the interests of the derivative stakeholder, Phillips advocates that management acknowledge and pay them heed for the sake of normative stakeholders.[86] Even though derivative stakeholders do not directly derive benefit from the moral obligations of the organization, they obtain their legitimacy as stakeholders nonetheless from their ability to affect and impact the normative constituent. Powerful derivative stakeholders can effectuate seismic influence and authority, and justify the moral decisions made by organization in support of the normative stakeholder.[87]

By virtue of their relationship to the organization, normative stakeholders are afforded greater moral consideration in corporate decision-making, than other social actors.[88] This does not suggest that the interests of derivative stakeholders are morally disregarded or diminished. But rather, there is an additional stakeholder-based moral obligation to address the needs and enrich the lives of the normative stakeholder. Normative stakeholders do not take entitlements away from derivative stakeholders. Rather, they are merely entitled to more. The subsequent chapters of this book reveal, in a centrifugal fashion, the entitlements and expectations of distinct normative stakeholder communities, and the moral obligation of the HCO to uphold their dignity and understand the values unique to them.

Because of the complexity of the interdependent interests within an HCO, and its susceptibility to disruption, stakeholder theory is a promising model for maximizing value creating opportunities in healthcare. It acknowledges moral agency and diversity of values[89] which appeals to the climate of the HCO and helps to ensure homeostasis. The following discussion briefly illustrates and contrasts the dominant normative stakeholder concepts – the ethics of care, and the principle of stakeholder fairness as advanced by their most notable theorists. These concepts reappear in subsequent chapters, consistent with the centrifugal style of this book to further underscore the value of human relationships in healthcare and the HCO's normative obligations to them.

Feminist Theory and Ethics of Care

In contrast to traditional economics-based views of management that are presumed to protect the interests of the corporation and its shareholders primarily, Friedman and Miles suggest that "stakeholder theory can be viewed as a *feminine* normative counterpart, whereby corporations seek to promote stakeholder satisfaction through a more cooperative, caring relationship."[90] This reconstitution of normative stakeholder theory supports the feminist ethics of care proposition that stakeholders are viewed as connected sets of relationships with each other, not merely with the organization.[91] In contrast to social contract theories, feminist moral theory looks beyond legalistic, right-based considerations of stakeholder interests, and elevates the value of relationship to ensure that those interests are brought to the forefront of managerial thought. Despite the feminist characterization, research indicates that preference for ethics of care over justice is identified with men as well as women.[92]

This brief discussion illustrates variations of feminine ethics of care, stakeholder theory, and analysis through the lens of distinct, but aligned theorists. These variations reappear in subsequent chapters addressing specific stakeholder communities. Care ethics is traced to Carol Gilligan's work. She undergirds her critique of previously dominant approaches to economics-based management by suggesting that stages of moral maturity transform inward assessments of the right course of action, into outward considerations of those with whom we are in rela-tion. Relationship requires connectedness with others, while differentiating the other from the self. This results in care for others.[93] Nel Noddings asserts that it is not merely those with whom we are in relation that should be the object of our caring, but rather, caring ought to be a universal attitude that we demonstrate to our wider shared society.[94] And, Ruth Groenhout considers ethics of care, by exploring its connection to human nature and human flourishing.

Stakeholder relationships exist between persons, groups of persons, organiza-tions, and those they serve. As such, the fundamental moral duty to treat people with respect, recognize their unique human dignity, treat them fairly, and avoid harm is multi-directional. Accountable leaders act in deference to their multi-di-mensional stakeholder obligations through commitments to fairness. The discus-sion of fairness in the following section is further developed in later chapters when addressing ethical accountability to specific stakeholder communities.

Stakeholder Fairness, Social Contracts, and Stewardship

Integrity, fairness, and trust are ethical concepts that comprise the moral princi-ples that should be applied in practical business settings.[95] The culture of ethical accountability within an HCO depends upon the degree to which these con-cepts and principles become rooted in the decisions of the organization and its leadership. The sheer breadth of normative stakeholders to whom an HCO is accountable makes employing the ethical concept of fairness one of the most ambitious demands placed upon leadership. Applying fairness requires that the needs, interests, and concerns of certain stakeholders be considered in relation-ship to others.[96]

Managing for HCO stakeholders seeks win-win outcomes through collab-orative and caring relationships. Complex situations, however, can result in zero-sum games where the gain of one individual or group is necessarily lost by another.[97] This seemingly inevitable reality does not presuppose that stake-holder theory is inherently prejudicial. On the contrary, Robert Phillips' nota-ble *principle of stakeholder fairness* argues that the obligations of fairness by and among stakeholders are *created* when benefits resulting from cooperative efforts are accepted by a group of stakeholders.[98] It is a reciprocal principle providing that those stakeholders who receive benefits have an obligation to fairness to cooperate with other stakeholders in a manner proportionate to the benefits they received. Rather than attempting to treat all stakeholders equally, which he believes is impossible, Phillips recommends the principle of equity to determine which normative stakeholder should receive more.[99] Although the work of Rawls is beyond the scope of this book, Phillips confesses that his work is based on John Rawls's principle of fair play which, according to Phillips, is the moral foundation of stakeholder theory.[100]

This notion of fairness, according to Freeman, presupposes basic equality among stakeholders as articulated in his *doctrine of fair contracts.* [101] His doctrine consists of six principles that impose duties of fairness on all agents participating in the social contract to serve the interests of all stakeholders. Freeman suggests that normative stakeholder considerations do not arise from one theory, but rather from a genre of theories to which the organization has a responsibility.[102] In contrast, the concept of *integrated social contract theory* espouses, according to Thomas Donaldson and Thomas Dunfee, a foundation for stakeholder theory that suggests management take into consideration stakeholder norms rather than interests.[103] Donaldson and Dunfee's model is communitarian in that it considers the normative voice of the relevant stakeholder communities which includes cultural context, beliefs, values, and standards unique to the community.

Stakeholder theories must also include policy and decision-making with respect to distribution of scarce resources, especially in healthcare. Justice and equity are key concerns[104] and are frequently central in the minds of management. However, morally accountable leaders are concerned with more than ensuring that resources are distributed with justice and equity. They are called to remain faithful to the ethic of stewardship in the management of stakeholders.

Stewardship in healthcare is an understanding that all the resources of the HCO, including real and intangible ones, are held in trust by the organization and its leadership for the good of others.[105] It is not merely an aspiration of good leadership. Stewardship is a fiduciary duty and a commitment to the organization and its stakeholders. Stewardship represents an ethic that transcends healthcare and is integral to nearly every discipline, including theology, information management,[106] environmental management, and economics. The principal difference in the value of stewardship within other disciplines has to do with the nature of the resource being managed. For example, the Catholic social tradition depicts stewardship as part of divine revelation for humankind to use the world's resources responsibly for the benefit of all.[107] Stewardship in information management prescribes responsible fiduciary oversight of how data is used. For an HCO, the value of stewardship requires that the care delivery system monitor and use its resources – varied as they are – ethically.[108]

Because the range of stakeholders in healthcare delivery is diverse, the ability of an HCO to achieve its mission, survive as a viable business, and provide for the good of others without encountering ethical tensions is dubious at best.[109] Add to this the fact that members of management are normative stakeholders themselves. As stewards, their obligation to safeguard the welfare of the organization requires a balancing of multiple claims of competing and conflicting stakeholders, including their own.[110] Despite this potential for conflict, by exercising moral agency through responsible discernment and decision-making, ethically accountable leadership can maintain homeostasis for the organization and its communities of stakeholders.

Conclusion

The contemporary healthcare organization (HCO), like the human body, is an interdependent system of form and function responding to internal and external environmental influences to survive and thereby maintain homeostasis. The business model of the HCO is extraordinarily complex as it is comprised of a series of interacting and coexisting touchpoints and relationships, each with their own unique self-interests, values, and objectives. Maintaining healthy order within such a heterogeneous system depends upon the ethical accountability of HCO leadership to its normative stakeholders. The discussion of moral soul in this chapter presents a foundation for the accountability arguments presented throughout the remainder of the book.

Moral agency, as the cornerstone of ethical leadership, provides the ability to discern, decide and act according to what is right, and to be accountable for those actions. The moral soul provides a metaphor for characterizing accountable leadership. Individual and institutional moral agents, possessing distinctive qualities and moral obligations acting on behalf of the HCO, showcase this moral soul. An organization is adjudged by the decisions, intentions, and actions of its agents, as well as by the values and principles it espouses.

Conversely, the absence of moral soul is recognized in such things as unresolved conflicts of interest, conflicts of conscience, and all too often deficiencies in moral judgment that result in stakeholder abandonment. When leaders are dispossessed of their moral agency and act in morally irresponsible ways, the soul of the HCO dies, as demonstrated through the AHERF case study.

Stakeholder theory, which considers interests beyond mere economic, is an approach to organizational ethics that heeds to the rights and interests of individuals who interact with and could be affected by the HCO's decisions. Stakeholder theory is concerned with the HCO's direct moral obligations to its constituents. The ethics of care and the principle of stakeholder fairness, and social contract are dominant stakeholder concepts which appeal to the responsibilities of the contemporary HCO. Respectively, these stakeholder concepts focus on the relational quality of moral human interaction, the principles of fairness, and stewardship as a fiduciary duty and commitment of the ethically accountable HCO to its communities of stakeholders.

Notes

1. Valerie C. Scanlon, and Tina Sanders, *Essentials of Anatomy and Physiology.* (Philadelphia, PA: F.A. Davis Company, 2015), 4.
2. Scanlon and Sanders, *Essentials of Anatomy and Physiology,* 6.
3. Linda Gambee Henry and James Douglass Henry, *Reclaiming Soul in Health Care. Practical Strategies for Revitalizing Providers of Care,* (Chicago, IL: AHA Press, 1999), 17.
4. Craig E. Johnson, *Meeting the Ethical Challenges of Leadership. Casting Light or Shadow.* 6th edition (Los Angeles, CA: Sage Publications, Inc., 2018), 159.
5. Patricia H. Werhane, "The Healthcare Organization, Business Ethics and Stakeholder Theory," In *Managerial Ethics in Healthcare: A New Perspective.* ed. G.L. Filerman, A.E. Mills, P.M. Shyve, ed. (Chicago, IL: Health Administration Press, 2014), 86.
6. Tom L. Beauchamp and James F. Childress, *Principles of Biomedical Ethics,* 7th edition (New York, NY: Oxford University Press, 2013), 3.
7. Beauchamp and Childress, *Principles of Biomedical Ethics,* 3, 13.

8. Beauchamp and Childress, *Principles of Biomedical Ethics*, 101–102, 202–204, 249–252.
9. Bernard Gert, Charles M. Culver, and K. Danner Clouser, *Bioethics. A Systematic Approach*, 36.
10. Bernard Gert, *Common Morality. Deciding What to Do*, (New York, NY: Oxford University Press, 2006).
11. Craig E. Johnson, *Organizational Ethics. A Practical Approach*, (Los Angeles, CA: SAGE Publications, Inc., 2016), 318.
12. E.M. Spencer, A.E. Mills, M.V. Rorty, and P.H. Werhane, *Organization Ethics in HealthCare*, (New York, NY: Oxford University Press, 2000), 17, 32.
13. Edmund D. Pelligrino, "Codes, Virtue, and Professionalism," in *Methods in Medical Ethics*, ed. Jeremy Sugarman and Daniel P. Sulmasy, (Washington, DC: Georgetown University Press, 2010), 92.
14. Pelligrino, "Codes, Virtue and Professionalism," 110.
15. Daniel P. Sulmasy and Jeremy Sugarman, "The Many Methods of Medical Ethics (or, Thirteen Ways of Looking at a Blackbird)," in *Methods in Medical Ethics*, 2nd edition. (Washington, D.C: Georgetown University Press, 2010); 7.
16. Albert Jonsen, *The Birth of Bioethics*. (New York, NY: Oxford University Press, 1998), 6.
17. Jonsen, *The Birth of Bioethics*, 7.
18. Jonsen, *The Birth of Bioethic*, 84.
19. Johnson, *Organizational Ethics. A Practical Approach*, 43.
20. R. Edward Freeman, *Strategic Management. A Stakeholder Approach*. (New York, NY: Cambridge University Press, 2010), 96–97.
21. Spencer, Mills, Rorty, and Werhane, *Organization Ethics in Health Care*, 9–14, 17–19, 69–76.
22. David A. Shore, *The Trust Crisis in Healthcare. Causes, Consequences and Cures*, (New York, NY: Oxford University Press, 2007), 4–16.
23. Spencer, Mills, Rorty, and Werhane, *Organization Ethics in Health Care*, 27–28, 200–217.
24. Shore, *The Trust Crisis in Healthcare. Causes, Consequences and Cures*, 3, 6–9, 173.
25. Craig E. Johnson, *Meeting the Ethical Challenges of Leadership. Costing Light or Shadow*, 377.
26. Patricia Grant and Peter McGhee, "Organizational Narcissism: A Case of Failed Corporate Governance?" in *The Heart of the Good Institution. Virtue Ethics as a Framework for Responsible Management*. ed. Howard Harris, Gayathri Wijesinghe, and Stephen McKenzie, (Netherlands: Springer, 2013), 100–101.
27. Geoff Moore, "Re-imagining the Morality of Management: A Modern Virtue Ethics Approach." In *The Heart of the Good Institution*. ed. Howard Harris, Gayahtri Wijesinghe, Stephen McKenzie, (Netherlands: Springer, 2013), 8–9.
28. Geoff Moore, "Re-imagining the Morality of Management: A Modern Virtue Ethics Approach." 25.
29. Spencer, Mills, Rorty, and Werhane, *Organizational Ethics in Health Care*, 76–82.
30. *Catechism of the Catholic Church*, 2nd ed., translated by the United States Conference of Catholic Bishops. (Vatican City: Libreria Editrice Vaticana, 1997), 1768.
31. *Catechism of the Catholic Church*, 1733, 1827.
32. Harris, Wijesinghe, and McKenzie, *The Heart of the Good Institution. Virtue Ethics as a Framework for Responsible Management*, 24–25; William O'Brien. *Character at Work. Building Prosperity Through the Practice of Virtue*. (Mahwah, NJ: Paulist Press, 2008), 8.
33. George Lakoff and Mark Johnson, *Metaphors We Live By*. (Chicago, IL: Chicago University Press, 1980) 5–25.
34. Lakoff and Johnson, *Metaphors We Live By*, 25–34.
35. Lakoff and Johnson, *Metaphors We Live By*, 15–16, 38–41; Spencer, Mills, Rorty, and Werhane, *Organization Ethics in Healthcare*, 54–59.

36. Linda Gambee Henry and James Douglas Henry, *Reclaiming Soul in Health Care. Practical Strategies for Revitalizing Providers of Care*, 8–16; Geoff Moore, "Re-imagining the Morality of Management: A Modern Virtue Ethics Approach," 24–27.
37. *Catechism of the Catholic Church*, 33, 362–365.
38. Margaret Benefiel, *Soul at Work: Spiritual Leadership in Organizations*, (New York, NY: Church Publishing, 2005), 1–12.
39. William J. O'Brien, *Character at Work. Building Prosperity through the Practice of Virtue*, (Mahwah, NJ: Paulist Press, 2008), 85–89.
40. Benefiel, *Soul at Work: Spiritual Leadership in Organizations*, 50–51.
41. Benefiel, *Soul at Work: Spiritual Leadership in Organizations*, 116–117, 122–123.
42. Marc A. Rodwin, *Conflicts of Interest and the Future of Medicine. The United States, France and Japan*. (New York, NY: Oxford University Press, 2011), 254–255.
43. Rodwin, *Conflicts of Interest and the Future or Medicine. The United States, France and Japan*, 11–21; 255; Holly Fernandez Lynch, *Conflicts of Conscience in Health Care. An Institutional Compromise*. (Cambridge, MA: The MIT Press, 2008), 73.
44. Rodwin, *Conflicts of Interest and the Future of Medicine. The United States, France and Japan*, 230–235; Fernandez Lynch, *Conflicts of Consciences in Health Care. An Institutional Compromise*, 99–110.
45. Johnson, *Meeting the Ethical Challenges of Leadership. Casting Light or Shadow*, 175.
46. Tracy Wilcox, "Embedded Moral Agency: A MacIntyrean Perspective on the HR Professional's Dilemma." In *The Heart of a Good Institution. Virtue Ethics as a Framework for Responsible Management*. ed. Howard Harris, Gayathri Wijesinghe, and Stephen McKenzie, (Netherlands: Sprinter, 2013), 129, 131–132.
47. Benefiel, *Soul at Work: Spiritual Leadership in Organizations*, 122–126; Spencer, Mills, Rorty, and Werhane, *Organizational Ethics in Health Care*, 1–54, 218.
48. Michael Maccoby, "Why People Follow the Leader: The Power of Transference," In *Harvard Business Review*, September 2004. https://hbr.org/2004/09/why-people-follow-the-leader-the-power-of-transference. (accessed April 3, 2019).
49. Patricia Grant and Peter McGhee, "Organizational Narcissism: A Case of Failed Corporate Governance?," 97.
50. Patricia Grant and Peter McGhee, "Organizational Narcissism: A Case of Failed Corporate Governance?" 105.
51. Spencer, Mills, Rorty, and Werhane, *Organization Ethics in Health Care*, 17–32.
52. Henry and Henry, *Reclaiming Soul in Health Care. Practical Strategies for Revitalizing Providers of Care*. 103–104.
53. Christopher Kutz, *Complicity: Ethics and Law for a Collective Age*, (New York, NY: Cambridge University Press, 2000), 66–74.
54. Kutz, *Complicity: Ethics and Law for a Collective Age*, 75–95.
55. Gerard Magill, "A Moral Compass for Cooperation and Wrongdoing," in *Voting and Holiness. Catholic Perspectives on Political Participation*. ed. Nicholas Cafardi. New York, NY: Paulist Press, 2012. 136, 139–142.
56. Kutz, *Complicity: Ethics and Law for a Collective Age*, 63, 104, 122–123.
57. Judith P. Swazey, *Merger Games. The Medical College of Pennsylvania, Hahnemann University, and the Rise and Fall of the Allegheny Health Care System*, (Philadelphia: Temple University Press, 2013). 14–27.
58. Swazey, *Merger Games. The Medical College of Pennsylvania, Hahnemann University, and the Rise and Fall of the Allegheny Health Care System*, 139.
59. Lawton R. Burns, John Cacciamani, James Clement, and Welman Aquino, "The Fall of the House of AHERF: That Allegheny System Debacle." In *Health Affairs*. 2000; 19(1). http://ww/medscape.com/viewarticle/409812print (accessed March 24, 2019).
60. Burns, Cacciamani, Clement, and Aquino, "The Fall of the House of AHERF: That Allegheny System Debacle," 4.

61. Burns, Cacciamani, Clement, and Aquino, "The Fall of the House of AHERF: That Allegheny System Debacle," 4, 18.

62. Swazey, *Merger Games. The Medical College of Pennsylvania, Hahnemann University, and the Rise and Fall of the Allegheny Health Care System,* 217; L.R., Clement Cacciamani, Clement and Aquino, "The Fall of the House of AHERF: That Allegheny Health System Debacle," 4.

63. Swazey, *Merger Games. The Medical College of Pennsylvania, Hahnemann University, and the Rise and Fall of the Allegheny Health Care System,* 87–89; L.R., Burns, Cacciamani, Clement J., and W. Acquino, "The Fall of the House of AHERF: The Allegheny System Debacle." *Health Affairs* (serial on the Internet 2000) 5–6; A.O. Adams, "Quality of Board Governance in Nonprofit Healthcare Organizations," *The Internet Journal of Healthcare Administration.* 205 Volume 2. DOI: 10.5580/251d http://archive.ispub.com/journal/the-internet-journal-of-healthcare-administration/volume-2 8-10. (accessed April 6, 2013 and January 1, 2019).

64. Swazey, *Merger Games. The Medical College of Pennsylvania, Hahnemann University, and the Rise and Fall of the Allegheny Health System,* 135.

65. Swazey, *Merger Games. The Medical College of Pennsylvania, Hahnemann University, and the Rise and Fall of the Allegheny Health System,* 209–217.

66. Burns, Cacciamani, Clement, and Acquino, "The Fall of the House of AHERF: That Allegheny System Debacle," 10.

67. Swazey, *Merger Games. The Medical College of Pennsylvania, Hahnemann University, and the Rise and Fall of the Allegheny Health System,* 229–236.

68. Steven D. Pearson, James E. Sabin and Ezekiel J. Emanuel, *No Margin, No Mission. Health Care Organizations and the Quest for Ethical Excellence.* (New York, NY: Oxford Press, 2003), 100–101.

69. Henry and Henry, *Reclaiming Soul in Health Care. Practical Strategies for Revitalizing Providers of Care,* 10–11.

70. Spencer, Mills, Rorty, and Emanuel, *Organization Ethics in Health Care,* 51–61.

71. Spencer, Mills, Rorty, and Emanuel, *Organization Ethics in Health Care,* 20–32, 36–39.

72. Pearson, Sabin, Emanuel, *No Margin, No Mission. Health Care Organizations and the Quest for Ethical Excellence,* 124.

73. Rodwin, *Conflicts of Interest and the Future of Medicine. The United States, France, and Japan,* (New York: Oxford University Press, 2011), 231–246.

74. Kenneth E. Goodpaster and John B. Matthews, Jr. *Can a Corporation Have a Conscience?* 163 *Harvard Business Review,* January–February 1982.

75. Jeffrey S. Harrison and Steven M. Thompson, *Strategic Management of Healthcare Organizations. A Stakeholder Management Approac.* (New York: Business Expert Press, 2015), 2, 13, 30–31, 35.

76. M.J. Gilmartin and R.E. Freeman, "Business Ethics and Healthcare: A Stakeholder Perspective," In *Healthcare Management Review* 2. Spring 2002. 52–65.

77. Joseph W. Weiss, *Business Ethics: A Stakeholder and Issues Management Approach. Cases. Principles. Practices.* 6th edition (San Francisco: Berrett-Koehler Publishers, Inc. 2015), 75.

78. Andrew L. Friedman and Samantha Miles, *Stakeholders: Theory and Practice.* (New York, NY: Oxford University Press, 2006, reprinted 2009), 19–20.

79. Werhane, "The Healthcare Organization, Business Ethics and Stakeholder Theory," 83.

80. Samuel F. Mansell, *Capitalism, Corporations, and the Social Contract. A Critique of Stakeholder Theory.* Cambridge, MA: Cambridge University Press, 2013) 8.

81. Friedman and Miles, *Stakeholders: Theory and Practice,* 5–8.

82. R. Edward Freeman, *Strategic Management: A Stakeholder Approach,* 46.

83. Robert Phillips, *Stakeholder Theory and Organizational Ethics,* (San Francisco, CA: Berrett-Koehler Publishers, Inc., 2003), 28.

84. Phillips, *Stakeholder Theory and Organizational Ethics*, 127.
85. Phillips, *Stakeholder Theory and Organizational Ethics*, 29.
86. Phillips, *Stakeholder Theory and Organizational Ethics*, 125.
87. Phillips, *Stakeholder Theory and Organizational Ethics*, 128.
88. Phillips, *Stakeholder Theory and Organizational Ethics*, 124.
89. Werhane, "The Healthcare Organization, Business Ethics and Stakeholder Theory," 83.
90. Friedman and Miles, *Stakeholders: Theory and Practice*, 65.
91. Brian K. Burton and Craig P. Dunn, "Feminist Ethics as Moral Grounding for Stakeholder Theory," In *Business Ethics Quarterly*, 6 (2), 1996, 133.
92. Craig E. Johnson, *Meeting the Ethical Challenges of Leadership. Casting Light or Shadow*, 159.
93. Carol Gilligan, *In a Different Voice*. (Cambridge, Mass: Harvard University Press, 1982), 63.
94. Nel Noddings, *Caring: A Relational Approach to Ethics and Moral Education*, (Berkeley, CA: University of California Press, 1984, 2003, 2013), 47–49.
95. Bob Tricker and Gretchen Tricker, *Business Ethics. A Stakeholder, Governance, and Risk Approach*, (London, UK: Routledge, 2014), 8–9.
96. Leonard J. Weber, "The Healthcare Organization as Employer: The Demands of Fairness and the Healthcare Organization," In *Managerial Ethics in Healthcare. A New Perspective*. ed. Gary J. Filerman, Ann E, Mills, and Paul M. Schyve (Chicago: IL: Health Administration Press, 2014), 177.
97. Weiss, *Business Ethics: A Stakeholder and Issues Management Approach. Cases, Principles and Practices*, 117.
98. Robert Phillips, *Stakeholder Theory and Organizational Ethics*, 92.
99. Friedman and Miles, *Stakeholders: Theory and Practice*, 61.
100. Phillips, *Stakeholder Theory and Organizational Ethics*, 85.
101. Friedman and Miles, *Stakeholders: Theory and Practice*, 58–59.
102. R. Edward Freeman, Jeffrey S. Harrison, Andrew C. Wicks, Bidhan L. Parmar, and Simone DeColle., *Stakeholder Theory, the State of the Art*, (New York, NY: Cambridge University Press, 2010), 216.
103. Friedman and Miles, *Stakeholders: Theory and Practices*. 55.
104. Katherine L. Acuff, "Healthcare Ethics, Public Policy, and Healthcare Organization," In *Managerial Ethics in Healthcare. A New Perspective*. ed, 224.
105. John Wallenhorst, "Ethics and Governance," in *Managerial Ethics in Healthcare. A New Perspective*, edited by Gary J. Filerman, Ann E. Mills, and Paul M. Schyve. (Chicago: Health Administration Press, 2014), 55.
106. Katherine O'Keefe and Daragh O. Brien, *Ethical Data and information Management. Concepts, Tools and Methods*, (London, UK: Kogan Page Limited, 2018), 102–105.
107. Mary J. McDonough, *Can a Health Care Market Be Moral? A Catholic Vision*. Washington, DC: Georgetown University Press, 2007, 25.
108. Anne Mills, "Ethics and the Healthcare Organization," in *Managerial Ethics in Healthcare. A New Perspective*. ed. Gary J. Filerman, Ann E. Mills and Paul M. Schyve. (Chicago: Health Administration Press, 2014), 21.
109. Katherine L. Acuff, "Healthcare Ethics, Public Policy, and Healthcare Organization," 226–227.
110. Friedman and Miles, *Stakeholders: Theory and Practice*. 48.

3 Ethical Challenges of Maintaining Stakeholder Confidentiality and Privacy

Introduction

Not all healthcare stakeholder interests are corporeal. Obtaining wellness of the body, mind, and spirit are patent concerns of most healthcare stakeholders. However, human flourishing and respect for human dignity also includes a person's right and interest in preserving that which is unique and personal to them – the confidentiality and privacy of their information, which is the source of their most intimate thoughts and facts. This chapter thoroughly explores the healthcare organization's (HCO) ethical accountability to this stakeholder interest by bifurcating them into distinct sections; one setting forth the duty of confidentiality, and the other illuminating expectations of privacy.

The timeless concept of confidentiality is embattled in an age where knowledge is power, predictive analytics dictates decision-making, and data has become "the raw material of the information age."[1] Confidentiality – the cornerstone of trust in healthcare – is weakened under the crushing influence of diverse organizations competing to consume as much health information as possible to advance their own interests, or those of their constituents. One reason for such obsession is that patient data holds the key to unlocking crucial medical advances. Patient data has become the lifeblood of the contemporary HCO, and as big data analytics innervates its body through algorithmic neural networks, personal privacy is endangered. Camouflaged within the infinite terrain of digital data elements, are the things which every human person has, holds sacred, and may even deny having at all – their secrets.

Preserving the confidentiality of patient secrets while satisfying legitimate competing, stakeholder interests is daunting. Accordingly, this chapter closely examines the concept of confidentiality as a multi-stakeholder interest in contemporary HCOs. It demonstrates the ethical justification for exceptions to the legal and professional obligations of the duty of confidentiality in clinical care, and the effects of those exceptions on patient and third-party expectations. It then illustrates the intersection of the individual's right to privacy in their personal information, the legal and ethical justification for use of patient information to do good, and the need for ethical guidelines and principles to minimize threats to privacy while respecting the dignity of the person

DOI: 10.4324/9781003229957-3

This chapter begins with an examination of the anatomy of a secret, the ethics of secrecy, and the fact that secrets are a natural part of humanness, according to the works of Sissela Bok and Anita Allen. It then illustrates how the revelation of patient secrets throughout the physician-patient relationship forms the seal of confidentiality, triggering the need for ethical principles, and the professional and legal strictures protecting them. This chapter explores the disruptors that justify disclosures of protected secrets in the clinical setting and the situations that imperil the ethics of physician-patient confidentiality.[2]

This chapter proceeds to discuss the role of autonomy and informed consent as a means for patients to exercise control over the disposition of their secrets. It discusses the need for physicians to avail themselves to their patient's autonomous voice when considering the scope of information necessary for a fully informed consent. It then shifts to the ethical dilemmas confronted by clinicians as they are called to be confidants and guardians of secrets.

Specifically, this chapter examines challenges to confidentiality that result from the clinicians' duty to protect secrets obtained throughout the psychotherapeutic practice. Adopting the assertion that mental health is a public good, it presents alternatives to absolute confidentiality in the form of duty to warn third parties. This dual allegiance between protecting the patient, and securing her secrets, and consideration for the welfare of others, presents a dilemma that implicates both legal and moral duties.

It then explores the duality of duty and the ethical dilemmas engendered through advances in genomic medicine. Genomic medicine, which includes references to genetic testing and whole genome sequencing, is pioneering promising and unprecedented advances in human health that will help to better understand the qualities of diseases.[3] At the same time, genomic findings expand the common understanding of secrets to include biological secrets which may never be known to anyone except the physician. In addition, this chapter illustrates how genomic medicine multiplies the breadth of third-party stakeholders who may obtain these secrets, and the ethical justification for preserving or foregoing their secrecy.

This chapter then shifts to the stakeholder expectation of privacy. It proceeds by briefly exploring the evolution of privacy as an individual claim, providing the foundation for current concepts articulated by several contemporary theorists Alan Westin, Daniel Solove, Adam Moore, Julie Inness, and Anita Allen. It also discusses the sanctity of privacy as both an inviolable right and a moral duty to respect intimacy, in addition to the effects on patient privacy from the transformation of American medicine and technology.

Considering the healthcare industry's appetite for protected health information, this chapter explores the legislative and regulatory activities enabling the access, use, and disclosure of individuals' health information. Protecting the privacy and autonomy of normative stakeholders while liberating data through health information technologies is also discussed. Specifically, this chapter explores interoperability of electronic medical records and its implications to the historically binary relationship between the physician and patient.

The proliferation of digital information, the ubiquity of the big data phenomenon, and the emergence of artificial intelligence, machine learning, and algorithmic decision-making not only drive healthcare innovation, but they also endanger patient autonomy. This chapter probes the opportunities and ethical complexities of big data and health data dependent technologies. In demonstrating how accountable healthcare leaders must consider the moral rights of their normative stakeholders, the chapter concludes with an exposition of an ethical framework for data use that has at its heart a better respect for human dignity.[4]

Confidentiality and the Ethics of Secrecy

Secrets live in the recesses of every person and define aspects of selfhood that intentionally remain hidden to preserve that which is uniquely human and different.[5] Much of human behavior is driven by the need to wall off others from access to secrets that reveal human aspirations, experiences, and desires. And the fear of public disclosure of private truths is often a strong motivator for concealment and even deception. However, trust is the antidote for such fear.

Trust in others is a human value that enables intimacy. It is most needed when one is no longer in control.[6] Surrendering control to a trusted other allows for the release of inhibitions that can obstruct human growth and flourishing. It creates a tie that binds the one who reveals an unknown to the recipient who now conceals, through the presumed inviolable bond of confidentiality. In such confidential relations, the confidant assumes the obligation not to use what has been revealed to harm the confider, or to share it with third parties without the confider's consent.[7] The trust imbued in such confidential relations is what seals the commitment of the moral agents to preserve entrusted secrets.

Moral agents cloaked under the seal of confidentiality are found anywhere and everywhere humans interact, including families, businesses, friendships, and professions. Particularly in the healthcare setting, the principle of confidentiality and the moral and legal obligations emerging from it can be thought of as a kind of security blanket protecting the secrets of a variety of stakeholders. However, confidentiality in healthcare today is a porous obligation, and it can be argued that the blanket is threadbare in many places. Medical secrecy in healthcare is a controversial matter as confidentiality is frequently abdicated to advance the interests of persons other than the patient.[8] What follows explores the anatomy of a secret and the moral agency that protects its vitality.

Keeping Secrets

Suggesting that humans are incapable of committing to an unbreakable confidence, Benjamin Franklin warned that, "[t]hree may keep a secret, if two of them are dead."[9] Franklin might be surprised to learn that according to some, if two of the three are dead, there are no secrets at all. Because traditional conceptions of secrecy hold that without a person from whom information is withheld, secrecy cannot occur. In essence, there is no secrecy at all when one is alone.[10] However, this book adopts the perspectives advanced by Slepian, Chun and Mason that "an individual has a secret from the moment he or she decides to withhold information" often long before they are in the presence of the person from whom they are concealing.[11] One's thoughts, and the details about their most intimate self that are not outwardly and openly expressed, are secrets. As such, keeping secrets – those facts or things that people intend to be "kept from the knowledge of others or shared only confidentially with a few"[12] – is a quality of humanness, because humans keep secrets.

Anita Kelly suggests that "secrecy is a nearly universal phenomenon and being able to keep personal secrets may even be seen as a sign of maturation."[13] It is self-control in the most literal sense. Keeping secrets about oneself demonstrates respect for the demarcation line between public and private life. It demonstrates respect for individual autonomy. Even though giving up control of a burdensome secret to another *can* be emancipating, collective, and individual dignity is enriched by the awareness that one can control their secrets. And it is important to note that while all deception requires secrecy, all secrecy is not meant to deceive.[14] Someone may keep secrets by omission – that is, intentionally withholding something about themselves – to avoid unpleasant or painful memories, without actively lying about the subject.

Sissela Bok's concept of the ethics of secrecy points to the importance of secrets in healthcare. She writes that humans are most comfortable and assured when they confront areas of life that they know intimately, or belong to, and "within that area, what we keep secret requires our most intense and active attention."[15] In contrast she contends that even amidst the many areas of life about which we know little, "we also experience as secrets the spaces from which we feel shut out."[16] Such is the case for the patient seeking care from a physician. The patient knows her body and her thoughts better than anyone and has elected to keep certain intimacies concealed, entrusting them to her physician. She similarly holds as secret that which she does not know but will soon discover from her physician.

Bok underscores that the sacred and the secret have been related through Latin etymology since antiquity.[17] The *secretum*, as something set apart and hidden, and the *arcanum* as that which is spiritually mysterious, are preserved in contemporary secret keeping. Keeping secrets is particularly sacrosanct in the physician-patient relationship. The confidentiality of secrets disclosed to physicians, either through direct communication or through physical revelation, is a fundamental presupposition of every medical encounter.[18]

Quality care depends upon mutual transparency and trust. It is widely recognized that patients who do not trust particular physicians, or healthcare generally, are less likely to seek care or be compliant with treatment protocols.[19] As such, the willing patient imparts information to her physician in confidence and trust[20] and once a secret is revealed, the physician's duty of confidentiality to keep her secret is invoked. In this regard, keeping secrets within the confines of the physician patient relationship has been long considered binary. Since secrets involve revealing information, presumably known only to the patient, so too is the truth of what is revealed.

To Tell the Truth

People typically choose to conceal information about their health long before they see a provider. Aches, pains, moods, and changes in a person's body may all be things that people keep secret, perhaps out of fear, indifference, independence, invincible ignorance, denial, or some combination thereof. Remaining true to themselves however, the intimate relationship that people enjoy with their own body and mind, according to Anita Allen, means that many diseases and injuries are invisible to other people. Because health conditions often remain hidden, most of what people learn about themselves and their conditions occur extra-professionally, through self-encounters.[21] Nevertheless, for the clinician to serve the patient's best interests, patients must realize some sacrifices to secrecy and willingness to tell the truth.

Many norms of social interaction are interrupted in the clinical setting. Questions are asked, and narratives are revealed during care that does not typically transpire in polite company. Discussing one's body and its conditions transparently and revealing one's experiences and emotions taps into the patient's fragility and vulnerability, which "follow individuals into their doctors' offices."[22] Considering all that is exposed through the clinical encounter, and in recognition of the fact that information is the most versatile resource in the healthcare setting,[23] the need for truthful disclosures is indisputable. Both the clinician and the patient are keepers of secrets in a trust-based relationship that is strictly dependent upon the moral imperative of veracity.[24]

But people often lie to manage information.[25] Of the many domains of human life where lying is prevalent, the healthcare delivery setting calls for special attention.[26] It is widely acknowledged that most patients lie to their doctors to avoid negative consequences, to escape embarrassment, and to be presented in a more favorable light. The most common are lies about diet, smoking, and alcohol habits, as well as sexual activities and preferences.[27] Some lies are also rooted in the patient's desire to achieve some economic gain such as public welfare benefits, or other attempts to defraud the healthcare system. Regardless of the motive, it is understood within the context of secrecy in healthcare, that "lying is an expression of a power relationship, whether it is used as a tactic to impose ones' power, or, on the contrary, to resist the other's power."[28]

The moral imperative to tell the truth is incumbent upon both the patient and the physician who have entered a treating relationship.[29] Conveying the truth provides the greatest opportunity for successful care delivery and outcomes. Intentionally providing inaccurate or untrustworthy facts may skew the physician's assessment and diagnosis. At its extreme, people with factitious disorders, or act as if they have illnesses or symptoms, produce unique, though not uncommon trials for the physician.[30] Although there is little formal guidance on the physician's duty to treat the knowingly untruthful patient, the physician-patient relationship "is a reciprocal one, and if patients don't meet their duty to be truthful, then doctors do not have a responsibility to continue to care for them."[31] Withholding the truth is dangerous. It is harmful to the patient, to the HCO, and may justify the physician's decision to discharge the patient from his care.[32] While truth telling is fraught with moral dilemmas, the physician's duty to keep secrets is derived from the ethical principle of patient autonomy as well as legal obligations respecting the patient's right of privacy.[33]

Professional Duty and Legal Obligation

Both mental health professionals and laypersons alike concur that confessing one's secrets is good for the soul, and that revealing secrets about oneself is cathartic.[34] In fact, relieving oneself of the burdens of their secrets is reported to have actual health benefits. Ridding oneself of secrets has been shown to improve immunological functioning, relieve stress, and even reduce the number of physician office visits. [35] While most of the research on secrets has focused on secrets about oneself, little work has been done on the willingness and ability of keepers of secrets to keep them confidential.[36]

However, since antiquity, respect for patient confidentiality has been a fundamental moral precept and professional responsibility of physicians. The promise to "not divulge, as reckoning that all such should be kept secret"[37] during the treating relationship resonates today. It can be argued that society's confidence in the sanctity of physician-patient communications is as relevant as the confidence held by the patient. However, the dynamics of modern healthcare, and the demands of civil society to adjudicate the truth are disruptors to many of the traditional rules of confidentiality, thus creating ethical dilemmas for clinicians. Thereby, leaving some to argue that confidentiality is dead.[38] Challenged by advanced data analytics, complex care management, patient data-dependent technologies, regulatory requirements, clinical collaboration, as well as the rules of civil and criminal procedure, the mantle of confidentiality is ambiguous.

The Duty of Confidentiality

Confidentiality and a patient's expectations of privacy are often mistakenly conflated and confused. To understand the difference requires a focus on the duties and rights of the confidant and confider, respectively. The physician's duty of confidentiality is supported by collateral and corresponding obligations to the patient. With the patient's interest at the forefront of his decisions, the physician has a duty to uphold the confidence in the physician/patient relationship generally, and the patient's legal right to privacy, specifically.[39]

The legal right to privacy, which is an expectation of confidentiality that is enforceable by and rooted in law, is a preeminent concern in contemporary healthcare. The legal right is addressed more fully later in this chapter. However, for purposes of this discussion it is important to recognize that patients forfeit some of their privacy rights when they enter treating relationships with their physician. Consenting for treatment often includes the patient's acknowledgment that certain information they provide may be subsequently redisclosed as required by law.

In some cases, confidentiality can be open-ended and must yield for the greater good. However, such yielding should only occur certain instances – when the severity of not disclosing, and the life and health of third parties would outmuscle patient confidentiality.[40] It may also be necessary for the sake of the patient that physicians share medical secrets with other clinicians on the treatment team, or even unaffiliated physicians in furtherance of population health, patient safety, or quality of care initiatives. Because the duty of confidentiality is no longer absolute; indiscretions and imprudent practices can result in breaches of patient confidentiality.

The intimacy of the physician-patient relationship enables physicians and other healthcare professionals to form subjective impressions of the patient, their habits, lifestyles, and other tangential activities. When sensitive information and impressions are shared beyond the patient treatment relationship, these disclosures can cause irreparable harm to patients, their reputations, and to their personal dignity.[41] Medicine today is often practiced in teams comprised of more than just the medical personnel involved in a patient's care. As these teams interact, largely innocent yet inappropriate disclosures of patient secrets as well as subjective impressions increasingly occur in public areas of the hospital such as corridors, elevators, stairwells, and cafeterias. Research demonstrates that breaches of confidentiality within the hospital care setting are a major problem – occurring as frequently as once every 62 hours.[42] And, physicians do not always know how to reconcile the need to share information with the obligation to avoid a breach.[43] This uncertainty is most evident when considering privileged communications.

The Evidentiary Privilege

Justice, according to principles of jurisprudence, refers to the restoration of balance by ensuring that which is morally due is delivered. For justice to be served, it is necessary to have full and transparent discovery and disclosure of relevant facts of a dispute. The failure to reveal something that may influence the restoration of balance in society can defile justice. All too often, the need to discover and reveal secrets through truthful testimony is the pivot point between justice and injustice. When facts become secrets shrouded in impenetrable confidentiality, the confidential relationship can make for a precarious foundation where secrecy and legal equity collide.

Not all evidence concerning a case or controversy is discoverable. The evidentiary privilege – the right of one to refuse to testify about matters or the right to prevent another from doing so – permits the suppression of evidence obtained through certain confidential relationships.[44] The physician-patient privilege, recognized alongside the attorney-client and priest-penitent privileges, accompanies, and sustains patient secrecy. This evidentiary privilege protects the communications made by both the patient *and* the physician.

Patient statements are protected from compelled disclosure in a legal proceeding. As the holder of the privilege, the patient may waive the privilege and allow for testimony that would make public the secrets she shared with her physician. However, the physician is not permitted to waive *his* privilege without her consent. With few exceptions, statements made by the physician to the patient are also protected as privileged. The evidentiary privilege is critical. It enshrouds and insulates the sacredness of physician-patient exchanges beyond the bounds of mere confidentiality. It asserts that there can be a greater societal interest in protecting trust and preserving secrecy than in revealing the information.[45] Reverence for the fiduciary relationship between the physician and the patient can, and frequently does, outweigh the need to provide testimony.

But the need for compelled disclosure of patient information to a third party – what is in effect a breach of confidentiality – can override the fiduciary relationship. Many departures from the duty of confidentiality are not unlawful or inappropriate at all but are essential to public health and policy, despite the impact on patient privacy.[46] Health oversight activities such as disclosures to public health authorities for infectious disease control, workers' compensation claims, and certain national priority disclosures are a few examples. Physicians may also disclose patient secrets when defending themselves in a lawsuit brought by the patient. But it must be noted that the lines between what is protected under the duty of confidentiality, what is required to be disclosed by law, and what is necessary for the benefit of society are not always clearly delineated. In healthcare, confidentiality is not absolute because is contextual. Determining when it is appropriate to break the seal of confidentiality requires consideration of the values and interests of the affected stakeholders as well as the facts and circumstances of the disclosure. The following section illustrates the complexities of the clinical environment and the need for principled and contextually based decision-making to support confidentiality.

Clinical Ethics

Applying ethical principles to guide moral decision-making, demands that the principles be "specific to the needs of the particular contexts."[47] Nowhere in healthcare do ethical principles align with specific contextual needs more than in direct clinical care settings. *Clinical care* defines the humanness of medicine through direct physical contact and observation and has the most notable impact on respect for human dignity and well-being. The therapeutic relationships created within the clinical setting are supported by the core principles of autonomy, beneficence, non-maleficence, and justice.[48]

Post, Bluestein and Dubler maintain that these core ethical principles cannot provide sufficient moral analysis if they are merely applied mechanically, or in a vacuum, as they are reliant on context and narrative. To contribute to ethical analysis, principles must be applied against the values and standards that matter most to patients and other stakeholders, as revealed through the patient narrative. The clinical context is fertile with ethical and value conflicts such as power imbalances, access to care, decisions to forego treatment, and informed consent, to name just a few.[49] As an instrument for moral reasoning, core ethical principles inform and guide those matters that resonate most profoundly with the gravitas of patient health. Specifically, this section examines how the ethics of secrecy exists in relationship with ethical principle of autonomy and the duty of confidentiality; particularly when these principles and values are in conflict.

Autonomy: *The Patient's Voice*

The duty of confidentiality, and the patient's expectation of privacy in health-care are constituents of the respect for the principle of autonomy.[50] Individual autonomy is generally accepted to mean the freedom to make choices without coercive and controlling influences. Those choices also include the patient's right to decide what, and to whom, personal information about them is to be used, disclosed, and stored. It also includes the patient's right to refuse access to information they otherwise do not know about themselves. Autonomy empowers patients with the tools to control decisions about their own health and well-being generally. It allows the patient to participate actively in their care. Respect for patient autonomy is respect for the patient's voice.

As a principle of common morality, autonomy imposes obligations on those who have a duty to protect the patient's interests. The patient's right to expect freedom from constraints, coercion, and influences impose what Beauchamp and Childress refer to as "negative obligations" on the actions of physicians and other moral agents. Avoiding paternalism, or the intentional countermanding of patient preferences by the physician because he believes his judgment of what benefits or harms the patient[51] is best, is an example of a negative obligation. Complementary positive obligations are also imposed on physicians and other healthcare professionals. An example of a positive obligation is the prescription that healthcare professionals provide sufficient information and facts to enable the patient to make informed decisions about themselves and their health.[52]

Beauchamp and Childress maintain that these positive and negative obligations are seminal for the moral principles of veracity/truth-telling as well as informed consent – which insulates "patient autonomy."[53] Respect for autonomy acknowledged through informed consent helps to ensure that dignity is preserved, choice is unencumbered, and the patient's voice is heard.

Informed Consent: *Telling It Like It Is?*

The original meaning of *inform*, from the Latin *informare*, meant to give form to something, to give it shape or to modify it; and eventually came to be used more narrowly to mean "instruct" or "educate."[54] The concept of informed consent as applied to clinical ethics is, in essence, a combination of both meanings. Within the context of clinical care, shared patient secrets are translated according to the clinician's understanding, clinical observations, and overall assessments. The secrets are further transferred into personal health information that, along with data from collateral sources such as lab and diagnostic information, consultative, and other relevant longitudinal information, become part of the patient's medical record.

Informed consent for treatment speaks to the right to self-determination, and the power to exercise control over oneself, avoiding exploitation, and especially making choices about how one's secrets are kept, shared, and used.[55] Originally a legal doctrine associated with any unwelcomed touching or battery, informed consent currently enjoys standing as a critical expression of patient autonomy, and occupies a dominant role in healthcare. For most patients, being a consumer of health services means purchasing services blindly. Meaningful informed consent emboldens patients to unmask the unknown. Done well, it provides the patient with necessary and appropriate information to help shape decisions. But, because the informed consent process is highly contextual, its effectiveness is not absolute.

The intersection of the principles of beneficence, non-maleficence, and justice with informed consent raises questions about the amount and kind of information provided to patients to adequately support their independent decision-making. Sawicki writes that legalists choose concepts like materiality and relevance of the information to define the scope of disclosure, despite the subjectivity of those measurements.[56] She further contends that many patients consider other subjective factors beyond medical efficacy when contemplating care decisions. Consideration for the burdens potentially imposed on caregivers and other third parties, costs, religious, and cultural values, and impacts to the quality of life also drive patient decisions. Ultimately, however, it is the physician who decides the type of information and the spectrum of issues disclosed during the informed consent conversation with the patient. The extent to which physician decision-making authority over patient secrets is ethically justified, implicates physician paternalism, violates confidentiality, or in the most extreme cases, creates potential abuses of power[57] must be a matter of further ethical discourse within specific clinical settings.

Dissecting the legal elements of the duty of disclosure under informed consent law in the United States is beyond the scope of this book. However, it is important to call attention to the inherent limitations of the legal doctrine which Thaddeus Pope maintains impede patient empowerment. Pope asserts the physician's duty to disclose is too narrow in that considerations about the information disclosed to the patient are measured only by what objective hypothetical patients would need to know, not his patient.[58] This hypothetical assumption fails to give credit to the patient's ability to consider other factors when contemplating treatment. Traditional views of informed consent fail to consider what matters most to the patient. As such, patient self-determination is compromised when subjective considerations are not respected.

HCOs share in the ethical responsibility for providing sufficient information to patients. To that end, policies and procedures addressing informed consent ought to be revisited and strategically reconsidered with the patient's voice in mind. Traditional views of informed consent must shift from check-box procedures to systemic approaches designed to include what matters to the patient. This must also include disclosures of patient quality measures, the types of data used to arrive at these measures, as well as the potential for subsequent redisclosures of data. Providing this information along with participation in meaningful communication with physicians will redefine the physician-patient dyad in order that patients can make *truly* informed decisions.[59]

Psychotherapy: Secrets Kept...Secrets Shared

Few areas of healthcare venture closer to the core of humanness than the psychotherapeutic practice. Barriers to secrecy are whittled away as the patient reveals the mosaic of her life; intimate pieces and parts of her past and present that may never otherwise be shared, except for the therapeutic encounter with the mental health provider. Psychotherapeutic practice has long respected the rule of confidentiality stating that information disclosed by the patient to the therapist during therapy may not be shared with others without the patient's prior express written consent.[60] Freud considered the need to preserve confidentiality of psychotherapy quintessential to successful treatment. So much so, that he encouraged patients not to even reveal the fact that they were *in* treatment with anyone else, including intimates, spouses, and other family members.[61]

Not surprisingly, concealing and even denying that one was in therapy in Freud's time did not require much persuasion. The centuries-old stigma associated with behavioral health and mental illness descends from a dark time when ignorance about people with behavioral issues was the norm. Mental illness has long been attributed to sin and the work of the devil, and those who suffered from it were often deemed insane, and were locked away in asylums or madhouses.[62] The stigma of mental illness remains a problem today, and persons with such conditions have encountered discrimination, even after laws were passed banning such activities.[63] To that end, the fear that privacy will be lost in psychotherapy is often a compelling reason why people forego treatment at all. The fear of laying bare the secrets of one's fallibility remains profound.

The rule of confidentiality protecting these secrets is an ethical principle, professional obligation, and in many jurisdictions is supported by state law.[64] Despite these safeguards, ethical and societal conflicts unique to behavioral health and psychotherapy arise when breaching confidentiality is necessary to prevent imminent harms to others, or to deliver justice. The tension between the principles of autonomy, beneficence, and non-maleficence are vividly illustrated in this moral dilemma.

Protecting a Public Good

United States Supreme Court associate justice John Paul Stevens, in his seminal opinion *Jaffee v. Redmond*, opined that mental health for the citizenry was "a public good of transcendent importance."[65] It is indeed. It is widely acknowledged that good health is an integral part of a good life, which includes, according to the World Health Organization, "a state of complete physical, mental and social well-being..."[66] Mental health for the citizenry presupposes that all who need it will receive it.

Underscoring the gravity of the psychotherapist privilege, Stevens distinguished it from the physician privilege according to the need for and ability to obtain personal information. He noted that physicians are, in most cases, able to treat patients through physical examination alone, or from limited objective information. This is most often the nature of emergency care, when many patients are unable to speak, or to aid the physician in evaluating symptoms.[67] Many diseases and conditions are treatable without the patient speaking a word.

That is not always the case for behavioral health. Psychotherapy requires the disclosure of secrets that are often not observable or discoverable until they are unleashed by the patient in probing exchanges with the therapist. People who keep secrets from themselves without realizing are said to be experiencing repression. In contrast, self-concealment occurs when one knowingly keeps things that they consider distressing or negative from others.[68] Treatment for both conditions depends upon transparency and assurances that these secrets, many of which invoke feelings of shame and guilt, are cloaked in privilege. Thus, the psychotherapist privilege, according to Justice Stevens, serves the public good[69] by enabling paths to treatment for infirmities that would otherwise remain hidden and unrealized.

Informed consent, as a path to treatment, is stringently upheld in the psychotherapeutic setting. Derived from the mental health professional code of ethics as well as respect for autonomy, informed consent in this context is the patient's right to voluntarily agree to participate in counseling and other mental health services. Consent can only be granted after the scope of services and counseling processes are described in terms sufficiently comprehensible to the patient.[70] However, an inherent irony concerning the efficacy of informed consent in the psychotherapeutic setting is that much of what the patient agrees to disclose may not even be known by the patient until the process of therapeutic self-discovery uncovers such inner secrets.[71] Successful therapy reveals the unconscious. Therefore, according to Lear, confidentiality is constitutive of the psychoanalytic process itself, and is not merely a value to consider. When the patient no longer keeps secrets from *themselves*, they transform their interests from being a secret-keeper to holder of privacy rights.[72] The contents of those secrets also may subject the therapist to a dual allegiance; that which they have to their patient, and that which they may owe to society.

Protecting the Public

The dual allegiance presents unique moral dilemmas for the therapist. It often forces the therapist to become a double agent, as his sole concern is no longer the welfare of his patient.[73] Consider for example, what happens when the patient who has been sexually abused tells her story. Doing so is an exercise of her freedom, and an expression of her willingness to surrender control to another whose judgment and discretion she trusts. The psychotherapist or other behavioral health professional takes possession of her story.[74] While telling her story, if the abused patient expresses violence toward her offender, or confesses that she wishes to engage in actions harmful to herself or others, the therapist's moral and legal obligations may change. The therapist must confront the moral dilemma that Mosher and Berman warn of when "unlocking one secret may require the creation of another."[75] Those secondary secrets and ancillary allegiances demonstrate that confidentiality is never absolute,[76] and that the therapist is obligated by principles of beneficence, and non-maleficence to fulfill his duty to necessary third parties as well.

The psychotherapeutic privilege – which the *Jaffee* Court deemed worthy of protecting the public good – is not an absolute privilege. Courts have created volumes of precedent to support serving the public good through evidentiary disclosure and testimony at the expense of patient confidentiality. The case of *Tarasoff v. Regents of the University of California* explored one of the most remarkable incidents in psychotherapy.[77] It examined the duty of a psychiatrist who learned, through outpatient counseling, that his client intended to, and eventually did, kill an unnamed, yet readily identifiable girl. The Court in *Tarasoff*[78] decreed therapists incur obligations to protect third parties when the patient expresses a serious intent to harm themselves or an identifiable other, and that harm is likely to occur in the present, or future.

This "duty to warn" obligation is an exception to the duty of confidentiality even when, under common law, there is no legal duty to prevent one person from harming another.[79] It bespeaks of the awareness of, and ethical justification for revealing patient secrets for the public good – a good that can be antithetical to the values of the patient. This public beneficence which seeks to "pursue and secure public benefits and minimize personal and public harm"[80] is also at the heart of debates surrounding genomic determinism and the disclosure of genomic secrets.

The Genomic Dilemma

The moral value of confidentiality, and the duty to respect secrets is no longer confined to those belonging to patients and research data subjects. When ethical conflicts and competing obligations such as those exemplified in psychotherapy arise, principles of beneficence and non-maleficence may override confidentiality for the sake of a *non-patient* third party, creating a moral dilemma.[81] Even when the third-party benefit is imperative, those principles may beget a moral predicament for the physician. Such predicaments must reconcile not merely how much information to disclose to the unsuspecting and perhaps disinterested patient or non-patient, but also *what kind* of information to disclose, and perhaps most importantly, whether to disclose information at all. These dilemmas are traversing unchartered terrain especially in the context of genomic mapping, genotyping, and genetic testing information.

Secrets released from whole genome sequences provide "important insights into the medical and related life prospects of individuals as well as their relatives – who most likely did not consent to the sequencing procedure."[82] Whole genomic sequencing unleashes a person's entire genome along with all its genetic variations or changes in the DNA sequence. These variants provide information about genetic traits, as well as disease carrier status, and susceptibility to catastrophic diseases such as some many cancers and late onset diseases such as Alzheimer's.[83]

The expansive and predictive power of genomic medicine creates an infinite constellation of health secrets belonging to patients, patients' family, as well as indeterminate groups of people. Even without the full sequence, many of these secrets are revealed from information obtained in the ordinary course of care itself – not directly from the patient. Discrete genetic tests examine specific genes among the more than 20,000 known human genes, to identify a particular disease variant, all without the patient uttering a single word to her doctor. Consequently, the physician then holds the power to disclose, to the patient or the patient's family and relatives, information he has learned through linked genomic information even when the individual has not shared any of his or her genetic information directly.[84] The duties of the physician and the rights of patients and others to know, and *not* to know, predictive genomic information is a probing matter that defies traditional understanding of the duty of confidentiality and the practice of medicine.

The Right to Know Oneself

Currently there are a variety of methods and justifications for knowing and understanding one's genomic information. It is widely held that patients can derive much benefit and personalized health advice from their genomic information. Pharmacogenomics, for example, can predict an individual's drug responses merely from the appearance of certain genetic factors, and nutrigenomics can determine potential adverse effects from food and specific food ingredients. Both discoveries may contribute to optimal health.[85] Obtaining genetic-based ancestry information through direct-to-consumer testing services can have life-altering effects on a person's sense-of-self and identity connecting them to unknown and unanticipated persons and conditions.

In addition, people can access their own genetic information obtained from tests administered in the clinical setting, typically involving a physician. This is the traditional venue for those who present with a medical indication, or symptom of a disease where genetic factors have been shown to play an important role.[86] Initially concerned with disease pathology alone, the idea of genomic information carries with it the preconception that it forecasts and foretells of doom-filled preconditions, impending maladies, and dreadful life and death predictions. However, Siddhartha Mukherjee reveals that "genetics has crossed over from the strand of pathology to the strand of normalcy."[87] That is to say that this new science can be applied to better understand culture, history, language, memory, and other characteristics of human life and human destiny;[88] essentially evolving toward a science of normalcy from which humankind can benefit.

In that vein, Prainsack aptly points out that advances in clinical genetic analyses often disclose incidental findings of information relating to conditions beyond what was intended by the test.[89] It is presumed, however, that the testing and extraction of information from the genetic fingerprint is an expression of the person's autonomy and free-will as validated by informed consent and serves their best interest to receive the unlocked secrets about themselves. When that information references the health of others such as monozygotic siblings or other filial relationships, or when it reveals undisclosed paternity or ancestry, the ethical, social, and psychological effects of knowing that information on such stakeholders are not trivial.[90] Whether one's autonomous right to learn their own genetic secrets should entail preventing such disclosures to family members who may share that genetic link is fodder for ethical debate. To that end, relational autonomy or feminist ethics suggests people also have moral responsibilities to each other because they stand in relationship with each other; they have an interest in maintaining family and community relations. In short, one person's choices affect another person's autonomy.[91]

Consider how the duty to warn balances the patient's expectations of confidentiality against harm to third parties. However, genomic analytic techniques provide insight into unanticipated findings concerning potential health conditions that could affect and harm third parties and family members, particularly if the predisposition to the condition remained unrealized and unmanaged.[92] The moral predicament for the physician is exacerbated when the patient refuses to share information concerning the risky hereditary condition to those who are affected.

While acting upon the knowledge of the unanticipated predisposition to disease or disability may prevent eventual harm to the third-party stakeholders or their offspring, unsolicited disclosure of disease susceptibility may also create more psychological harm to them than benefit.[93] Clearly there are legitimate beneficent reasons for disclosing such information to third parties. Equally important however, when assessing arguments from beneficence and non-maleficence, is the family member who, because of the information learned, has been unwittingly exposed to troubling realities. For them, the bell cannot be un-rung.

The Right to Be Forgotten

Consider how, in a world where wearable devices and the Internet of Things gather and store digital information on everyone, the increased aggregation of "the quantified self" portends that people will know things about themselves that were never contemplated.[94] The expanse of the digital data environment means that a person's genomic information may also be accessible outside of the HCO as well. For many, that is a welcomed opportunity. Moreover, the commercialization of genomics, and the explosive interest in personal ancestry and do-it-yourself genomic testing information, suggests that there is an unmet need to know more about one's genomic profile.[95] It may be argued, however, that persons may obtain information about themselves that they would prefer not knowing, particularly if certain of their genetic factors produce unexpected characteristics or associations with different communities of people.[96] Ross suggests that even though most of this commercial genomic testing information provides a snapshot, and not the full genomic sequencing, there is great potential for false worry and misinformation.[97]

This potential for false worry is ever present with genetic analysis performed within clinical settings as well. Consciously avoiding harms from worry and anxiety is the preeminent ethical justification for a physician to withhold the truth from their patients. While veracity and truth-telling are essential to respect autonomy, the matter of disclosing genomic information brings to bear the distinction between telling the truth, and the right to the truth. And while the right to be told the truth is a core component of informed consent, clinicians are confronted with the moral dilemma to determine when it is right and just to be told something less.[98]

Much of the moral dilemma confronting the physician, who straddles the duty of confidentiality and the duty and obligation to disclose, or not to disclose genomic information, lies in the fact that medicine has changed. Sheila Jasanoff contends that the primary mission of medicine, to make sick people well and to enable the apparently well, but at-risk, to remain healthy is vexed by genetic science. "Knowing bodies in a new way, through a person's genetic code, opens up the prospects for unprecedented intrusions on cherished rights of liberty, equality and privacy"[99] which the physician, and even the HCO, must now factor into their decisions. The physician not only must consider these consequences as they relate to his patient, but also through the lens of someone he may not know.

Frequently cited justifications for disclosing genetic information to family members include the importance of conveying reproductive risks of inheritable conditions in order to enable timely reproductive decisions.[100] In addition, it has been argued that genetic information is familial rather than personal and therefore is communal in nature, and not to share it with at-risk family members would be selfish.[101] In either case, it is widely recognized that, at the very least, the physician has an ethical obligation to attempt to persuade the patient to discuss the hereditary risk with the affected family members.[102] The success of these persuasive attempts, while difficult to assess, underscore the critical role that the physician plays in respecting the ethics of secrecy hidden within the patient's family tree; the roots of which encroach upon the privacy of all of those identified.

Privacy

Privacy is a timeless concept. Judith Decrew asserts that the earliest expressions of privacy date back to antiquity, and beyond.[103] Shame and its association with good and evil has been a consequence of privacy invasions since Adam and Eve took to wearing fig leaves.[104] Noah further exhibited shame, anger, and a preference for decency over his bodily privacy, when he discovered how his sons treated his unanticipated nakedness.[105] Even the political divide between the public and private spheres of life, espoused by Aristotle, bespeaks of a desire to shield citizens from unwarranted intrusions. And, of course, humans have been whispering what they do not want others to hear since they began communicating with words and sounds. Notwithstanding its persistence for thousands of years, and despite the eager willingness of people to decry violations to their individual privacy today, it is not a concept that is well defined or understood.[106]

Privacy evokes feeling and is often defined by that feeling in the same way that "freedom" and "peace" are more emotive than precise in their meanings. This vagueness contributes to the disarray that Solove contends is the state of play for privacy today.[107] There are likely as many perceptions of privacy as there are occasions to evoke its feeling.

Considered the founding father of contemporary privacy, Alan Westin, taught that privacy is an "…[i]ndividual's claim to determine what information about himself or herself should be known to others…when such information will be communicated or obtained, and what uses will be made of it by others."[108] Despite this clear definition, what besets those who think about privacy is the need to understand more deeply what is at the core of privacy. Because it is emotive, sensitivities to privacy go beyond the act of communicating information. Whether respect for privacy is a moral claim, or legal one; whether it is an individual, or collective condition, and even the degree to which it is a societal issue are the ponderings of theorists and advocates.

Concepts and Values

Westin argued that privacy is a set of expectations created from social values that are defined by culture. It is both a psychological and physical condition originating from choices and preferences, as well as a right that one must assert an expectation for legal protection.[109] He believed that privacy debates are infinite, as they are tied to societal norms supporting human conduct that is acceptable, neutral, or advancing the public good.[110] Much of the disarray espoused by Solove is fueled by cultural variances driving privacy values and expectations. Adam Moore takes culture's influences on privacy a step beyond. He supports the notion that culture exerts significant influence on privacy but sees privacy itself as a cultural universal that drives his compelling theory that privacy is about control.

According to Moore, as a societal value, privacy is a fundamental moral claim that washes over the various privacy interests and concerns which are innately human and provides a necessary equilibrium to the examination of those interests.[111] He calls attention to the fact that privacy interests speak necessarily to the human need to control one's world. This includes the right of control over property and one's physical world, control over one's body and its capacities, the right to control decisions (often referred to as decisional privacy) as well as control over informational privacy.[112]

For Moore, "privacy…is a core human value – the right to control access to oneself is an essential part of human well-being or flourishing."[113] It is worth noting that Moore's position is consistent with the understanding of secrets suggested earlier; control over what others know about oneself does not necessarily presuppose an intent to deceive. To the contrary, privacy validates the innately human need to protect those unique facts that help to construct uniquely human lives. Moore's theory is especially appealing in healthcare as its central mission is complimentary to it – to promote human welfare. The intersection of Moore's claim of control and the acknowledgment of respect for humans is the launching point for Julie Inness's intimacy theory of the concept and value of privacy.

Inness suggests that the value of privacy is found in the moral duty to respect individuals as loving, liking and caring, autonomous and rational beings with the capacity to freely choose, and to form and develop close relationships.[114] She accepts the notion that claims to privacy are moral claims to control aspects of life, as well as to separate oneself from certain life conditions. But she suggests that merely exercising control over access to information, to oneself, or the intimate decisions of the person, are individually too narrow, and collectively too broad.[115] Instead, she refines the moral claim to control over aspects of life that involve "decisions about *intimate* information, *intimate* access and *intimate* action (emphasis added)."[116]

Intimacy claims, for Inness, are the core of privacy. Whether something is intimate depends upon the roles that the particular aspect of life plays for the individual in furtherance of that which they love, like, or care about.[117] For example, a patient sharing private aspects of her life with her physician in the course of treatment is intimate, according to Inness's theory, in that she wishes to exercise control while advancing that which she likes – her health – with someone she has engaged in a caring relationship. The value of intimacy cannot be overstated and is but one installment in Anita Allen's claim for self-directed accountability vis-à-vis personal privacy.

"Privacy," admits Allen, "is purposely personal."[118] Yet, privacy is also a foundational good of our society that is required of freedom, dignity, and the preservation of individual and collective good character. This fundamental good demands of people, in addition to the moral obligation to respect others' privacy, "a moral or ethical obligation to protect their own privacy."[119] That is to say that while moral duties are typically other-oriented, Allen's accountability theory argues that a duty to self, while a second order duty, is necessary to support the duty to others.[120] Bi-directional privacy accountability is especially cogent in healthcare as the failure of someone to reasonably protect his own health information from unauthorized use could foreseeably cause downstream harm to his intimates, or other close associations within his community. This conflation of other and self-oriented moral agency reflects the importance of stakeholder accountability in matters of personal privacy.

Privacy as a Healthcare Value

Whether the idea of privacy generates an emotional response, or a collective reaction to specific legal doctrines, or the absence of any such doctrines, privacy remains an amorphous concept.[121] There are, however, applications of personal privacy that are clearly valued for the ends they achieve.[122] Privacy for the sake of ensuring that people are protected from unwarranted intrusions into their home, or to their physical person is rooted in the tenets of civilized society. However,

Solove underscores the reality that "the matters we consider private change over time...because of changing attitudes, institutions, living conditions and technology"[123] and are often contextual. Yet, few examples of the value of privacy are as controversial as in contemporary healthcare. How much, and to what extent must stakeholder privacy be protected, or even sacrificed to ensure that the HCO meets its obligations to deliver care for the common good is an evolving moral dilemma.

Intimate details about a patient's body, their mind, and all their life experiences, including those surreptitious trials that may affect their health and dignity, are bathed in privacy. In healthcare, physical privacy is understandably limited, though not without reasonable protections against unwarranted contact or exposure, as are aspects of decisional privacy, which generally fall within the purview of informed consent.[124] Informational privacy is concerned with the discipline around preventing unauthorized access, use and disclosure of a person's protected health information (PHI). This chapter is concerned with the legal and moral challenges created by physical, decisional, and informational privacy; although as demonstrated throughout this writing, the demarcation line between all three is blurring.

There is great irony in the idea that individual privacy in healthcare is controversial. On its face, the physician-patient encounter is steeped in privacy protections stemming from the duty of confidentiality. Presumably, the physical environment also bespeaks of secrecy. Consider the curtains separating patients in the emergency department, computer monitors rendered unreadable by snoopers, and increased preference for private inpatient rooms. "Patients' privacy in hospital settings is widely recognized as important for patients' well-being and satisfaction."[125] In addition, healthcare privacy is heavily regulated in the United States, and is subject to a wide array of state and federal laws and regulations restricting data use.[126] Nevertheless, the law cannot protect against all the unintended consequences from use of health data, nor can compliance with it alone resolve the privacy challenges.

Technology and medical advances, and the insatiable hunger for more data, better data, and faster access to it nearly always conflict with decades-old laws governing their use. Yet, nothing can happen without access to data. Every aspect of the transformation of American healthcare described hereunder is dependent upon better access to patient health information. The introduction of evidenced-based medicine at the turn of twenty-first century medicine, whereby clinical decisions relied upon research evidence rather than clinician judgment alone, virtually demanded access to aggregate and unmasked patient information. Eventually evidenced-based alone gave way to value-based medicine. Value-based medicine is "the integration of best research evidence with clinical expertise and patient values."[127] As with the concept of privacy, value in this sense is a relative term, and has evolved to mean decisions that yield increased life expectancy and quality of life.[128] The transformation translates to an increased need for more and more patient data. Accordingly, the shift in focus to a value-based enterprise means that health information is increasing dominating the list of organizational concerns from the boardrooms to the operating rooms.[129]

Protected Health Information and the Need to Know

Healthcare is an information business. Treatment, quality measures, patient safety, efficacious clinical outcomes, clinical research, and reliance on advanced technology are just a handful of the objectives that depend upon the acquisition and use of patient information.[130] But personal patient data has not always been the commodity that it is today. Prior to the introduction of computerized data in the 1970s, most data sets were created manually from the individuals treating the patients.[131] As recently as twenty years ago, physician notes and the mental impressions of his patient encounters were still written by hand, memorialized on paper, and treated with confidential reverence. All of that has changed.

Regardless of its form, patient healthcare information is rich with data that can serve many purposes. Aside from its clinical attributes, it contains demographic insights about patient preferences and lifestyles, can provide economic forecasts for the HCO, exposes a financial snapshot of the patient, and can even include information about U.S. government agencies. Many organizations not in the business of healthcare collect and use patient health information from their vendors as part of doing business with them; insurance, financial institutions, education, and real estate, to name a few.[132] To that end, the mobilization of public policy wishing to protect health insurance for unwell employees during the 1990s, whetted appetites for what would amount to a far-reaching liberation of personal patient information.

Access, Use, and Disclosure: Stakeholder Expectations

The Health Insurance Portability and Accountability Act of 1996,[133] was introduced as part of the Clinton Administration's attempt to socialize healthcare in the United States. It brought to light the need to ensure that workers would not lose their health insurance if they changed jobs or had pre-existing health conditions. Among the portability provisions, HIPAA established administrative simplification requirements enabling insurance claims and payments to process more efficiently between providers and insurance companies. Establishment of uniform electronic transmittals of transaction code sets provided for greater ease of sharing patient information.[134]

Today, the acronym HIPAA is synonymous with healthcare privacy, yet the Act is not a per se privacy regulation. In fact, establishing a privacy right was never part of the original legislative intent. Rather, concern for the privacy of individual medical information was a regulatory after-thought. As compliance with HIPAA required that volumes of medical information be converted to rapid-pace electronic transmittals, Congress became increasingly concerned with the privacy and security of the PHI. Through a series of legislative and executive missteps, and political posturing, the Department of Health and Human Services promulgated the HIPAA Privacy Rule (2002) and Security Rule (2005) to address the need for and create the individual's codified right to privacy in their PHI.[135]

Since then, controlling how protected health information is accessed, used, stored, and disclosed has become an imperative in contemporary healthcare. The HIPAA Privacy Rule provides federally protected patient privacy rights to access, amend, restrict, and account for disclosures of their personal health information.[136] Many states also enacted statutes providing civil and criminal protection against misuse of medical information, as well as laws that afford greater privacy protection for certain sensitive medical information such as HIV/AIDS, mental health, and substance abuse treatment.[137] But policies and regulations don't protect patient privacy, or ensure that decisions rendered from data use are also fair and just, people do. Despite the snarl of privacy regulations, healthcare as a politically infused industry appears to have emancipated volumes of patient information.

Although it is a restrictive regulation requiring patient authorization and consent for most disclosures of PHI to third parties, the HIPAA Privacy Rule allows for many exceptions that do not require consent. Health plans, most providers, and healthcare clearinghouses ("Covered Entities") are permitted to access, use, and disclose the *minimum necessary*[138] amount of their patient's PHI without the patient's authorization. Specifically, if the disclosure of PHI is for treatment, payment, or any one of several healthcare operations activities, there is no need to obtain any patient consent at all.[139] The absence of consent does not itself mean that private information is shared indiscriminately or without patient awareness. Patients are provided notice, have a right to certain accountings, and in some limited instances may opt-out of the disclosure altogether.[140] However, the many exceptions to the consent requirement have practically swallowed the Rule entirely, thereby unleashing what often appears as an unconstrained flood of personal health information into the wild. As such, the case for expanded physician access and the proliferation of technology that is dependent upon digital data are in palpable tension with patient stakeholder privacy preferences, their exercise of control, their values, and expectations.[141]

Health Information Technologies

In 2004, the Bush Administration pronounced through Executive Order, that every American would have an electronic health record by 2014. This Executive Order was motivated by the need to improve the quality of care and reduce healthcare costs through enhanced clinical decision-making through expanded access to information. In addition, it recognized the need to reduce errors of omission and commission from illegible and poorly handwritten physician notes and prescription drug orders. These objectives ignited the launch of the electronic health record.[142]

The Office of the National Coordinator for Health Information Technology (ONC) was spawned from this Executive Order and was formally mandated in 2009 through the Health Information Technology for Economic and Clinical Health Act (HITECH). HITECH was enacted as part of the Obama Administration's American Recovery and Reinvestment Act (ARRA). Under the direction of the Department of Health and Human Services, the ONC is charged with constructing and implementing a nationwide health information system comprised of a variety of information and communication technologies (ICTs). The ONC's goal is to have an interoperable health information ecosystem stood up by 2024.[143] In furtherance of this ambitious goal, the 21st Century Cures Act ("Cures Act") was signed into law in 2016.[144]

ICTs focusing on healthcare including patient registries, adverse-event databases, and data-mining tools[145] are being designed, tested, and implemented at a pace that is nearly impossible to accurately gauge in real-time. Personal health records (PHRs), patient portals, telemedicine delivery channels, and health information exchanges (HIEs) are a few of the most recognized technologies that rely on acquiring, aggregating, and analyzing patient health data to extract value for a diverse set of stakeholders. The eHealth Exchange™ is an example of a private sector HIE which transitioned from the ONC in 2012. It is a network of hospitals, pharmacies, federal agencies, medical groups, and dialysis centers spanning all 50 states that links health data belonging to approximately 100 million patients.[146] Except for the patients, whose information is automatically pushed to HIE unless they opt-out, all participants mutually agree to certain data sharing standards and specifications. The intent is to send and access patient information to reduce costs and improve clinical outcomes, improve patient safety, and facilitate business planning.

The most ubiquitous ICT by far, and the undertaking of several presidential administrations is the electronic health record or EHR. EHRs are anticipated to be longitudinal, comprehensive, and interoperable. They contain PHI attributed to identifiable individuals from cradle to grave. They include all clinical encounters with wide ranges of providers that are accessible electronically by any EHR user to whom access is granted.[147] Although any electronic record carries privacy concerns, the interoperability of technology sought by the ONC, presents the greatest opportunity for threats to privacy.

Interoperable technology allows providers who use different electronic health records to communicate with each other directly through an integrated single EHR.[148] The interoperability of medical records further underscores the reality that the physician-patient relationship is no longer binary. Nearly all information conveyed during the treating relationship, presumed to be confidential, will now be accessed and used by hundreds, if not thousands of entities; many of whom will be unknown to the patient. Just as important, users will likely only know the patient as an identifiable data set, and never understand them as a unique and distinct person.

The Cures Act was designed to enhance interoperability and information sharing and between patients, providers, and healthcare systems by removing data access barriers to achieve efficiency and improve health outcomes. It purports to increase innovation and competition by creating an ecosystem of applications and application program interfaces (APIs) to provide users with real-time access to EHR information. APIs facilitate data sharing between software programs and servers that are hosted by third-party vendors.

Another objective of the Cures Act is to enhance patient autonomy by increasing transparency and providing patients with unfettered access to all their information to ensure they are fully informed participants in their care. Patients can now access their structured or unstructured information – data that includes physician clinical notes, diagnosis, plans of care, ethics consultation notes, and other confidential information – at no cost to them through APIs. It is important to note that the data transmitted through the applications and APIs are also accessible to third-party application administrators who are outside the control of the provider, HCO, and patient. To access information, patients are expected to consent to the data sharing and attest that they understand the privacy and security risks. The effectiveness of this consent presupposes that they fully appreciate how their secrets may be accessed by unknown users. And, since the Cures Act connected ecosystem is a constituent of big data, the number of those unknown end users grows exponentially.

Big Data, Big Opportunities

Evidence and value-based approaches to healthcare management, and provider incentive payments based on good health outcomes necessitate analysis of considerable volumes of patient clinical data. Preventive medicine, public health initiatives, fraud detection, and innovations in biomedical technology similarly rely upon analysis of health information. Accordingly, big data is, in measurable ways, an instrumental disruptor in healthcare today.[149] It exerts tremendous influence on advances in medicine and care delivery. Big data is widely understood to mean "large, diverse, complex, longitudinal and/or distributed data sets" that are generated from a wide variety of digital sources such as email, Internet transactions, various applications, sensors and connected wearable devices.[150] However, what really matters about big data is not so much what it is, but rather how it is used.[151] The panoply of uses is limited only by the imagination.

Very few, if any, of the downstream uses of healthcare big data are contemplated or understood at the time the patient grants her informed consent for treatment. Assume for the sake of argument that the patient sufficiently understood the cornucopia of purported big data health benefits and attendant uses of her information. To be *fully* informed, she must also understand that her data could potentially reside in a repository that can be accessed, ingested, interpreted, and even identified by any researcher anywhere in the world, for any number of downstream uses.[152] The notion of fully informed consent must be balanced against the risk that once she becomes aware of the constellation of accesses her data, she may decline care or refuse to consent out of privacy concerns. It is important to recognize, however, that despite privacy concerns, big data can benefit important facets of human life in innumerable ways.

Big Data: Defined, Connected, and Exposed

Big data is often defined contextually according to how it is used. In such instances the term is used synonymously with "big data analytics" to describe the *practice* of combining "volumes of diversely sourced information" which are then analyzed using algorithms to assist decision-making.[153] And, there is virtually no limit to the diversity of the data that populates the big data environment; and it is not all attributed to natural persons. That is, sensors that track the weather, the timing of streetlights, and home security systems share a commingled data community with information from EHRs, smartphones, wearable devices, and motor vehicle global positioning systems, to name just a very few.

Nearly everything about the way that we now acquire data, and the knowledge produced from it has changed. The Internet of Things (IoT), the now antiquated term used to describe "…[t]he ability of devices to communicate with each other using embedded sensors that are linked through wired and wireless networks"[154] further increased the exponential explosion of digitized data. According to Alec Ross, approximately 90% of the world's digital data has been created in just the few years since 2014.[155] Being connected is ubiquitous and getting connected has never been easier. The Internet, social media, tens of thousands of mobile applications, commercial and government databases, and nearly every modern convenience is Internet-enabled – from coffee pots to condoms. These connections pour incalculable volumes of digital information into to the universe of big data.

The permeation of healthcare data into the Internet connected universe, in tandem with government's appetite for "interoperative and electronic access to data across a myriad of information systems"[156] offers societal benefits unmatched through any other means. As predicted by former European Data Protection Supervisor, the late Giovanni Buttarelli, by 2020 connectivity has become a standard feature, with more than 25 billion connected objects. Among other things, they are "able to detect blood clots and to monitor fitness and wound healing."[157] By amassing large quantities of data, valuable health insights are gained from granular data points. In other words, by having a haystack, data scientists can find the needle they seek.[158] Yet, without a framework for balancing big data's societal benefits against the individual and community stakeholder, and societal harms from misguided and malevolent use,[159] the big data haystack could become a hornet's nest.

For example, the ubiquity of cloud computing – storing data on connected networks via the Internet – is appealing to the HCO. However, the fact that many cloud providers provide multitenancy data storage, that is, many clients sharing data space on the same pieces of hardware (public cloud), rather than solely occupied (private) storage[160] is hardly if ever, understood by the patient. Cloud providers frequently store patient data in countries outside the United States, where they can be further accessed by sources unknown to the patient.

In addition, big datasets stored on mobile computing devices are susceptible to accidental loss or theft.[161] As Verizon unveiled in its 2017 report, healthcare was distinguished as a top industry for data loss in 2016.[162] The risk of loss of aggregated and identifiable patient data from big data sources adversely affects more than the HCO and the impacted patients directly. It impacts the physician-patient relationship particularly, and the integrity of healthcare's reputation generally. The mere threat of a loss is sufficient to reshape the patient's willingness to share sensitive information with their physician.[163]

The Big Data Haystack

Recording data about the world is nothing new. Since earliest man painted his experiences on cave walls, humans have kept records. But never before has recorded information been thrust upon humankind with such unprecedented volume, with such a diverse variety, and with such velocity as in the present digital information age.[164] The nearly continuous generation of data from limitless connected sources offers society unproven, theory-free objective sources of conclusions largely because "data can offer connections that radiate in all directions."[165] As the availability of clinical data connections expand, clinical decisions can be made based upon inferential connections, as well as the experiences reported by colleagues with similarly situated patients in real-time.[166] The direct and indirect health benefits to patients from this new way of creating knowledge are unquantifiable. And, in many ways, so are the harms.

Not all health information is subject to protection from unauthorized disclosure under the HIPAA Privacy Rule. HIPAA only protects PHI created, used, and disclosed by and between Covered Entities. Medical information websites, health chat rooms, medical apps, and online genetic testing sites may be subject to Federal Trade Commission (FTC) consumer protection but are not necessarily subject to use restrictions.[167] What this means is that health and wellness data sets that were uploaded from personal connected devices, that were not intended to be used to make inferential medical decisions, are susceptible to such uses.

Maintaining good health means more than disease management. More than ever, it includes a focus on preventive health and disease avoidance, which looks to personal lifestyle choices and preferences, family ancestry and other social determinants, to predict and address health issues and outcomes.[168] As such, data from Internet-enabled activity trackers that measure how much a person walks, eats, sleeps, and sits idle can be aggregated and accessible to their physician. He can then make wellness-related assumptions about the patient, even when she is not seeking treatment from him. In addition, Internet-enabled household items, such as the smart refrigerator, can alert a person when they are out of a particular item such as their favorite ice cream, or triple-cheese pizza. With access to accurate data logs, health insurance companies may be able to assess the healthiness of their members' diets and perhaps correlate the size of their grocery list to the size of their insurance premiums.[169]

Although nearly all privacy laws require some form of individual notice and consent, or authorization when those who acquire data seek to use it for a particular purpose, the sheer number of data users renders consent impracticable and unmanageable in the big data context.[170] The big data universe is not a person-centered environment. Consumers who consent to having their data digitally connected through their Internet-enabled "smart" devices typically are not afforded the opportunity to question the secondary or tertiary third-party uses of their data once they are connected. Moreover, the opportunity to review and approve the terms of the consent routinely occurs after the person has purchased the device or service and is already committed to its use.

Notwithstanding consent limitations, it is unlikely they could contemplate how much of their personal identity, and their closely held secrets would be revealed through manipulation of their unstructured and even anonymized data. Cynthia Dwork illustrates the power of linkage attacks – the ability to connect auxiliary information from one privately connected source, to data from other databases – in order to identify individuals and their sensitive information; including their personal health records.[171] In short, privacy laws that rely upon consent alone cannot sufficiently reconcile the phenomenon of big data vis-à-vis the patient's expectation of privacy.[172]

Algorithmic Decisions

In addition to its predictive capacity, big data's ability to monitor human behavior individually and collectively is appealing to healthcare. It is important to note that the bigness of big data is not so much that data is massively amalgamated. Rather, the bigness refers to its nearly irrepressible capabilities. Capabilities which "connect disparate datasets through algorithmic analysis" that cobble together unpredictable relationships from data collected at various times and places, in various forms and formats, drawing inferences for a myriad of purposes.[173]

Algorithms draw from and feed off an ever-expanding universe of data about persons and weigh them against prescribed metrics, to arrive at computer-generated, rather than human-contemplated decision-making. Within healthcare, predictive algorithms provide decision-support tools for physicians whenever they face uncertainty or clinical ambiguity. There are unlimited algorithmic possibilities. For example, algorithms can predict the risk of patient readmission in patients with heart failure. They monitor prescription drug use as well as prescribing habits to detect and mitigate opioid misuse. They can also predict the risk of neonatal infection which could influence the physician's decision whether to prescribe costly and potentially unnecessary antibiotics.[174] Predictive algorithms are also highly effective in expediting research and development of new drugs and related clinical treatment pathways by eliminating time constraints, and human-induced delays. These results can run through a database, and algorithms will identify relevant trials for cancer patients with certain types of tumors.[175] As more and more mathematical algorithms replace human discernment and contemplation, humans will move away from making their own decisions, and move toward "tools that make decisions without a person in the loop."[176]

Real Data...Artificial Intelligence

"Data is not information, information is not knowledge, knowledge is not understanding, and understanding is not wisdom."[177] By describing the world of information according to what it is *not*, Clifford Stoll illustrates that knowledge obtained from information requires a process of applied learning and continual improvement, and refinement of data. All with the goal of achieving some great outcome.[178] The evolutionary progression from raw data to knowledge and then to action is typically the purview of the data scientists whose job it is to pour over and tease through terabytes of data to interpret and analyze presumably for some anticipated good of the organization and its stakeholders. Today, algorithmic decision-making is an inflection point in information processing and provides the means for decisions that were once made by data scientists to be made by computer systems.[179]

An algorithm, in computer science, refers to a well-defined set of facts or rules that are to be followed to accomplish a particular goal or calculation. The rules themselves are resident within a system's source code which provides the fuel for what is recognized today as machine learning,[180] or the ability to perform activities based solely on recognition of data patterns. Although the terms are often used interchangeably, machine learning (ML) and artificial intelligence (AI) are not the same.

Artificial intelligence is a broad concept that describes the ability for a device to act "smart" or intelligently, as a human would.[181] It is an area of computer science that seemingly gives machines the ability to mimic cognitive functions normally attributed only to the human mind; essentially imitating human intelligence. [182] *Generalized artificial intelligence* is a type of AI that includes ML. Machine learning gets its education from continually correcting and improving upon the accuracy of the probabilities and predictions it makes, thereby refining its decision-making capabilities. For example, smartphone technology becomes obsolete almost immediately as its decision-making and task-performing functionality becomes refined through enhanced ML. *Applied artificial intelligence* refers to the application of machine learning to perform specific acts, such as autonomous driving vehicles or drone navigation, to name only a few.[183] As more information about physical interactions and private facts are digitized, digital records of these facts and whereabouts procreate and propagate, and artificial intelligence tells humans what do and how to do it, humans will make decisions according to direction provided by a machine. Not only will machines make decisions, but they will also perform activities that were once solely within the province of humans.

Artificial intelligence is the single most important tool in the delivery of healthcare today. Unleashing algorithms to identify patterns within haystacks of data is accelerating the science and practice of medicine. For example, increasing speed and accuracy of diagnosis, expedited research and drug development, and disease surveillance that is critical for public health purposes have all been enhanced by AI. By accelerating delivery times beyond that which human intervention alone can produce, machine learning and artificial intelligence have revolutionized healthcare.

Nearly all the major technology companies in the world have ventured into the healthcare with notable successes and failures. In the 12-month period between June 2020 and May 2021, Google expanded its presence in healthcare by partnering with dozens of health systems, institutes, innovative start-ups, and universities throughout the United States.[184] Through its collaboration with many hospital systems, IBM ingested massive amounts of data into its supercomputer, Watson, whose artificial intelligence was initially a boon to healthcare. It was purportedly designed to offer genomic sequencing and diagnostic analysis to oncologists to make advanced diagnosis, precision medicine, and treatments accessible to patients who may not otherwise have access to such exclusive care.[185] However, Watson is an example of the pitfalls of technological hype surrounding AI. Watson's impressive strength in natural language processing proved to be an inadequate solution to real-time cancer diagnosis and has since been repurposed. Physicians were frustrated with the amount of time wasted on ineffective technology that could have been spent caring for patients,[186] underscoring the incomparable value of human interaction.

Ceding Control…Enabling Discrimination

Throughout the history of humankind, the authority to choose for oneself, and the respect for free will has been cherished as the most revered source of human authority.[187] Such humanism also undergirds healthcare, as autonomy and the control over one's body, as well as the private information about oneself is inextricably attributed to respect for human dignity. Yet, as Schneier asserts, civil society often requires that people cede power and control over themselves to others, despite the inherent risk in doing so.[188]

As dataism, which sees the world and its decision-making power as a series of data flows, dominates the world, it argues that humans will no longer be able to see clear of all the information available to make decisions. Dataists argue that at some point, the algorithms will know a person better than they know themselves. Therefore, control over decision-making will be ceded to artificial intelligence.[189] While this insurgent view has not been fully actualized, it is fair to say that in healthcare, a large part of decision-making control has been ceded to algorithmic analysis, but not necessarily at the will of the patient.

With the advent of the interoperable electronic health record, many HCOs use risk engines to apply algorithms across all forms of medical information about their patients. Health information is combined internally with other data points. Some data points, commonly referred to as social determinants of health, include environmental and lifestyle factors that can be used to determine health outcomes for individuals and populations.[190] When coupled with data from medical interventions, they create predictive profiles of the probable diseases and other maladies that could affect the patient based on the algorithmic output. Big data analytics can not only open predictive doors that can help people live longer and flourish, but it can also discriminate.

Paul Ohm contends that "Although we have banned discrimination based on race, big data helps companies find a reasonable proxy for race."[191] There are enough unregulated data elements available today that even if a data source did not specifically contain information about a person, the inferences drawn could. When algorithms draw inferences from commingled social determinant and electronic health data, and people are profiled based on their zip code, credit scores, or other socio-economic factors, discriminatory red flagging occurs.[192] The person who lives in a low-income zip code or does not own an automobile could be red flagged by an insurance company as a patient who may be slow to pay by their insurance company or is likely to be a no-show at their doctor's office. The algorithmic thought process is subject to spurious correlations.[193] Such correlations can weaponization data invoking harm upon the person on the other side of the algorithm.

When considering data-driven discrimination, what is conspicuous by its absence from algorithmically inspired decisions is human moral judgment. The ethical challenge for algorithmic decisions is to inculcate the uniquely human capacity for moral judgment into data use. For according to Purves, Jenkins and Strawser, "[h]uman moral judgment is not codifiable, i.e., it cannot be captured by a set of rules. Moral judgment requires…the ability to perceive certain facts *as* moral considerations."[194] Moral judgment and moral agency allow the HCO to recognize the values that matter most to its stakeholders concerning their data. Considering those and other individual values, before patient data is consumed and used, can help to avoid discrimination, forestall value conflict, and benefit society while respecting individuality and dignity. Such is the impetus for establishing and implementing a data ethics framework in healthcare.

Ethical Guidance

The fear of intrusive technology plagued the minds of Samuel Warren and Louis Brandeis more than a century ago. Their prescient paranoia argued for one of the most fundamentally human rights in American jurisprudence – the right to be let alone.[195] Intrusive technology, and the nosiness of governments, scientists, clinicians, hospital executives, marketers, and actuaries invokes similar healthy stakeholder paranoia today. The erosion of individual control exacerbated by artificial intelligence and robotics, facial recognition, undetected wearable technology, and augmented realities threatens to alter the sanctity of privacy. To that end the future of privacy in healthcare must be transformed from the maturation of a legal right to the respect for human values and flourishing in a digitally networked world.

It is apparent, more so than ever, that the ethical commitment to privacy is an indivisible constituent of human dignity that cannot be digitalized. Ethical decisions and moral judgment require human influence. So much so, that privacy is revitalizing the field of ethics. According to Forrester Research, "ethical privacy practices will be the next consumer-driven, values-based source of differentiation"[196] between HCOs and other derivative stakeholders or competitors.

There is an acute and urgent demand for a practical and comprehensive ethical guidance for accountable leaders to follow to harmonize the voracious hunger to understand infinite points of healthcare data, with patient autonomy, dignity, and personhood. Yet, there is currently little consensus on how to approach applied ethics in this new age. What is clear, however, is that a purely automated data-driven world that is devoid of moral judgment must demonstrate human accountability. To do that, according to Martin Abrams, "it will be necessary to depend on people to build ethics into the objectives for the systems through accountable data governance...that ensures the outcomes are legal, fair and just to the various stakeholders."[197]

Accountability and Data Ethics

The data created for and about patients every second of every day will continue to persist under the control of others[198] who may have no direct relationship with the HCO and their patient stakeholders. Of course, the loss of patient control is but one of the value conflicts that accountable HCO leadership must solve for when they seek to harness the power of data for the benefit of many stakeholder interests. The ethical justification for recognizing individual privacy as a moral duty, a social value espoused for the common good, and a core human desire to control access to oneself to catalyze human flourishing comes down to respect for individual dignity. To that end, ensuring that data is used and managed ethically on behalf of stakeholder interests necessitates the creation of an ethical framework that considers what is fair, just, and in harmony with their values.

In support of this assertion, Buttarelli argued that objectification – using a person or their information as a tool to serve someone else's purposes – which is an undercurrent of big data analytics, is a violation of privacy and human dignity.[199] His position, of course, is representative of the view espoused by the European Union, and other countries, that consider privacy a fundamental right of all humans. This is significant since data analytics and algorithmic decision-making is a global phenomenon. As such, appreciation for principles of fairness, justice, and individual values must transcend jurisdictional and geographic limitations thereby encouraging an international commitment to ethical principles of accountable data stewardship.

A striking example of this commitment, the World Health Organization recently published its first global guidance document on artificial intelligence. In it, the WHO contends that although AI holds great promise for public health and the practice of medicine, it presents ethical challenges for HCO, physicians, and stakeholders of all types.[200] The risk of racial, gender, income, and age biases from unchecked non-human algorithmic decisions cannot be overstated. Moreover, because the world's most prominent technology companies are entering into healthcare, the expansion of unregulated care delivery and data use can present real harm to people throughout the world. As such, the WHO argues that ethical considerations, and human rights must be at the center of design and deployment of AI technologies.[201] To that end, it proposes principles of ethics for organizations to adopt along with existing regulations as the basis for responsible global AI governance.[202]

Despite the inherent limitations of regulations as a mechanism for protecting privacy, there is a basis in law, both domestically and internationally, for principles of fairness and justice. Originally promulgated in 1973 by the Department of Health, Education and Welfare (now the Department of Health and Human Services – DHHS) the Fair Information Practice Principles (FIPPS) became the cornerstone set of principles for personal data collection and creation of record keeping systems.[203] Concerned with individual rights, the FIPPs evolved and became the prime influencer of a number of standards adopted by the ONC, the Organization for Economic Co-operation and Development (OECD) the ONC, and the FTC, to name just a few. However, the FIPPS were designed to empower consumers with the limited ability to control information through notice and choice but do little to ensure information disclosed is not used in unfair or harmful ways.[204]

For behavior to be unfair according to the FTC, the practice must cause substantial injury that cannot be reasonably avoided by the individual and is not outweighed by the benefits.[205] Proving legal injury in big data misuse is tenuous at best, as the customary litmus test is most often economic harm. In other contexts, fairness also presupposes that the benefits inured are outweighed by the risks and do not create biases that disadvantage the benefactor or beneficiary.

However, in the big data space, Solove argues that the harm from unfair data use is the dehumanizing effect on people. Because data emanating from aggregated databases "fails to capture the texture of our lives. Rather than provide a nuanced portrait of our personalities, they capture the stereotypes and the brute facts without the reasons."[206] Accordingly, to preserve the cherished texture of their patients' lives and to ensure fairness in the use of their data, accountable healthcare leaders must consider the privacy rights, interests, and values of their normative stakeholders when setting data use and strategy policies. Such reflective consideration must include any foreseeable adverse consequences as well as those that are not so obvious. Data policies affording such consequential reflection must consider ethical principles respecting autonomy, fairness, transparency, inclusivity as well as assimilation of the norms driving these principles.

An ethically accountable HCO can transform its approach to using patient data by reframing their overall data strategy to advocate for and support an enterprise-wide culture of data ethics. A culture of data ethics presupposes that organizations and their moral agents will look beyond the law to consider the values and norms of its normative stakeholders with respect to how their data is used and the consequences of such use. A culture of data ethics reflects an organization's acknowledgment that just because they can use their customer's secrets in a particular way does not mean they should.

As illustrated in earlier chapters, the ethical character and culture of an HCO reflects its most significant norms and values. Similarly, according to O'Keefe and O'Brien, "[a]n ethical framework in the context of modern information management will need to consider organizational values, processes, and development of technology in the context of fundamental ethical principles such as human rights and dignity."[207] Examining an HCO's relationships with its normative stakeholders to understand the contextual significance of these and other ethical principles is critical to establish a culture of data ethics. The value of connected relationships, as suggested by feminist ethics of care theories, is that the values and preferences that individuals hold with respect to their information should become part of the caring process, not viewed separately. Caring for an individual's health must include care for their most private secrets. A culture of data ethics is a marker of ethical accountability.

Since ethical codes are markers of accountability in many professions and is most profoundly present in healthcare, establishing a code of data ethics would create a "forum to translate identified ethical principles into defined ethical actions and practices in their organizations as part of their information governance model."[208] This presupposes that such code would accompany routine ethical reviews and consultations of data uses, processes, and activities. Ethical data reviews may conclude that certain uses are deemed necessarily off limits[209] for the sake of patient dignity, and alignment with institutional norms and values.

But ethical data review may also serve as an early warning system of sorts for approved initiatives involving patient data that are particularly innovative and novel. As a discernment tool, ethical data review considers stakeholder values through the lens of codified ethical principles. It also considers the values and norms of the HCO vis-à-vis its normative stakeholder values. Through this discernment process, ethical data review affords data scientists, leaders, and healthcare professionals the opportunity to forestall value conflicts by developing and deploying algorithms according to ethical recommendations. Data ethics helps to ensure HCOs innovate responsibly.

Recalibration: Reshaping Our Norms

Westin wrote that the norms of privacy in society depend upon political, sociocultural, and personal settings.[210] Schneier's perspective similarly contends that norms of personal privacy are cultural and situational – changing across generations.[211] This observation is well-grounded and validated by society's undaunted reliance on the smartphone camera today, in contrast to Warren and Brandeis' virulent distrust of the Kodak "snap camera" in 1890. Privacy norms are contextual, too. Privacy offenses in healthcare are likely to have a greater gravitational pull on one's senses than privacy breaches in other contexts. The vulnerability and fragility of human dignity that is the hallmark of the healthcare experience context is sufficient to ignite deep emotional responses to offenses against that dignity.

Nevertheless, in the ordinary course of our lives, the constellation of digital data footprints that are left everywhere, by virtually everyone, seems to suggest that few people are likely to ponder, or even consider where their data is, where it is going, or how it is used today. Consequently, expectations of privacy have been reoriented such that most people believe they have less privacy today, instead of more.[212] What matters most about this reorientation, aside from the danger of privacy apathy, is the need to recalibrate today's privacy norms, rather than dismiss them as meaningless. We may, in fact, have less privacy today, but there has hardly been a time in in history when we need it more than now.

Inviolate respect for privacy engenders patient trust in the HCO, and its leadership. At the heart of trust generally is the act of surrendering control to another.

In addition to surrender, Malhotra's view that it is the willingness to be "vulnerable to the discretionary behavior of others...based upon the positive expectations regarding the other person's motivations and/or behavior."[213] Human beings trust with their hearts and their heads, and that is particularly important as privacy is both a feeling as well as a right. Patient trust also relies mightily up the hearts and heads of the clinicians and executive leadership. However, algorithms, which are emerging as dominant decision makers, and machine learning tools, predict and inform without human feeling or thinking.

Ethical accountability in an age of big data, artificial and machine-driven decision-making, and continuously innovative advanced analytics means that normative conceptions of privacy and trust, must change. Patient stakeholders may eventually be expected to accept that they are vulnerable to the discretions and indiscretions of algorithmic-generated intelligence. And while surrendering control to an algorithm cannot replace trust in another human being, patients ought to begin to recognize that machine learning is, at the very least, a derivative stakeholder to the contemporary HCO. Realistically, artificial intelligence and machine learning are not going to replace physicians, but they will most definitely modify what a physician needs to know, as well as what will occupy their time.[214]

Humankind's necessary coexistence with data vis-à-vis those aspects of life which are entitled to privacy protection will necessarily entail a shift in norms. Alec Ross boldly warns that as information about our fallibilities, flaws, fantasies, and foibles becomes accessible and indelibly preserved in big data, the greater the likelihood that the things we prize as novel or even scandalous will eventually be neither.[215] Nothing is likely to surprise anyone anymore – including those unique aspects of being human which are most cherished. He further observes that even "serendipity fades with everything we hand over to algorithms."[216] Cohabitation in harmony with big data will mean that humans must fill the moral gaps left by algorithmic decision-making. Decision makers must realize the need to exercise their moral judgments in place of that which artificial and machine interventions cannot do. When that happens, patient privacy will embrace a world of artificial intelligence that affords humankind the opportunity to be more authentically human.

Conclusion

Keeping secrets is innately human. Secrets afford people the opportunity to control aspects of their life and to establish necessary boundaries between themselves and society.[217] The ethics of secrecy in healthcare presupposes that trust is indispensable to ensure transparency and confidence in the relationship between the physician and patient. Nevertheless, many secrets are no longer binary between the patient and her physician. Many features of modern medicine present challenges to patient confidentiality. Among those features, the contemporary healthcare environment is both enriched *and* complicated by a data-driven hunger supported by advances in digital technology such that, "secrets get exposed sooner than they used to...making them harder to keep."[218]

Of the many challenges that the information age imposes on healthcare stake-holders, the ability to maintain the seal of confidentiality concerning patient secrets is paramount. It is supported, in many cases, by law, ethical principles, and by the seal of privileged communications which protect against arbitrary dis-closure. The universal principles of respect for autonomy, beneficence, and non-maleficence are the primary justifications for confidentiality based upon the best interest of the person[219] and the context of the clinical setting.

With few exceptions, most stakeholders are autonomous, and need sufficient information to make sound decisions.[220] Informed consent necessitates that the physician understand his patient's autonomous voice when determining what she needs to know to consent to treatment, *and* to the sharing of her secrets. For the most part, the duty of confidentiality, the expectation of the patient, and the sufficiency of information necessary to confer informed consent, are formulated and executed on behalf of the patient. However, third-party stakeholder interests, as revealed in the psychotherapeutic setting, often present compelling and legiti-mate threats to the principle of confidentiality.

From its earliest days, the secrets shared in the psychotherapeutic setting were sacrosanct. Many of the truths revealed through the therapist/patient relationship may not even have been realized by the patient at the time that informed consent was given, as psychotherapy is in many ways a deliberate process of mining for secrets. The duty to protect these secrets is derived from professional codes, eth-ical principles, as well as by sources of law. However, the duty to warn – resulting from the seminal *Tarasoff rule* – considers public beneficence as compelling justi-fication sufficient to override patient confidentiality, and creates ethical dilemmas for the health professional.

Advances in genomic medicine present another set of ethical dilemmas for the physician and patient with respect to confidentiality. Despite all the good that genomic medicine promises, the secrets revealed place the physician and the patient in an unprecedented predicament. A predicament that must con-sider who has a right to know the realities of the genetic discovery, how much should be told, and whether they can decline knowing the genetic secrets entirely. Healthcare is barely approaching the threshold of this new frontier in medicine and the ethical considerations relating to the confidentiality protecting these secrets will emerge along with the science. The ethical obligations to these var-ied stakeholders will rely upon deliberate moral decision-making, which includes respect for the ethics of secrecy.

The relationship between the patient and her doctor is enmeshed in a complex constellation of data sharing exchanges that expose secrets disclosed that were once presumed sacred. There is a powerful push for interoperability, and ubiqui-tous digital technologies that force patient data into environments that are not individual-centered and lack the capacity to respect patient autonomy and other values. Flooded with big data from incalculable sources, healthcare decisions that once were the province of human beings are subordinated to technologies pow-ered by algorithms, artificial intelligence, and machine learning tools. Thus, there is a rapid erosion of the time-held demarcation lines between a patient's physical, decisional, and informational privacy rights, and entitlements. The absence of clear boundaries presents moral challenges and conflicts for the healthcare professional, the HCO, and stakeholders who entrust their secrets to them.

The ethically accountable HCO has a moral duty to its stakeholders to invest in a data strategy that advances, at its core, a culture of data ethics supported by principles of data ethics to reflect respect for the human rights and dignity of its normative stakeholders. These principles of data ethics are to be embedded within and throughout the HCO to undergird ethical review and analysis of data uses across the enterprise. A culture of data ethics will seek to understand the norms and values of the HCO and its normative stakeholders, and identity and forestall value conflicts relating to data use before they occur. As norms, values, and expectations surrounding privacy in healthcare continue to evolve, ethically accountable leaders must reconcile the tension between technology and algorithmic decision-making with the recognition that moral judgment is the province of humans, not machines.

Notes

1. Alec Ross, *Industries of the Future*, (New York, NY: Simon and Schuster, 2016), 182.
2. Sandra Petronio, Mark J. DiCorcia, and Ashley Duggan, "Navigating Ethics of Physician-Patient Confidentiality: A Communication Privacy Management Analysis," in *The Permanente Journal* 16 (2012): 41–45.
3. Presidential Commission for the Study of Bioethical Issues, *Privacy and Progress in Whole Genome Sequencing* (October 2012), 22.
4. Giovanni Buttarelli, "Towards a New Digital Ethics, Data, Dignity and Technology." Paper Presented at the European Data Protection Supervisor (EDPS), Brussels, Belgium. (September 11, 2015): 12.
5. Paul W. Mosher and Jeffrey Berman, *Confidentiality and Its Discontents. Dilemmas of Privacy in Psychotherapy*, (New York, NY: Fordham University Press, 2015), 1.
6. Barbara J. Evans, "Barbarians at the Gate: Consumer-Driven Health Data Commons and the Transformation of Citizen Science," in *American Journal of Law and Medicine* 42 (2016): 683.
7. Neil C. Manson and Onora O'Neill, *Rethinking Informed Consent in Bioethics*, (New York, NY: Cambridge University Press, 2008), 124.
8. Andreas-Holger Maehle, *Contesting Medical Confidentiality, Origins of the Debate in the United States, Britain and Germany*, (Chicago, Ill: University of Chicago Press, 2016), 1.
9. Benjamin Franklin, *Poor Richard's Almanac*, 1735.
10. Michael L. Slepian, Jinseok S. Chun, and Malia F. Mason, "The Experience of Secrecy," in *Journal of Personality and Social Psychology* 113 (July 2017): 1.
11. Slepian, Chun and Mason, "The Experience of Secrecy," 3.
12. *Merriam-Webster Online*, accessed May 26, 2017, http://www.merriam-webster.com/dictionary/secret.
13. Anita E. Kelly, *The Psychology of Secrets*, (New York, NY: Plenum Publishers, 2002), 10.
14. Sissela Bok, *Secrets: On the Ethics of Concealment and Revelation*, (New York, NY: Vintage Books, 1989), 7.
15. Sissela Bok, *Secrets: On the Ethics of Concealment and Revelation*, 10.
16. Sissela Bok, *Secrets: On the Ethics of Concealment and Revelation*, 10.
17. Sissela Bok, *Secrets: On the Ethics of Concealment and Revelation*, 6.

18. Samuel Reis, Aya Biderman, Revital Mitki and Jeffrey Borkan, "Secrets in Primary Care: A Qualitative Exploration and Conceptual Model," in *Society of General Medicine* 22 (2007): 1246.
19. Nadia N. Sawicki, "Informed Consent as Societal Stewardship," in *Journal of Law, Medicine and Ethics* 45 (Spring 2017): 47.
20. Thomas L. Beauchamp and James F. Childress, *Principles of Biomedical Ethics*, 7th edition (New York, NY: Oxford University Press, 2013), 318.
21. Anita L. Allen, *Why Privacy Isn't Everything. Feminist Reflections on Personal Accountability*, (Lanham, MD: Rowman & Littlefield Publishers, Inc., 2003), 121.
22. Allen, *Why Privacy Isn't Everything. Feminist Reflections on Personal Accountability*, 127.
23. Linda Farber Post, Jeffrey Bluestein, and Nancy Neveloff Dubler, *Handbook for Health Care Ethics Committees*, (Baltimore, MD: The Johns Hopkins University Press, 2007), 49.
24. Post, Bluestein and Dubler, *Handbook for Health Care Ethics*, 51, 53.
25. Els Van Dongen and Sylvie Fainzang, "Lying, Misery and Illness: Towards a Medical Anthropology of the Lie," in *Anthropology and Medicine* 9 (2002): 89.
26. Van Dongen and Fainzang, "Lying, Misery and Illness: Towards a Medical Anthropology of the Lie," 87.
27. Diana Klebanow, "Everybody (Well, Almost) Lies...to Their Doctor," in *USA Today Magazine* 142 (March 2014): 66.
28. Van Dongen and Fainzang, "Lying, Misery and Illness: Towards a Medical Anthropology of the Lie," 93.
29. Beauchamp and Childress, *Principles of Biomedical Ethics*, 303.
30. Rebecca Volpe, Maria Baker, George F. Blackwell, Gordon Kauffman, and Michael J. Green, "A Case of Deceptive Mastectomy," in *Narrative Inquiry in Bioethics* 3.2 (2013): 177.
31. Volpe, et al, "A Case of Deceptive Mastectomy," 180.
32. Dennis Auckley, "When the Patient-Physician Relationship is Broken," in *AMA Journal of Ethics* 10 (September 2008): 550.
33. Beauchamp and Childress, *Principles of Biomedical Ethics*, 320.
34. Kelly, *The Psychology of Secrets*, 67.
35. Kelly, *The Psychology of Secrets*, 69.
36. Robin Marie Kowalski, Chad Alan Morgan, Elizabeth Whittaker, Brittany Zaremba, Laura Frazee, and Jessica Dean, "Will They or Won't They? Secret Telling in Interpersonal Interactions," in *Journal of Social Psychology* 155 (2015): 86.
37. Oath and Law of Hippocrates (circa 400 B.C.), in *Harvard Classics* 38 (Boston, MA, 1910), accessed November 23, 2017, http://www.cirp.org/library/ethics/hippocrates/.
38. Deb Matthews, "Protecting the Privacy of Patients; Quiet Death of Doctor-Patient Confidentiality," in *The Toronto Star*, February 13, 2014, A18.
39. Jorgen Husted, "Autonomy and a Right Not to Know," in *The Right to Know and the Right Not to Know. Genetic Privacy and Responsibility*, ed. Ruth Chadwick, Mairi Levitt, and Darren Schickle (Cambridge, UK: University Press, 2014), 25.
40. Chris Cotton, David W. Crippen, Farhad Kapadia, Arthur Morgan, Holt N. Murray, and Gill Ross, "Ethics Roundtable Debate: Is a Physician-Patient Confidentiality Relationship Subservient to a Greater Good?" accessed August 26, 2017, http://ccforum.com/content/9/3/233, 236.
41. Cristina M. Beltran-Aroca, Eloy Girela-Lopez, Eliseo Collazo-Chao, Manuel Monteo-Perez-Barquero and Maria C. Munoz-Villanueva, "Confidentiality Breaches in Clinical Practice: What Happens in Hospitals," in *BioMed Central DOI* 10.1186/s12910-016-0136-y (September 2, 2016) published online. 1–2.
42. Beltran-Aroca, et al, "Confidentiality Breaches in Clinical Practice: What Happens in Hospitals," 8.
43. Beltran-Aroca, et al, "Confidentiality Breaches in Clinical Practice: What Happens in Hospitals," 9.

44. Daniel J. Solove and Paul M. Schwartz, *Information Privacy Law*, (New York, NY: Wolters Kluver, 2015), 483–484.
45. Ronald Goldfarb, *In Confidence. When to Protect Secrecy, and When to Require Disclosure*, (New Haven, CT: Yale University Press), 25.
46. Mark A. Rothstein and Meghan K. Talbott, "Compelled Disclosure of Health Records: Updated Estimates," in *Journal of Law, Medicine, and Ethics* 45 (Spring 2017): 149.
47. David Degrazia and Tom L. Beauchamp, "Philosophy: Ethical Principles and Common Morality," in *Methods in Medical Ethics*, ed. Jeremy Sugarman, and Daniel P. Sulamasy, (Washington, DC: Georgetown University Press), 40.
48. Post, Bluestein, and Dubler, *Handbook for Healthcare Ethics Committees*, 15.
49. Post, Bluestein, and Dubler, *Handbook for Healthcare Ethics Committees*, 17.
50. Beauchamp and Childress, *Principles of Biomedical Ethics*, 106.
51. Beauchamp and Childress, *Principles of Biomedical Ethics*, 215–216.
52. Beauchamp and Childress, *Principles of Biomedical Ethics*, 107.
53. Beauchamp and Childress, *Principles of Biomedical Ethics*, 107.
54. Neil Manson and Onora O'Neill, *Rethinking Informed Consent in Bioethics*, 34.
55. Salon Baracas and Helen Nissenbaum, "Big Data's End Run Around Anonymity and Consent," in *Privacy, Big Data, and the Public Good*, ed. Julia Lane, Victoria Stodden, Stefan Bender, and Helen Nissenbaum, (New York, NY: Cambridge University Press, 2014), 56.
56. Sawicki, "Informed Consent as Societal Stewardship," 42.
57. Beauchamp and Childress, *Principles of Biomedical Ethics*, 219.
58. Thaddeus Mason Pope, "Certified Patient Decision Aids: Solving Persistent Problems with Informed Consent Law," in *Journal of Law Medicine and Ethics* 24 (2017): 16.
59. Kenneth Campbell and Kayhan Parsi, "A New Age of Patient Transparency: An Organizational Framework for Informed Consent," in *Journal of Law, Medicine and Ethics* 45 (2017): 60, 62.
60. Jeremy Sugarman and Daniel P. Sumasy, *Methods in Medical Ethics*, (Washington, DC: Georgetown University Press, 2010), 41.
61. Craig Tomlinson, "The Early History of the Concept of Confidentiality in Psychoanalysis," in *Confidentiality. Ethical Perspectives and Clinical Dilemmas*, ed. Charles Levin, Allananah Furlong, and Mary Kay O'Neill, (New York, NY: The Analytic Press, Inc. 2012), 143.
62. George Rosen, *The History of Public Health*, (Baltimore, MD: Johns Hopkins University Press, 1993), 120.
63. Nuffield Council on Bioethics, *Public Health: Ethical Issues*, (Cambridge, UK: Cambridge Publishers Ltd, 2007), 269–270.
64. Solove and Schwartz, *Information Privacy Law*, 513–515.
65. *Jaffee v. Redmond*, 518 U.S.1, 9 (1996).
66. Nuffield Council on Bioethics, *Public Health: Ethical Issues*, 15.
67. *HIPAA Privacy Rule*, 45 C.F.R Part 160 and 164.
68. Kelly, *The Psychology of Secrets*, 5.
69. *Jaffee v. Redmond*, 518 U.S. 1, 11.
70. C. Emmanuel Ahia, *The Danger-to-Self-or-Others Exception to Confidentiality*, (Lanham, MD: University Press of America, Inc. 2010), 7.
71. Paul W. Mosher and Jeffrey Berman, *Confidentiality and Its Discontents. Dilemmas of Privacy in Psychotherapy*, 1.
72. Jonathan Lear, "Confidentiality as a Virtue," in *Confidentiality. Ethical Perspectives and Clinical Dilemmas*, ed. Charles Levin, Allananah Furlong, and Mary Kay O'Neill, New York, NY: The Analytic Press, Inc. 2012), 5.
73. Robert L. Pyles, "The American Psychoanalytic Association's Fight for Privacy," in *Confidentiality. Ethical Perspectives and Clinical Dilemmas*, ed. Charles Levin, Allananah Furlong, and Mary Kay O'Neill, (New York, NY: The Analytic Press, Inc. 2012), 263.

74. David Sundelson, "Outing the Victim: Breaches of Confidentiality in an Ethics Procedure," In *Confidentiality. Ethical Perspectives and Clinical Dilemmas*, ed. Charles Levin, Allananah Furlong, and Mary Kay O'Neill, (New York, NY: The Analytic Press. 2012), 196.

75. Mosher and Berman, *Confidentiality and Its Discontents. Dilemmas of Privacy in Psychotherapy*, 1.

76. Daniel W. Shuman, "Legal Boundaries on Conceptions of Privacy: Seeking Therapeutic Accord," in *Confidentiality. Ethical Perspectives and Clinical Dilemmas*, ed. Charles Levin, Allananah Furlong, and Mary Kay O'Neill, (New York, NY: The Analytic Press. 2012), 270.

77. Mosher and Berman, *Confidentiality and Its Discontents. Dilemmas of Privacy in Psychotherapy*, 10.

78. *Tarasoff v. Regents of the University of California*, 17 Cal. 3d 425 (Cal 1976).

79. Ahia, *The Danger-to-Self-or-Others Exception to Confidentiality*, 9.

80. Presidential Commission for the Study of Bioethical Issues, *Privacy and Progress in Whole Genome Sequencing*, 28.

81. Beauchamp and Childress, *Principles of Biomedical Ethics*, 208.

82. Presidential Commission for the Study of Bioethical Issues, *Privacy and Progress in Whole Genome Sequencing*, 2.

83. Presidential Commission for the Study of Bioethical Issues, *Privacy and Progress in Whole Genome Sequencing*, 19.

84. Victoria Stodden, "Enabling Reproducibility in Big Data Research: Balancing Confidentiality and Scientific Transparency," in *Privacy, Big Data and the Public Good*, ed. Julia Lane, Victoria Stodden, Stefan Bender and Helen Nissenbaum, (New York, NY: Cambridge University Press, 2014), 122.

85. Ruth Chadwick, Mairi Levitt, and Darren Shickle, "The Right to Know and the Right Not to Know: The Emerging Debate," in *The Right to Know and the Right Not to Know*, ed. Ruth Chadwick, Mairi Levitt, and Darren Shickle, (Cambridge, UK: University Press, 2014), 19.

86. Barbara Prainsack, "DIY genetics: The Right to Know Your Own Genome," in *The Right to Know and the Right Not to Know. Genetic Privacy and Responsibility*, ed. Ruth Chadwick, Mairi Levitt, and Darren Shickle, (Cambridge, UK: University Press, 2014), 103.

87. Siddhartha Mukherjee, *The Gene. An Intimate History*, (New York. NY: Simon & Schuster, Inc., 2016), 330.

88. Mukherjee, *The Gene. An Intimate History*, 330.

89. Prainsack, "DIY genetics: The Right to Know Your Own Genome," 103.

90. Jeantine Lunshof and Ruth Chadwick, "Genomics, Inconvenient Truths and Accountability," in *The Right to Know and the Right Not to Know*, ed. Ruth Chadwick, Mairi Levitt, and Darren Shickle, (Cambridge, UK: University Press, 2014), 121.

91. Sandi Dheensa, Angela Fenwick, Anneke Lucassen, "Is This Knowledge Mine and Nobody Else's? I Don't Feel That." Patient Views About Consent, Confidentiality and Information-Sharing in Genetic Medicine," in *Journal of Medical Ethics* 42 (2016): 174.

92. Barbara J. Daly, Ashley Rosko, Shulin Zhang, and Hillard M. Lazarus, "The Devil is in the Details: Confidentiality Challenges in the Age of Genetics," HEC Forum 27 (2015): 84–85.

93. Husted, "Autonomy and a Right Not to Know," 24.

94. Brian Wassom. *Augmented Reality Law, Privacy and Ethics. Law, Society and Emerging AR Technologies*, (Waltham, MA: Elsevier, Inc., 2015), 293–294.

95. Ross, *Industries of the Future* 48.

96. Chadwick, et al, "The Right to Know and the Right Not to Know: The Emerging Debate,"19.

97. Ross, *Industries of the Future*, 57.
98. Claude Richard, Yvette Lajeunesse, and Marie-Therese Lussier, "Therapeutic Privilege: Between the Ethics of Lying and the Practice of Truth," in *Journal of Medical Ethics* 36 (June 2010): 353.
99. Sheila Jasanoff, *The Ethics of Invention. Technology and the Human* Future, (New York, NY: W.W. Norton & Company, 2016), 120.
100. Dheensa, Fenwick, and Lucassen, "Is This Knowledge Mine and Nobody Else's? I Don't Feel That" Patient Views About Consent, Confidentiality and Information-Sharing in Genetic Medicine," 176.
101. Dheensa, Fenwick, and Lucassen, "Is This Knowledge Mine and Nobody Else's? I Don't Feel That" Patient Views About Consent, Confidentiality and Information-Sharing in Genetic Medicine,"175.
102. Michael Gallagher, "The Intersection of Relational Autonomy and Narrative Ethics for the Patient Unwilling to Disclose Genetic Diagnosis Information," in *Life Sciences, Society and Policy*, A Springer Open Journal, (March 2014): http://www.lsspjournal.com/content/10/1/7.
103. Judith Wagner DeCrew, *In Pursuit of Privacy. Law, Ethics, and the Rise of Technology*, (New York, NY: Cornell University Press, 1997), 9–13.
104. Genesis 3:7.
105. Genesis 9:21–27.
106. Daniel J. Solove, *Understanding Privacy*, (Cambridge, MA: Harvard University Press, 2008), 5.
107. Solove, *Understanding Privacy*, 1.
108. Alan F. Westin, *Privacy and Freedom*, (Portsmouth, ME: IAPP), xxxi.
109. Westin, *Privacy and Freedom*, xxxi.
110. Westin, *Privacy and Freedom*, xxii.
111. Adam D. Moore, *Privacy Rights. Moral and Legal Foundations*, (University Park, PA: The Pennsylvania State University Press, 2010), 5.
112. Moore, *Privacy Rights. Moral and Legal Foundations*, 2, 5.
113. Moore, *Privacy Rights. Moral and Legal Foundations*, 6.
114. Julie C. Inness, *Privacy, Intimacy and Isolation*, (New York, NY: Oxford University Press, 1992), 11, 95.
115. Inness, *Privacy, Intimacy and Isolation*, 9.
116. Inness, *Privacy, Intimacy and Isolation*, 10.
117. Inness, *Privacy, Intimacy and Isolation*, 83.
118. Anita L. Allen, "The Duty to Protect Your Own Privacy," in *Privacy, Security and Accountability. Ethics, Law and Policy*, ed. Adam. D. Moore, (London, UK: Rowman and Littlefield, 2016), 29.
119. Allen, "The Duty to Protect Your Own Privacy,"32.
120. Allen, "The Duty to Protect Your Own Privacy," 24–26.
121. Wassom, *Augmented Reality. Law, Privacy and Ethics. Law, Society and Emerging AR Technologies*, 43.
122. Solove, *Understanding Privacy*, 84.
123. Solove, *Understanding Privacy*, 50.
124. John C. Moskop, Catherine A. Marco, Gregory Luke Larking, Joel M. Gelderman and Arthur R, Derse, "From Hippocrates to HIPAA: Privacy and Confidentiality in Emergency Medicine – Part I: Conceptual, Moral and Legal Foundations." In *Annals of Emergency Medicine* 43 (January 2005):53.
125. Chaham Alalouch, Peter A. Aspinall, and Harry Smith, "Design Criteria for Privacy-Sensitive Healthcare Buildings," in *ISCSIT International Journal of Engineering and Technology* 8 (February 2016): 32.
126. Daniel Solove and Paul Schwartz, *Information Privacy Law*, 482.
127. Jong-Myon Bae, "Value-Based Medicine: Concepts and Applications," in *Epidemiology and Health* 37, accessed September 6, 2017, http://dcx.doi.org/10/4178/ephi.e2014014.

128. Bae, "Value-Based Medicine: Concepts and Applications," 2.
129. Jane Hyatt Thorpe, Elizabeth A. Gray and Lara Cartwright-Smith, "Show Us the Data: The Critical Role Health Information Plays in Health System Transformation" in *Journal of Law, Medicine and Ethics* 44 (2016): 592.
130. Burke W. Mamlin and William M Tierney, "The Promise of Information and Communication Technology in Healthcare: Extracting Value from the Chaos." In *The American Journal of Medical Sciences* 351 59 **[fix cite]**.
131. Martin Abrams, "The Origins of Personal Data and Its Implication for Governance," the OECD Expert Roundtable Discussion in Paris, France: *Protecting Privacy in a Data-Driven Economy: Taking Stock of Current Thinking.* (March 21, 2014): 2.
132. Verizon, 2015 *Protected Health Information Data Breach Report*, 5–6.
133. 45 C.F.R. §§160–164.
134. Solove and Schwartz, *Information Privacy Law*, 516.
135. Daniel J. Solove and Paul M. Schwartz, *Privacy Law Fundamentals 2017.* (Portsmouth, ME: IAPP, 2017), 99.
136. U.S. Department of Health and Human Services, Office for Civil Rights, Summary of the HIPAA Privacy Rule, 12–13.
137. Solove and Schwartz, *Privacy Law Fundamentals 2017*, 98–99.
138. 45 C.F.R. §§164.502(b), 164.514(d).
139. 45 C.F.R. §164.506.
140. 45 C.F.R. §§ 164.520, 164.528 and 164.510.
141. Kelly Caine and Rima Hanania, "Patients Want Granular Privacy Control over Health Information in Electronic Medical Records," in *Journal of American Medical Information Association* 20 (2013): 7.
142. Donald W. Simborg, MD, "Promoting Electronic Health Record Adoption. Is it the Correct Focus?" in *Journal of American Informatics* Association 12 (March–April 2008), 127.
143. Thorpe, Gray, and Cartwright-Smith, "Show Us the Data: The Critical Role Health Information Plays in Health System Transformation," 593.
144. *21st Century Cures Act: Interoperability, Information Blocking, and the ONC Health IT Certification Program*, 45 C.F.R. Parts 170 and 171.
145. Ethimios Parasidis, "The Future of Pharmacovigilance. Big Data and the False Claims Act," in *Big Data, Health Law, and Bioethics.* ed. I. Glenn Cohen, Holly Fernandez Lynch, Effy Vayena, and Urs Gasser (New York, NY: Cambridge University Press, 2018), 74.
146. The eHealth Exchange Overview, accessed September 11, 2017, http://sequoiaproject.org/ehealth-exchange/about/.
147. Mark A. Rothstein, "The Effects of Health Information Technology on the Physician-Patient Relationship: The Hippocratic Bargain and Health Information Technology," in *The Journal of Law, Medicine and Ethics* 38 (Spring 2010): 7.
148. Thorpe, Gray, and Cartwright-Smith, "Show Us the Data: The Critical Role Health Information Plays in Health System Transformation," 594.
149. I. Glenn Cohen, "Overcoming the Downsides of Big Data," in *Big Data, Health Law and Bioethics*, ed. I. Glenn Cohen, Holly Fernandez Lynch, Effy Vayena, and Urs Gasser (New York, NY: Cambridge University Press, 2018), 69–72.
150. National Science Foundation, Solicitation 12–499: *Core Techniques and Technologies for Advancing Big Data Sciences and Engineering (BIG DATA)* 2012, accessed April 30, 2017, http://www.nsf.gov/publs/2012/nsf12499/nsf12499.pdf.
151. Executive Office of the President, *Big data: Seizing Opportunities and Preserving Values*, (May 2014), 3.
152. Carl Landwehr, "Engineered Controls for Dealing with Big Data," in *Privacy, Big Data and the Public Good. Frameworks for Engagement.* ed. Julia Lane, Victoria Stodden, Stefan Bender, and Helen Nissenbaum, (New York, NY: Cambridge University Press, 2014), 211.

153. Buttarelli, "Towards a Digital Ethics. Data, Dignity and Technology," 6.
154. Executive Office of the President, *Big data: Seizing Opportunities and Preserving Values*, 2.
155. Ross, *Industries of the Future*, 154.
156. Alan T. Belasen, Barry Eisenberg, and John W. Huppertz, *Mastering Leadership. A Vital Resource for Health Care Organizations*, 233.
157. Buttarelli, "Towards a New Digital Ethics, Data, Dignity and Technology," 7.
158. Executive Office of the President, *Big data: Seizing Opportunities and Preserving Values*, 7.
159. Katherine Strandburg, "Monitoring, Datafication and Consent: Legal Approaches to Privacy in the Big Data Context," in *Privacy, Big Data and the Public Good. Frameworks for Engagement*. ed. Julia Lane, Victoria Stodden, Stefan Bender, and Helen Nissenbaum, (New York, NY: Cambridge University Press, 2014), 5.
160. Landwehr, "Engineered Controls for Dealing with Big Data," 227–229.
161. Landwehr, "Engineered Controls for Dealing with Big Data,"212.
162. Verizon, 2017 Data Breach Investigations Report, 19th edition, Verizon, 56.
163. Verizon, 2015 Protected Health Information Data Breach Report, 10.
164. Executive Office of the President, *Big data: Seizing Opportunities and Preserving Values*, 7.
165. Jacob Metcalf, Emily F. Keller, and Dana Boyd, "Perspectives on Big Data, Ethics and Society," in *The Council for Big Data, Ethics and Society*, (May 23, 2016), 6.
166. Belasen, Eisenberg, Huppertz, *Mastering Leadership. A Vital Resource for Health Care Organizations*, 236–237.
167. Strandburg, "Monitoring, Datafication and Consent: Legal Approaches to Privacy in the Big data Context," 26.
168. Craig Konnoth, "Data Collection, EHRs, and Poverty Determinations," in *Journal of Law, Medicine, and Ethics* 46 (2018): 622.
169. Wassom, *Augmented Reality Law, Privacy and Ethics. Law, Society and Emerging AR Technologies*, 66.
170. Strandburg, "Monitoring, Datafication and Consent: Legal Approaches to Privacy in the Big Data Context," 30.
171. Cynthia Dwork, "Differential Privacy: A Cryptographic Approach to Privacy Data Analysis," in *Privacy, Big Data and the Public Good. Frameworks for Engagement*. ed. Julia Lane, Victoria Stodden, Stefan Bender and Helen Nissenbaum. (New York, NY: Cambridge University Press, 2014), 297.
172. Strandburg, "Monitoring, Datafication and Consent: Legal Approaches to Privacy in the Big Data Context," 31.
173. Jacob Metcalf, Emily F. Keller, and Danah Boyd, "Perspectives on Big Data, Ethics and Society," 5.
174. Ravi B. Parikh, Ziad Obermeyer, and David Westfall Bates, MD, "Making Predictive Analytic a Routine Part of Patient Care," in *Harvard Business Review* (April 21, 2016) accessed September 9, 2017.
175. Agnes Shanley, "The Future of Pharma. Innovating in a Value-Based World," in *Pharmaceutical Technology*. (May 2017):20.
176. Derek E. Bambauer, "Uncrunched: Algorithms, Decision-making, and Privacy," 4.
177. Clifford Stoll. BrainyQuote.com, Xplore Inc., 2017, accessed April 30, 2017. http://brainyquote.com/quotes/quotes/c/cliffordst212166.html.
178. Shane J. Downey, *One Data. Achieving Business Outcomes through Data*, 7.
179. Joshua A Kroll, Joanna Huey, Solon Barocas, Edward W. Felten, Joel R. Reidenberg, David G. Robinson, and Harlan Yu, "Accountable Algorithms," 165 *Univ. of Penn L. Rev.* 633: 636.
180. Kroll, et al, "Accountable Algorithms," 638.
181. Bernard Marr, "What Is the Difference Between Artificial Intelligence and Machine Learning?" accessed June 29, 2017. https://www.Forbes.com/sites/bernard-marr/2016/12/-6/what-is-the-difference-between-artificial-intelligence-and-mach-ing-learning/2/#7/c53944f483d. 1.

182. Katherine O'Keefe and Daragh O'Brien, *Ethical Data and Information Management. Concepts, Tools and Methods, Ethical Data and Information Management. Concepts, Tools and Methods.* (London, UK: Kogan Page Limited, 2018), 84.
183. Bernard Marr, "What Is the Difference Between Artificial Intelligence and Machine Learning?"
184. Katie Adams, "Google Deepens its Healthcare Presence: A Timeline of the Last Year," in *Becker's Hospital Review,* (June 23, 2021), accessed June 30, 2021, https://www.beckerhospitalreview.com/healthcare-information-technology/google-deepen.
185. Steve Lohr, "IBM, Is Counting on Its Bet on Watson, and Paying Big Money for It." in *The New York Times,* (October 17, 2016): B1.
186. Steve Lohr, "Watson's Life After Jeopardy!" in *The New York Times,* (July 18, 2021): BU.
187. Yuval Noah Harari, "Yuval Noah Harari on Big Data, Google and the End of Free Will." (blog), *The Financial Times Ltd.,* 1, accessed September 9, 2016, https:///www.ft.com/content/50bb-4830-6a4c-11e6-ae5b-a7ccdd5a28c?siteeditin+intl.
188. Bruce Schneier, *Data and Goliath. The Hidden Battles to Collect Your Data and Control Your World.* (New York, NY: W.W. Norton Company, Inc. 2015), 189.
189. Yuval Noah Harari, *Homo Deus. A Brief History of Tomorrow.* New York, NY: Harper Collins Publishers, 2017), 372–373.
190. Craig Konnoth, "Data Collection, EHRs, and Poverty Determinations," 622.
191. Paul Ohm, "Changing the Rules: General Principles for Data Use and Analysis," in *Privacy, Big Data and the Public Good. Frameworks for Engagement.* ed. Julia Lane, Victoria Stodden, Stefan Bender, and Helen Nissenbaum, (New York, NY: Cambridge University Press, 2014), 101.
192. Virginia Eubanks, *Automating Inequality. How High-Tech Tools Profile, Police, and Punish The Poor,* (New York, NY: Picador, 2018), 3, 5, 7.
193. Ross, *Industries of the Future,* 183.
194. Duncan Purves, Ryan Jenkins, and Bradley J. Strawser, "Autonomous Machines, Moral Judgment, and Acting for the Right Reasons," in *Ethical Theory and Moral Practice* 18 (2015) 1–2.
195. Samuel D. Warren and Louis D Brandeis, *The Right to Privacy,* 4 Harv. L. Rev. 193 (1890).
196. Fatemeh Khatibloo, *The New Privacy: It's All About Context. Vision: The Customer Trust and Privacy Playbook,* Forrester Research, Inc. Forrester Research, Inc. (June 30, 2017): 2.
197. Martin Abrams, John Abrams, Peter Cullen, and Lynn Goldstein, "Artificial Intelligence, Ethics and Enhanced Data Stewardship," in *IEEE Security and Privacy* (March–April 2019), 17–30.
198. Executive Office of the President, *Big Data: Seizing Opportunities and Preserving Values,* 9.
199. Buttarelli, "Towards a New Digital Ethics, Data, Dignity and Technology," 12.
200. World Health Organization, *Ethics and Governance of Artificial Intelligence for Health: WHO Guidance.* Geneva, 2021, xi.
201. World Health Organization, *Ethics and Governance of Artificial Intelligence for Health,* v.
202. World Health Organization, *Ethics and Governance of Artificial Intelligence for Health,* 23–30.
203. U.S. Department of Health and Human Services, "Examining Oversight of the Privacy and Security of Health Data Collected by Entities Not Regulated by HIPAA," (June 16, 2016): 19.
204. Ohm, "Changing the Rules: General Principles for Data Use and Analysis," 96–99.
205. Section 5, FTC Act, 15 U.S.C. §45 (n).
206. Daniel J. Solove, Privacy and Power: Computer Database and Metaphors for Information Privacy, 53 Stan. L. Rev. 1393 (2008): 1425.

207. O'Keefe and O'Brien, *Ethical Data and Information Management. Concepts, Tools and Methods*, 162.
208. Katherine O'Keefe and Daragh O'Brien, *Ethical Data and Information Management. Concepts, Tools and Methods*, 142–143.
209. O'Keefe and O'Brien, *Ethical Data and Information Management. Concepts, Tools and Methods*, 143.
210. Westin, *Privacy and Freedom*, xxxi.
211. Schneier, *Data and Goliath. The Hidden Battles to Collect Your Data and Control Your World*, 270.
212. Schneier, *Data and Goliath. The Hidden Battles to Collect Your Data and Control Your World*, 271–272.
213. Deepak Malhotra, "Too Big to Trust? Managing Stakeholder Trust in Business in the Post-Bail-Out Economy," in *Public Trust in Business*. ed. Jared D. Harris, Brian T. Moriarty, and Andrew C. Wicks. (Cambridge, UK: Cambridge University Press, 2014), 58.
214. Rowena Lindsay Staff, "What will Artificial Intelligence Look Like in 15 years? In *The Christian Science Monitor*, (September 6, 2016).
215. Ross, *Industries of the Future*, 179.
216. Ross, *Industries of the Future*, 181.
217. Lenore Manderson, Mark Davis, Chip Colwell, and Tanja Ahlin, "On Secrecy, Disclosure, the Public, and the Private in Anthropology," in *Current Anthropology* 56 (December 2015): 183.
218. Bruce Schneier, *Data and Goliath. The Hidden Battles to Collect Your Data and Control Your World*, 187.
219. Beltran-Aroca, et al, "Confidentiality Breaches in Clinical Practice: What Happens in Hospitals," 1.
220. Thomas Schick and Ida Critelli Schick, "The Ethics of Keeping Corporate Secrets," in *Public Relations Strategist* 4.2 (Summer 1998): 30.

4 Community Stakeholders in Healthcare
Pediatric Populations

Introduction

Corporate social responsibility refers to an organization's duty to respond to its stakeholders with a continuing commitment to look beyond its core business to the externalities that affect all its stakeholders and constituents. To that end, the morally responsible organization must realize, understand, and harmonize its decisions amidst the complex interconnectedness between social and economic externalities pressing on its normative stakeholders.

Ethical accountability to stakeholders in healthcare requires a moral commitment from HCOs to the common good, and to the sustained well-being of the communities they serve. Providing for the common good is both an expectation of members of society, and a duty of those so empowered. Since healthcare is a common good of a moral and civil society,[1] principles of stewardship and the duty to provide for the common good require a commitment from HCOs to disrupt the status quo and mobilize change for the good of at-risk stakeholders. Pointedly, HCO's must create opportunities for their normative stakeholders, especially the most vulnerable amongst them, to flourish. The remainder of this book explores the HCO's ethical accountability to select normative stakeholder groups who are the most vulnerable and disempowered across the life continuum. This chapter is dedicated to the second of the three stakeholder categories: the treatment of pediatric populations.

Focusing on the beginning of the life continuum, this chapter centers on children and their attendant vulnerability. It commences with an ethical justification for transcending risk and upholding the moral obligation to promote children in clinical and social research studies. It opens with an explication of the concept of vulnerability as a condition of humanity[2] as interpreted by several moral theorists, including Mackenzie, Rogers, and Dodds. It then provides a view into the grim history of exploitation in human subject research, and its evolution into modern-day clinical research, with a particular focus on children.

Within the context of clinical research, physicians and researchers are often the same person. As moral agents, they confront moral predicaments when their commitments as treating physicians run counter to those expected of researchers engaged in scientific inquiry. To illustrate, referring to people who

DOI: 10.4324/9781003229957-4

participate in research as *subjects*, can dehumanize, enabling researchers to forget the humanity of the *patient*.[3] In addition, as moral agents, these clinicians must navigate ethical challenges specific to the clinical, cultural, social, and contextual considerations that are unique to their patients and subjects. This chapter explores these specific research considerations and risks, as well as the moral duty of HCOs and their agents to expand opportunities for ethical research participation.[4] Particularly, it looks at vulnerable pediatric communities: children and adolescents with HIV, abused and maltreated children, and those with cognitive disabilities.

While none of these risks can be eliminated entirely, this chapter concludes that the risks to these children as participants in HIV, child abuse, and cognitive disability research can be ethically managed and even mitigated. Adoption of the goodness-of-fit model espoused by leading theorists, including Celia Fisher,[5] speaks to the moral obligation of the ethically accountable HCO and its clinician leaders to advocate inclusion and research that respects human dignity and promotes empowerment. The goodness-of-fit model is also useful when approaching the ethical dilemmas concerning pediatric HIV status, as well as strategies for healthcare professionals to mitigate and even prevent the life-threatening adverse effects of abuse, and obesity on children.

As a multi-factor condition, pediatric obesity is a public health threat. The remainder of this chapter examines it through the lens of societal, socio-cultural, and environmental influences. It addresses the ethical and legal strategies for managing pediatric obesity by describing the problems and societal impacts of the disease generally. It then considers the various obesogenic environments and community influences that support, enable and propagate these environments that can threaten the life of a child.

The long-term medical consequences of pediatric obesity are indisputable. This chapter delves deeply into the psychosocial as well as physiological effects of this condition, particularly considering Western culture's obsession with thinness. For many children, in addition to the adverse physical effects, being labeled obese often subjects them to humiliating stigma, prejudice, and suffering.[6] These psychosocial consequences most often persist throughout the child's life, traversing into adulthood. Since they are socially constructed, these psychosocial harms result in social costs that warrant community intervention to execute remediation strategies.

Because the HCO's ethical accountability extends beyond its internal stakeholders, it has a moral duty to protect those who cannot yet fully protect themselves. As such, this chapter presents an argument for principled communitarianism combining the principles of the duty to do what is good, and to avoid harm, with the individual's right to be left alone, and the community's duty to advance its best interests. To that end, the legal theory of *parens patriae* is introduced to cases of persistent obesogenic environments engendering medical neglect. It further argues that, as a social parent,[7] the HCO's moral duty to protect its pediatric stakeholders involves intervention and cooperation with its full community.

Transcending Risks to Serve the Vulnerable

Centuries before the Information Age, the Enlightenment period triggered humankind's desire to discover and uncover the answers to life's mysteries through inquiry and scientific thought. One of hallmarks of this historic time was the notion that knowledge is power. It was believed that knowledge and understanding endowed people with power and control over their own lives. It was in thinking about the world that humankind recognized its humanness.[8] The more knowledge humankind acquired and the more it learned about its world, the more apparent it became that the *absence* of knowledge precipitated vulnerability, disadvantage, and disempowerment. Control manifested through self-determination and autonomy, permitted enlightened people to rise above oppressive rulers to take dominion over their own lives and destinies. In many ways, knowledge and power defeated death, and translated into survival.

Toward the end of that era, survival began to mean more than prevailing against domination. The same motivation to control and take dominion over human life sparked the quest to understand the cause and prevention of disease, and "to stamp out or radically limit death or disease."[9] Because of its success as a scientific endeavor, the use of human subjects in clinical and social research initially garnered enthusiasm and public support.

However, the pursuit of knowledge of the world does not come without risks. While it can help and heal, the pursuit of knowledge from human research can also bring with it infinite harms that may *disempower* specific populations if not obtained ethically. This is particularly true when the research subjects are members of a highly vulnerable class such as children, and doubly so when the children have special needs, diseases, or are victims of abuse.

In addition, society's long-held preconception that women and children were weak cloaked them under layers of protections and safeguards that excluded them from participation in clinical research trials. Such exclusions resulted in a dearth of research on women and children, and a general lack of clinical understanding of them, including meaningful prevention and treatment. Overly protectionist policies also have the effect of characterizing entire populations of people as vulnerable so that few potential research candidates *are not* classified as such. This reduces the pool of viable research participants. Such expansive labeling also has the tendency to diminish the significance of vulnerability, or worse, exacerbates the consequences of stereotyping and discrimination.[10] Overly exclusionary policies can further harm vulnerable populations when the policies fail to consider the indirect consequences of the disease or condition.

The profound impacts of the COVID-19 pandemic on children illustrate the significance of pediatric research to better understand child and adolescent health. In addition to the dire need for effective pediatric vaccines and treatment, the need to mitigate *indirect harms* from the effects of radical changes in the way children have lived throughout the pandemic is significant. For example, the intermediate and long-term consequences on physical and behavioral health from social isolation, physical distancing, increased screen time, and decreased physical distancing will demand coordinated, collaborative, and ethical research.[11] Balancing the rights of vulnerable children to participate in research and protecting them from unreasonable risks and harms are the principal challenges for conducting this kind of research ethically.[12] Transcending these risks is the charge of accountable leadership.

Understanding Vulnerability and Moral Duty

First appearing in the late seventeenth century, the etymology of "vulnerable" stems from the Latin *vulnerare* meaning "to wound," and *vulnus* meaning "wound." Accordingly, *vulnerability* is having the ability or capability to be wounded, and is the meaning adopted throughout this book. From this broad perspective, it can be argued that all of humanity are vulnerable. According to Mackenzie, Rogers, and Dodds, as embodied, social beings with material and physical dependencies that are both susceptible to and dependent upon environmental and internal influences, vulnerability is a condition of human life. As such, "within bioethics vulnerability is variably viewed as an ontological condition of all human existence and as a marker to identify those who require extra care, where the especially vulnerable are those whose autonomy, or dignity or integrity are capable of being threatened."[13] Although humans are ontologically susceptible to vulnerability, there are contextual considerations that shape various other theories and characteristics of human vulnerability.

Contingent susceptibility theory suggests that vulnerability is relational. That is to say that "[i]nequalities of power, dependency, capacity or need render some agents vulnerable to exploitation by others."[14] Such exploitation is enabled because humans are inherently dependent upon others for care and support in satisfying those needs, and largely exist within interdependent, relational communities. According to Mullin, "It is our needs that make us vulnerable…We are therefore, vulnerable to others not only because they may attack or wound us, but also because our neediness and limited ability to meet our own needs makes us dependent on others for care…"[15] Children are supreme examples of a population predisposed to contingent vulnerability theory in this context.

Rogers similarly argues that vulnerability involves two concepts. She contends that the first concept of *universal vulnerability* is inherent and inevitable as part of the human condition. And the second concept of *contextual vulnerability* "is associated with contextual factors, which signifies precariousness or greater risks of harms for particular individuals."[16] Much of what is understood as vulnerability within healthcare today contemplates this precariousness and looks at "the social, cultural or economic context the individual finds themselves in, rather than a stringent categorization measured against the ability to give consent or to make an autonomous choice."[17] As Mackenzie, Rogers, and Dodds suggest, both concepts of vulnerability ought to be incorporated into ethics of vulnerability discussions. This book adopts and advances this blended perspective of vulnerability.

One challenge with the concept of contextual vulnerability is the temptation to understand the almost infinite number of characteristics and conditions that comprise vulnerable subgroups. To illustrate, the Belmont Report, the Declaration of Helsinki, and the Council for International Organizations of Medical Science (CIOMS) identify as many as 19 specific populations deemed particularly vulnerable because of contingent forms of vulnerability.[18] There are obvious populations such as children, older persons, and patients with incurable diseases, to less visible groups of lower-income people, nomads, or displaced persons, and subordinate members of hierarchical groups. Many of these populations experience a layering of conditions. Solbakk suggests that such layered conditions overlap each other and are both persistent (universal) and variable (accidental or "fallen victim") conditions of vulnerability. The differences are determined by the kinds of protection or remediation necessary, and the rights to which the vulnerable are entitled.[19]

To understand accountability to the vulnerable, Mackenzie, Rogers, and Dodds contend that two theories undergird the moral obligations. The first suggests that the vulnerability itself is the source of a moral obligation, while the second perspective argues that the vulnerability is more akin to a signal pointing to other moral obligations such as providing for an unmet need, or mitigating or avoiding harm.[20] Accordingly, it is both the inherent nature of human vulnerability as well as the situational conditions that give rise to the moral obligation and ethical duty to mitigate threats and protect the vulnerable. By illuminating Goodlin's proposition, Mackenzie, Rogers, and Dodds maintain that this duty inures to "anyone who is in a position to assist but most especially on those to whom a person is most vulnerable. Thus, persons who are in positions of power and authority have special responsibilities..."[21] Within the context of vulnerable pediatric population is necessary to look at the effects of all authoritative relationships on the child. This chapter begins with the authority relationships influencing pediatric research.

Expanding Medicine Through Research, or Exploitation?

In preserving the ancient principle that medicine should do no harm, the practice of medicine has historically been a patient-centric endeavor supporting the physician's commitment to promote health and protect – one patient at a time. The quest for knowledge per se, was rarely the objective of good medicine. It was a relational and largely paternalistic endeavor. It was the physician, who in seeking to protect the life and the dignity of her patient, often made decisions for her on the basis of the best-individualized therapy.[22] As the practice of medicine sought to cure the sick and relieve pain and suffering, research looked to expand knowledge in an effort eliminate disease globally, understand the treatment, and delay or even prevent death.[23] The need for biomedical research emerged since progress and survival necessitated a broader and more utilitarian understanding of disease.

Biomedical research came to be defined as those interactions which tested hypotheses and sought generalizable knowledge about diseases to sustain and enhance the good of society and humanity by improving the practice of medicine.[24] Although the terms biomedical research and clinical research are often used interchangeably, most of the *biomedical research* is conducted on animals and their tissue, not human subjects. The outputs of biomedical research typically support medicine generally. *Clinical research,* on the other hand, involves humans and is designed to enhance therapeutic interventions.[25] As such, medical advancements are often realized from the knowledge obtained from clinical research on human subjects. Unless otherwise stated, all references to research throughout this chapter shall mean clinical research.

Much of the quest for research-based knowledge throughout the nineteenth and twentieth centuries, and the medical discoveries made during this period were the collateral effects of wars, military conflicts, and attempts to understand the casualties associated with them. Although understanding therapeutic interventions and disease management was indispensable during military conflict, it was significant in the postwar period as well. Despite the valuable contributions to medicine that emerged during this time, the crimes against humanity from unspeakable human experiences occurring behind the front lines remain the hallmark of this period. Incalculable numbers of human beings were involuntarily selected and exposed to physical and emotional experimentation designed to test the limits of human tolerance and biology. Prisoners of war were involuntarily immersed in tanks of ice water to observe the boundaries of hypothermia, and pressure-chamber experiments were performed on children to induce epileptic seizures.[26] Dissection and organ extraction of live persons, and the intentional wounding of women prisoners' legs in order to understand the efficacy of injected sulphonamide were but a few of the ghastly and macabre tortures performed in the name of research during World War II.[27] These inceptive days of human subject research drew attention to the fundamental truth that respect for human life could not be forfeited by treating participants as a means to an end.[28]

These fundamental truths provided the backdrop for the groundbreaking Nuremberg Code, promulgated by U.S. judges following the Nazi trials of World War II. As a foundational document, it is based upon natural law and human rights, and sets forth basic moral, ethical, and legal concepts undergirding research involving human subjects.[29] A 10-point statement of principles outlining professional ethics for medical researchers, the Code influenced all subsequent standards of conduct for human participant research.[30] A central, and most celebrated tenant of the Code punctuated the need for participants' voluntary informed consent.

Despite the positive influence of the Code, exploitation of humans participating in research proliferated for decades under the guise of ethical research. As late as the 1970s, many inhumane experiments were discovered and disclosed, revealing questionable procedures surrounding selection of participants and volunteers as well as insufficient informed consent processes. For example, the Tuskegee Syphilis Experiment remains an example of an indelible moral failing within the United States. Treatment to an identified population of American black men infected with advanced syphilis was intentionally withheld to gauge progression of the untreated disease.[31] National and international codes were developed to supplement the full and universal adoption of the Code. Regulations and codified principles defining ethical research, justice in selection, and protocols to ensure bi-directional flow of information between the researcher and the vulnerable research subject ensued.[32]

Rules, Regulations, and Rights

The paternalistic presumption that women and children were vulnerable and therefore required greater protections, historically excluded them from participation in human research trials.[33] While the desire to protect was laudable on its face, the consequences of exclusion were that women and healthy children were under-researched and therefore little was known about them medically. Since the view of ethical human research was largely concerned with distributing the risk to the sturdiest and most resilient, opportunities to provide needed services were often missed, as were prospects to avoid harmful ones. Effective treatments, understanding drug dosages, reactions and interactions, and the pathology of disease, for women and children were virtually unknown[34] while men between the ages of 16–60 were the most tested. Women and children became therapeutic orphans.[35]

However, children who were institutionalized or otherwise deemed defective were not always orphaned in this way. To the contrary, they were often so objectified as to be considered expendable resources and were victimized as subjects for nontherapeutic research; that is, research which is not likely to have any direct benefit to the participant child.[36] The horror discovered within the walls of the Willowbrook State School for persons with intellectual disabilities is an example of the most atrocious abuse of non-therapeutic research on children since World War II. Resident children were intentionally given the hepatitis virus to understand the effects of gamma globulin on them.[37] Defenders claimed that because the hepatitis virus was already present throughout the institution, the virus was likely to infect the children anyway. In many ways, the children *became* the human experiment. Rising public awareness of the exploitation of these vulnerable children and the sentiments at that time, induced debate and a push for legislation and guidelines. Such pronouncements shifted the mindset from excluding children from research as a *risk* avoidance tool to one that permitted research but sought fairness in the distribution of the *benefit*.[38]

A series of promulgations followed the Nuremberg Code seeking to respect autonomy and human rights while balancing the harm and benefit to protect human research participants, including children.[39] For example, the Belmont Report, published in 1979 by the National Commission for the Protection of Human Subjects Biomedical and Behavioral Research, codified the moral principles of respect for persons through autonomy, beneficence, and justice, into the bedrock principles of research ethics.[40] This principled approach established strict criteria for ethical human subject research. For its time, the Report powered a moral stir by illuminating the practice of selecting children for nontherapeutic research which had no relation to the child's own health. This led to the National Institute of Health and other agencies' push for regulations. Acknowledging the need for research with children, but cognizant of their vulnerability and history of exploitation, these regulations landed within the purview of the Department of

Health, Education, and Welfare. That agency – which is now the Department of Health and Human Services – addressed the acceptability of research involving children in the form of the Federal Policy for the protection of Human Subjects, specifically Subpart D of the Common Rule.[41]

Promulgated in 1991 and effectively revised in 2019, The Common Rule amplified the Belmont Report and further set forth ethical provisions and parameters. These included the establishment of the institutional review Board or IRB. The IRB ensured that research protocols and plans were sufficiently vetted, risks to research subjects were minimized, and that they received the protections they were owed. IRBs continue to occupy a central role in human subject research.[42]

Subpart D of the Common Rule sanctions research with all children according to nine statutory provisions which parallel the principles of the Belmont Report. Subpart D provisions range from the assessment of risk and prospect of benefit to the role of the IRBs, the requirement of parental consent and child's assent, protections for highly vulnerable children, as well as processes for conducting unapproved research with children.[43] In 1998 the National Institutes of Health published policies and guidelines supporting inclusion of children as research participants, and in 2002 Congress adopted legislation promoting increased drug trials involving children.[44]

Applying the Principles to Pediatric Research

Because they differ from adults, research with children is essential to understand the pathology of disease and disorders involving them. Some diseases are unique to children and because they are not little adults, nor are they non-adult beings, their physiology and psychology must be understood within the pediatric context. Although including children in clinical research is critically essential to understanding child health, this species of research remains a source of controversy.[45]

Respecting the humanness of children demands first that they be accepted as fully human. Early nineteenth-century biology and philosophy viewed children as *human becoming* who were pre-competent and although they were developing into full humans, they were essentially biology-in-progress. Because they were considered incomplete, their completeness was thought to impair the quality of the research data, and their developmental level was considered short of the requisite capacity necessary to consent to research.[46] Their completeness and competence was measured against an adult world rather than the everyday world of a child.

Research involving children, and particularly those who are contextually vulnerable often involves reliance on knowledge obtained from children's subjective experiences in natural contexts, which is fraught with potential misinterpretations and misunderstandings. Even the meaning of the word *children* is subjective in that, it includes a broad spectrum of meanings. It includes infants and teenagers, girls and boys, and varied social, ethnic, and religious backgrounds, including able-bodies and those with physical and sensory impairments.[47] The Belmont Report provides the widely accepted definition of the term *children*. It holds that children are persons who have not attained the age of legal consent to medical care according to the law of the jurisdiction in which the research is conducted.[48] But this definition alone is insufficient to understand what it means to be a child, as children are much more than their defined legal status. They are inherently and conditionally vulnerable, as they cohabitate with others in a world of complex relationships, cultural contexts, and unique experiences.

Accepting and understanding children's experiences and their world as they understand them, will help to reinforce the notion that they are competent human beings, rather than deficient adults with no opinion, expressions, and thoughts.[49] It is the differentiated quality of children, rather than their perceived incompleteness, which challenges the ability to consistently apply the Belmont Report's ethical principles and related guidance. In addition to the moral commitment to ethical principles, what matters most in pediatric research is understanding what matters most to the child.

Foundations of Ethical Research: Inclusion and Choosing Justly

Understanding which children should participate in research is essential to understanding how to serve all children fairly, so that every child, including the highly vulnerable, can *benefit* from the outcomes, or at least not be *harmed* by them. Highly vulnerable children, such as those with special cognitive needs, have been the object and subject of unethical and unjust research practices since the eighteenth century, but it was the Willowbrook State School case that stirred worldwide controversy.[50] The aftermath of Willowbrook marked, once again, a movement away from including children in research.

Becoming therapeutic orphans by default, statistics from the post-Willowbrook period demonstrate that children were disempowered and vulnerable as both research subjects and patients, particularly in drug safety. Infant deaths from diethylene glycol poisoning and birth defects from exposure to thalidomide during pregnancy are a few tragic examples. At that time, most drugs prescribed for children were not tested in children; only about 20% of FDA-approved drugs were cleared for pediatric use.[51]

It was not until the Food and Drug Administration Modernization Act of 1997 that pediatric clinical trial infrastructure began to take shape.[52] Henceforth, legislation such as the Pediatric Research Equity Act of 2003 (PREA) and the Best Pharmaceuticals for Children Act of 2002 (BPCA) helped facilitate pediatric drug studies, as well as the approval of more than 730 labeling changes for drugs prescribed to children.[53] Similarly in Europe during this time, most drugs prescribed for children were done so off label due to insufficient safety, and efficacy information. Beyond drug studies, the burden of proof for pediatric researchers today has shifted from the need to demonstrate *why* children should be included in research to whether there are ethical reasons why they should *not* be included. The welfare of children in pediatric research must be balanced against the need to protect them from harm. In pursuit of that balance, it is necessary to examine whether justice in the participation process implies a moral duty to participate in research in the first instance.

As a principle of morality, Rosamond Rhodes submits that to the extent humankind demands more out of science "we should each see the need to participate in studies by contributing and sacrificing some of our time, energy, comfort, blood, bodies, and privacy."[54] To that end she argues that research amounts to a collaborative necessity to include people of every sort from infants and adolescents to pregnant women, the elderly, and persons with diseases and conditions of every type. This collaborative necessity is a moral duty, according to Rhodes, that is fair and just since biomedical science is for the common good, and the benefits of research inure to the broader society. It is further dramatically amplified to impose duties on clinicians, researchers, and IRB protocol reviewers to consider their own willingness to enroll in studies when reviewing potential study participants.[55]

In contrast, Yarborough asserts that supporting common good of healthcare through participation in clinical research, either tacitly or expressly, is not a moral duty even though the societal benefits of research can inure to anyone who has occasion to access the fruits of healthcare.[56] His sentiments suggest that those who do not participate in or advocate for support of clinical trials are not guilty of a moral failing because much of clinical research is itself a failure. Citing that much of research is wasteful, he points to the statistically high fail rate of many forms of clinical research to rebut the obligation of individuals "to take on risks for the sake of clinical research." [57] According to Yarborough, approximately half of completed trials never get published in full, and that many of the drug trials published in high-impact journals appear to have been designed for marketing purpose.[58] He further contends that much of pre-clinical research is fraught with software coding error, mislabeled cell lines, and inaccurate data that adversely affect quality and safety of the finalized clinical trial. For Yarborough, such inaccuracies diminish the societal benefits and increase the likelihood of adverse consequences, and harm.

With respect to children, Fleishman and Collagan contend that placing some children at risk for the sake of all is acceptable on condition that there are necessary and sufficient methods in place to protect the children enrolled in the research. These safeguards are important to ensure that they are not exposed to undue risk, without any direct benefit.[59] This seemingly straightforward solution to inclusion has not been met with universal acceptance. The debate surrounding pediatric research is fueled nationally and internationally by divisive theological and philosophical opinions; from staunchly conservative to radically liberal.

Protestant theologian, Paul Ramsey, argued against research involving children contending that doing so was only justified if it furthered the medical interests of the child. He further posited that nontherapeutic research ought never to be performed without the consent of the child subject. For Ramsey, the argument that the children who do not benefit directly from research would develop moral character from the altruistic act of participation was fallacious. According to Ramsey, the child could not develop moral character from performing acts that were unwilled by them.[60]

On the other hand, Roman Catholic theologian Richard McCormick, argued that research with children was necessary to improve the health and well-being of this population collectively. As such, parental consent would sufficiently protect their interests since parents know their children best and are perfectly suited to make sound decisions on their behalf. He broadly assumed that most children if they were able to consent, would want to participate in experiments that contribute to generalizable knowledge for the common good.[61]

Both the United States and international communities attempted to harmonize the perspectives within their policy positions and related codes/regulations, to justify research with children. Despite the effort, it is not surprising that there is not a clear, universally adopted position. The Belmont Report recognized that research involving children is justified to cure childhood diseases and to improve well-being provided that their vulnerabilities were recognized, and protections for them prevailed.[62] The Report underscored that the concept of equitable selection, as a matter of social justice, established an order of preference in the selection of certain classes of research subjects, ensuring that protections prevailed. To that end, research ought to take place first on animals, then on adults, and then on older children, prior to including infants.[63]

The Declaration of Helsinki contains two preconditions supporting research with children. The research must be indispensable to promote pediatric health, and it cannot otherwise be conducted on populations who are able to give their own consent. Refining the Declaration's position, the Convention on Human Rights and Biomedicine set parameters around research with vulnerable persons but did not expressly advocate research with children. However, the Council for International Organizations of Medical Science does support children in research to avoid dangerous reliance on drugs and treatments that have only been tested on adults. Accordingly, it supports pediatric research only in those instances where the knowledge sought cannot be obtained by research carried out on adults.[64]

Understanding which children should participate in research is critical to understanding how to comprehensively and fairly serve children so that every child, especially those belonging to vulnerable subpopulations, can benefit from the outcomes. As the COVID-19 pandemic has shown, the global nature of health demands global solutions.[65] Harmonizing regulations and practices relating to ethical clinical research for vulnerable populations is a global aspiration[66] for everyone's benefit.

Understanding children through pediatric research has pendulously evolved from periods marked by exploitation to over-protection and orphaning, reverting to exploitation, to what is now a presumption that ethical research with children is a necessary moral imperative. This elevates the significance of informed consent, the assent and competency of the child, and the assessment of risks and benefits as vital ethical considerations. Respect for the autonomy of the person requires that legally competent, as well as incompetent persons be given the chance to choose whether to participate in research, to the extent they are able.[67]

Foundations of Ethical Research: Respect for Autonomy and Informed Consent

The Belmont Report's assertion that respect for persons entails respect for their autonomy is what drives informed consent in clinical research. Ensuring that human research subjects validly grant their consent prior to commencing participation helps to preserve autonomy; the respect for the person's ability to make informed decisions about their health that is free from interference and limitations that may obstruct their decision-making.[68] Truly informed decision-making is predicated on the notion that sufficient information is available. The 2017 revised Common Rule approached information sufficiency by enacting key provisions invoking the reasonable person standard.[69] Prospective participants or their legal representatives must receive "information that a reasonable person would want to have in order to make an informed decision about whether to participate, and an opportunity to discuss that information."[70]

The reasonable person standard exists in the common law to determine what is fair and just when determining and measuring the legal responsibility and accountability of a party to a particular matter. Its application to medical disclosure law vis-à-vis the revised Common Rule reflects for the first time an explicit need for investigators, and physicians, to be aware of and address what information a reasonable person would need to know, not merely what the researchers and IRBs consider relevant.[71] This further helps to ensure that research subjects or their surrogate, especially children who may have diminished autonomy and special needs, have an adequate understanding of the circumstances and conditions in order to maintain control over their lives.[72] Respect for autonomy and informed consent does not guarantee the safety of the therapy or procedure, but it does help to provide reasonable assurance that people participating in human research are able to exercise their free-will. The ability to exercise control and free-will sufficiently and validly, including the ability to assent to take part in a research study, requires that people be fully informed of the facts necessary to give consent.

The principle of informed consent consists of three primary considerations. Consent requires first, the competence of the research participant to make a rational decision; secondly, whether the participant can comprehend the relevant information provided as well as the consequences of their decision, and finally the extent to which that individual's consent decisions are voluntary.[73] Voluntariness necessitates that the decisions are free from significant or undue controlling influences of coercion, persuasion, and manipulation.[74]

While the legal and ethical underpinnings of valid consent are critical components of research, the *intrinsic* value of consent in the pediatric context is what enables children to project their voices and views throughout the research experience. Valid informed consent helps to empower the vulnerable. It gives them a voice. Respect for the autonomy of a child and her ability to make decisions for herself necessitates that the ethically accountable researcher endeavor to understand the child's voice, viewpoint, perspective, and wishes. Given that children organize their thoughts differently than adults and do not always express their viewpoints in ways that adult investigators instinctively understand, a child's true intent may not be known.[75] Moreover, the child may not even comprehend the information provided, or may be influenced by factors that are unknown to the investigator. Balancing the respect for autonomy and these ambiguities against the need to procure legally valid consent supports the need for parental or other third-party intercession and consent.[76]

Accordingly, "informed consent in pediatric research means the permission of parents, (biological or adoptive) or other legal representatives or 'guardians' (individuals authorized under state or federal law to consent on behalf of the child)."[77] The rudiments of informed consent are not controversial; rather, it is the administration and effectiveness of it that present ethical issues. If there is a direct benefit to the child, or there is minimal risk to them from participation in the research study, then an IRB may determine that consent of only one parent is sufficient. In the case of non-therapeutic research that involves more than minimal risk, both parents must consent. However, parental permission and assent of the child may be waived entirely if the minimal risk research could not be carried out without the waiver. The child subjects will be provided with relevant information following the research, and the waiver itself does not impact the rights or well-being of the subjects. In addition, unless an IRB determines that the capacity of the child is so limited that they cannot be consulted concerning the research, the Common Rule provides that the assent of the child, or affirmative agreement to participate ought to be solicited.[78] It is worth noting the important distinction between capacity and competence. The terms *capacity* and impaired capacity refer to results of clinical evaluation, while *competence* and incompetence refer to the legal status of someone to make their own decisions.[79]

Competency, capacity to understand, voluntariness, and having enough information are so interdependent upon one another that they should not be uncoupled and treated as independent from one another. Informed consent should be assessed and valued as an indivisible continuum of processes to uphold the autonomy and dignity of the research subject, rather than a compliance checkbox item that more closely resembles an exchange of executed permission slips.[80] Arnason, Li, and Cong defend the idea that informed consent is a communicative process involving mutual listening, sharing and timely response.[81] Underscoring the importance of communication, Nancy E. Kass, of Johns Hopkins Berman Institute of Bioethics contends that informed consent documentation and the process for procuring it ought to prompt and guide further conversation about the research. To that end, "looking someone in the eye, getting a sense of whether they're with you, and even asking them to repeat back what they understand is the most likely strategy to achieve meaningful understanding."[82] The sufficiency of this process is subjective and largely stakeholder specific, beginning with an assessment of the quality of information, an examination of the likelihood that it has been understood, and ensuring that coercion or unreasonable external manipulations were not exerted to influence consent. This subjectivity is exceedingly important when examining the sufficiency of and processes for obtaining informed consent when the research subject is a child.

Foundations of Ethical Research: Benefit, Harm and Assessing Risk

The Belmont Report also obligates researchers to adhere to the principle of beneficence by maximizing benefits, while minimizing harms to the research subjects.[83] For purposes of this discussion, a *benefit* is defined as something of positive value related to health and welfare. *Harms* can be physical, psychological, legal, social, or financial injuries, and must be evaluated from the perspective of the research subject. In the case of a child, the harm must be evaluated from their perspective and perception, not the adult researcher or parent. Hence, the positive value is subjective. The concept of *risk* considers the potential harm to the research subject as well as their family, or community.[84] In short, beneficence obligates ethically accountable researchers, and all involved in human research to acknowledge and support the best interest of the child subject and help to ensure that their well-being is promoted wherever possible.

As set forth in Subpart D of the Common Rule, research involving children is permissible if it offers the prospect of direct benefit to the child and is aligned with appropriate risk stratifications. The regulation, however, does not define what is meant by *direct benefit*, and there is little agreement on the ambitious definitions offered by a variety of researchers. The concepts of direct and indirect benefits were introduced by the National Commission to bolster protections for those who could not provide their own, independent informed consent. Because it feared exposing vulnerable groups of people to heightened risks in pursuit of benefits that may be speculative or realized in the distant future, the National Commission espoused the position that direct benefits must be "fairly immediate."[85] Others like Keyserlingk, Glass, and Gauthier argue that research must afford vulnerable research subjects benefits of *significant* magnitude.[86] And other views consider the degree of "tangible positive outcome" such as pain relief and increased mobility.[87]

Useful for this discussion, Nancy King proffers three types of benefits. *Direct benefits*, according to King, are therapeutic benefits that inure to the child directly from the intervention or experiment. *Collateral benefits* are those arising merely from being a research subject even if the child did not receive the intervention or participate in the study. Examples of collateral benefits include receiving a free medical exam, or the altruistic benefit resulting from involvement with the study. And, *aspirational benefits* provide social value, and are benefits that inure to the broader society, as well as future patients.[88]

The different perspectives on what constitutes direct benefit can subvert confidence in the protections against harm that are necessary for those who cannot exercise their autonomy and informed consent.[89] Particularly for children who are unable to assess and appreciate the gravity of risk and benefit to themselves, and especially for those who serve as their surrogate decision-maker, risk-benefit calculations are difficult. To that end, Friedman, Robbins, and Wendler suggest that when considering the degree of accompanying risks vis-à-vis the potential direct benefits, not all benefits are created equal.[90] Notably, in cases of nontherapeutic research – or research with no prospect of direct benefit – it is necessary to assess the risk of harm according to a thorough balancing, and non-arbitrary analysis,[91] prior to seeking informed consent.

In establishing the strict criteria for research involving children, the National Commission classified risk into three categories according to its probability: minimal risk, a minor increase over minimal risk, and more than a minor increase over minimal risk.[92] Accordingly, with respect to children, it defined minimal risk, as "the probability and magnitude of physical or psychological harm that is normally encountered in the daily lives, or in the routine medical or psychological examination of healthy children."[93] It is important to note that the Common Rule definition of minimal risk, which does not appear in Subpart D involving children, but rather Subpart A, makes no reference to healthy children. Rather, it considers the daily lives of the general population. For the sake of particularly vulnerable children, some argue that the risk standard ought to be relative to the individual child who is the subject of the proposed research – not the healthy child.

Probability and severity of harm can be influenced by the condition of the child entering the study. That is to say that a child with a disorder may be vulnerable to greater harm from a research procedure than a child who does not have one. Conversely, some argue that children who are healthy ought to remain so and are therefore entitled to greater protection. These relative positions are part of the ongoing conversation surrounding risk of harm assessments.[94]

The idea of avoiding harm, proffering benefit, and minimizing risk to children in clinical research has many dimensions. Harms are wide-ranging and dynamic. They range from the physiological, to unanticipated intrusions into privacy and embarrassment, to offenses to personal dignity and self-respect. All of which must be balanced against the interests of research participants, and those who may benefit in the future.[95]

Benefits are not always known and are often not detected until long after the study closes and may not even inure to the study participants themselves. Further, they may be misinterpreted altogether if the informed consent process failed to counter a therapeutic misconception, or if any potential benefits were misconstrued as cures or something more than collateral.[96] Risk assessments look at the probability and severity of harm through the lens of what is reasonably foreseeable or what is already known to have occurred. Evaluating the likelihood of harm to a child requires unique insight into the experiential as well as a conjectural understanding of what it means to be a child, which, in the absence of meaningful clinical research, remains unknown. Despite the conundrum, understanding the vulnerability of children relies, to some extent, upon knowledge obtained through ethical clinical research.

Pediatric Vulnerability in Three Contexts

As moral agents, ethically accountable HCOs have a moral duty to address the needs of its community of stakeholders. Many vulnerable populations of stakeholders within the purview of an HCO, are dependent upon it to satisfy a variety of their physical and emotional needs. Since vulnerability is both a source of moral obligation, and an indicator of conditions that give rise to such obligations, HCOs have an incontrovertible duty to its vulnerable stakeholders.

Power and authority demand moral responsibility, and the HCO is a wellspring of both. Children are inherently and conditionally vulnerable. "They need care not only to survive but also to develop their basic physical, intellectual and emotional capacities,"[97] and are entirely dependent, albeit often temporally, upon the authority and power of others to decide most matters for them.

The most common metric of vulnerability within healthcare is the autonomy of the individual, specifically, assessing the competence and capacity to give informed consent.[98] However, an autonomy-based understanding of vulnerability alone is too limiting because vulnerability is contextual. The taxonomy of contextual vulnerability looks to the types of vulnerability according to the circumstances, surroundings, environments, and other related factors affecting the individual. Representative factors include *institutional vulnerabilities*, such as those experienced by prisoners. *Deferential vulnerability*, which considers gender, race, or socioeconomic contexts, as well as medical, cognitive, and communicative vulnerability.[99] *Contextual vulnerability*, considers more than the intrinsic characteristics of the individual; it considers the contexts in which they find themselves.[100] This section explores pediatric research as a contingent vulnerability by illuminating the contextual vulnerability unique to children with HIV, victims of abuse and maltreatment, and children with special cognitive and developmental disorders. Because healthcare and clinical research are relational, the significance of interpersonal and social relationships and the influence of authority figures such as physicians, researchers and IRBs, legal proxies, and other caregivers, underscore the need for relational ethics.

Children With HIV

Human immunodeficiency virus (HIV) is a virus spread through the exchange of certain body fluids that attack CD4 cells, also known as T-cells, which support the body's immune system and help it to fight off infections. Unlike other viruses, the human body cannot fully rid itself of HIV; therefore, once a person acquires the virus, they have it for life. Over time, if left untreated, HIV outnumbers and destroys the CD4 cells, rendering the body susceptible to other infections, particularly opportunistic infection-based cancers. When these infections overpower the immune system, it is an indication of their progression toward the final stage of HIV or acquired immunodeficiency syndrome – AIDS.[101]

Although there is no cure, antiretroviral therapy (ART) can significantly reduce the viral load – amount of HIV present in the body's blood – to amounts that are virtually undetectable thereby preventing further transmission of HIV. Although ART has greatly reduced HIV prevention and management and has contributed to a 48% reduction in AIDS-related deaths, it "does not remove replicative HIV from the body and is not a cure."[102] In order to maintain the reduction in viral load and transmission prevention, ART must be administered for the life of the patient with HIV. In the absence of cure, HIV remains a chronic disease carrying a devastating prognosis in its active stages.

Approximately 37.9 million people worldwide live with HIV;[103] including 1.8 million children under 15 years of age. Children and youth can acquire HIV through perinatal, or mother-to-child transmission (MTCT), through sexual contact, or through other non-vertical/nonsexual encounters such as unsafe intravenous drug use,[104] and blood transfusions. Ninety percent of pediatric HIV cases occur from MTCT either in utero, during labor and delivery, or postnatally through breastfeeding.[105] ART administered during pregnancy has resulted in significant reductions in rates of perinatal transmissions and has improved morbidity and mortality rates. Despite the significance of ART, HIV is a chronic infectious disease still in need of a cure. HIV cure research seeks therapeutic interventions to control or eliminate HIV such that further medical interventions are unnecessary to maintain health.[106]

HIV-infected children are contextually vulnerable. Consistent with Solbakk's theory, they also live with layered conditions that magnify their vulnerability. At one time, HIV-positive children were not expected to live past childhood. However, with longer lifespans today, children and young people growing up with HIV face considerable challenges to their physical and mental health as well as developmental processes.[107] Although adolescence is a time of high risk generally, those with HIV can be particularly susceptible to psychosocial challenges as they face not only developmental vulnerability but also HIV-related stressors.[108] Regardless of how the HIV was acquired, "distinctive features characterize the experience of learning to make sense of and live with a communicable and highly stigmatized infection during childhood and adolescence."[109] The stigma associated with HIV infection also raises one of the most controversial matters in pediatric HIV; that is, determining if and when to disclose the HIV status to the affected child.

The presence of HIV is most often attributed to stigmatized behavior such as high-risk sexual activity, intravenous drug use, and same-sex sexual behavior. Because most HIV-infected children acquire the virus through MTCT, disclosing the infection often unveils other family secrets such as paternity, socioeconomic status, patterns of parental sexual behavior, and drug use.[110] In such cases, the public health risks of non-disclosure directly conflict with the child's right not to know their HIV status. Yet, children who are unaware of their HIV serostatus can unwittingly engage in behaviors that create risks. Risks from non-compliance with medication – the purpose of which they do not understand – increase the potential for transmitting ART-resistant strains of the virus. Moreover, children who do not know they are infected are unable to participate in HIV cure research studies.

Failing to disclose their perinatal HIV infection to them increases the child's vulnerability. Currently, there is little published research to evaluate the most appropriate time to disclose, and the psychosocial effects of HIV disclosure or non-disclosure on the child. However, practitioners confront disclosure issues with great frequency, and there is some clinical consensus on recommended guidelines.[111] Although, Sabharwal, Mitchell, and Fan contend that recommendations alone are not enough to encourage disclosure. They argue that considering their emotional, psychological, and cognitive development, HIV-infected youth must be aware of their serostatus, regardless of parental desire to delay disclosure.[112]

To that end, HIV-infected children are subordinate to the authority, power, and competing interests of caregivers upon whom they are dependent. Such power and dependency mandate that parents, caregivers, and providers have a moral duty to provide physically and emotionally supportive environments for children and adolescents with HIV. That duty entails comprehensive consideration of the dynamic cultural, social, familial, and emotional contexts these children experience, as well as the context of their relationships with these authority figures. Accordingly, Marhefku, Turner, and Chenneville advocate for research to better understand "[t]he antecedents, processes and outcomes of disclosure to children."[113] Ethically enabling appropriate species of research on these children must be reconciled with their contextual vulnerability. *Relational ethics* recognize the interpersonal contexts; its application is essential to addressing the contingent vulnerability of this distinct pediatric population.

According to the goodness-of-fit model of relational ethics, the vulnerability of a child is considered beyond just her age and capacity. It evaluates the goodness-of-fit between clinical context of treatment and research, and the child's development, which includes caregiver and parental comprehension, their personal values, and cultural norms.[114] The model focuses on collaboration between the clinician, the investigator, the families, and the child, and is relevant to all aspects of clinical treatment and research, including informed consent and considerations of capacity to understand. Goodness-of-fit shifts the judgment "[a] way from an exclusive focus on assumed child or guardian vulnerabilities to an examination of the clinical or experimental setting that can reduce or facilitate informed choice."[115] It requires a holistic awareness of cultural values, as well as "[h]ow HIV stigma is differentially distributed across social groups."[116]

Because there is little available research on HIV-infected children, the goodness-of-fit framework necessitates an independent effort on the part of the ethically accountable physician and researcher to understand the relational dynamics of this vulnerable stakeholder group. Rahill, Joshi, and Lescano prescribe professional and cultural training and education to help the healthcare professional understand the impact of culture and personal values on the child and their caregivers. In addition, "Education and training can also help clinicians and researchers develop a clearer understanding of their own cultural beliefs and values in relation to the multiple identities that a racial, religious, ethnic, disabled or sexual minority youth who is also HIV positive may be experiencing."[117] Such cultural humility is an essential component of moral accountability vis-à-vis the needs of vulnerable children, as further illustrated by those who are victims of abuse.

Child Maltreatment

Intentional harm to children is not a modern-day phenomenon. Evidence of infanticide, abandonment, beatings, terrorization, and child sexual abuse is seen as far back as the ninth century B.C. Children typically occupied the lowest social strata in ancient times, and their maltreatment was considered rather unremarkable. The perception that children were impediments whose existence placed strains on society extended into Elizabethan England. Social policies were designed to protect society from vagrancy, idleness and other delinquencies attributed to children.[118]

It was not until the late nineteenth century that the consequential story of Mary Ellen Wilson brought the reality of child abuse into the public arena. Because there were no relevant laws protecting children, 8-year-old Mary was rescued, according to animal cruelty laws, from horrendous physical abuse at the hands of her foster parents. Her suffering helped illuminate the need for public attention and legislation.[119] Over the next several decades, child abuse centers as well as state and federal child abuse advisory boards emerged, establishing the basis for a child protection system in the United States.[120] Albeit imperfect, the system established civil and criminal protections for maltreated children. As the evolution of child abuse protection efforts intersected with the expansion of medical research, hyper-protective concerns for abused children isolated them from meaningful research. The few studies conducted introduced compelling evidence of the short and long-term effects of maltreatment on children.

The legal definitions of *child maltreatment* and abuse generally align with the specific provisions of individual state penal codes and statutes. Because it is universally recognized, this book adopts the definition provided by The Centers for Disease Control and Prevention (CDC): "[a]ny act or series of acts of commission or omission by a parent or other caregiver that results in harm, potential for harm, or threat of harm to a child."[121] Child maltreatment recognizes four main types of abusive acts: physical abuse, sexual abuse, emotional, or psychological abuse, and neglect.[122] Each type identifies specific harms such as beating, shaking, abusive head trauma, scalding and poisoning, sexual contact and exploitation, blaming, intimidating, degrading and isolating, and failure to provide for or supervise a child – to name just a few.[123] According to the CDC definition, and consistent with most statutory frameworks, only a caregiver can perpetrate maltreatment. Acts and injuries by all others are considered criminal assaults and/or batteries.[124]

The physiological and psychological harms from maltreatment are far-reaching. Findings from early research on child and adolescent development revealed that girls who were sexually abused reported having more instances of gynecological problems, persistent sleep issues, obesity, cognitive challenges, HIV risk, and early puberty, than non-maltreated girls.[125] "Neglect, the most prevalent type of child maltreatment, is associated with restricted growth of the corpus callosum, dental disease, failure to thrive, and a variety of mental, emotional and behavioral impairments among children."[126] "Adults who were mistreated in childhood are at significantly greater risk of experiencing serious illness and premature mortality from a variety of conditions, including drug/alcohol addiction, cancer, lung disease, severe obesity, heart disease, asthma and liver disease."[127] The consequences of child maltreatment trauma can develop across the child's lifespan. However, not all children who experience maltreatment necessarily develop physiological and mental health problems. A child's resiliency to such problems can be enriched through protective factors such as familial and social support mechanisms.[128]

Child maltreatment is a serious public health matter and "[t]he consequences… are pervasive, spanning multiple domains of functioning."[129] According to the Administration for Children and Families, in 2019 there were 4.4 million reports of child maltreatment involving 7.9 million children in the United States.[130] As this rate increases, its prevalence and recognition as a childhood illness requires research to improve its diagnosis, treatment, and prevention. To that end, Guttman, Shouldice, and Levin contend that "there is a moral duty for researchers to be active in this area."[131] The ethical and legal considerations, however, associated with child maltreatment research, are challenging, arduous, and present multiple unique dimensions because of the nature of the *illness*. The depth of ethical issues ascribed to child maltreatment research is well beyond the scope and limits of this chapter. Rather, it calls attention to the moral duty of the HCO, through its accountable physicians, researchers, and other professionals to recognize the necessity and value of child maltreatment research as a multi-stakeholder concern and to pursue it actively. Because it is post-hoc, most of the research in child abuse will result in a benefit to the common good of society, rather than to the child participant. In fact, the mere disclosure of the abuse could result in more harm to the child. Therefore, not unlike risks from disclosure of HIV-infected children, moral accountability requires that "studies be designed to protect against and avoid further harm and trauma" from the disclosure of abuse.[132]

Ethical research practices avoid inducing injury or illness and typically require examining the illness in its naturally occurring setting. The nature of child maltreatment research, which is in effect injury research involving children who are already contextually vulnerable, presents risks that are per se sufficiently high. Although injury research typically involves children who have been identified through case reports, studies on prevention and intervention strategies may reveal undetected incidents of prior, current, or imminent abuse.[133] Detecting and exposing abuse can cause the child to undergo additional abuse. Child maltreatment is trauma that is unique because it is non-accidental. The intentionality of the parent or caregiver perpetrator, who is most often the logical proxy for informed consent based on the presumption that they have the best interest of the child in mind despite abusive evidence to the contrary, is an ethical paradox.[134]

Even if the informed consent requirement is waived to protect the child from additional trauma, child maltreatment research presents ethical challenges to the researcher and clinician. The risk of causing distress to a child during an interview process, appropriately handling the discovery of abuse that was never reported, and identification of perpetrators[135] are just a few of the unique challenges of this species of research. The relational ethics model of pediatric research may palliate these challenges. One way is for healthcare professionals to recognize the centrality of culture, cultural influences, and rights to cultural autonomy in their work with this vulnerable population.[136]

In the same way as it applies to the goodness-of-fit approach in HIV research, culture is important in all aspects of detection, prevention, intervention, and treatment of child maltreatment.[137] Because culture influences all dimensions of child-rearing, child development, and maturation into adolescence and adulthood, it is an essential component of relational ethics in child maltreatment research. Cultural considerations help to determine how resilient the child is to potential harm, how the child's family setting may influence the abuse as well as the interventions employed, and the extent to which culturally influenced social systems may protect, or expose the child to greater vulnerability.[138] Thus, researchers and clinicians working with abused children must possess cultural competence as well as cultural literacy; that is, an understanding of the perspectives and experiences of the victims and their parents/caregivers – in order to adapt the research and practices accordingly.[139] An ethically accountable HCO is duty-bound to provide methods for understanding the role of culture within the child's exosystemic framework to its researchers, clinicians, caregivers, and children. The moral duty of the HCO to mitigate risks to vulnerable children in research is further examined through the lens of those with special cognitive needs.

Children With Intellectual and Cognitive Disabilities

Developmental disability is a term that broadly describes intellectual, or physical impairment, or a combination of the two that generally manifests before an individual reaches age 22. A developmental disability likely continues indefinitely and results in substantial limitation of life activities such as self-care, receptive-expressive language, self-direction, learning, and capacity for independent living.[140] "Intellectual disability (ID) encompasses the 'cognitive' part of this definition, that is, a disability that is broadly related to thought processes...It is characterized by significant limitations in intellectual functioning (reasoning, learning and problem-solving), and in adaptive behavior."[141]

Intellectual disability includes those congenital cognitive disorders that are likely to be diagnosed in early childhood such as Down syndrome, Fragile X syndrome, and autism.[142] Today, the term intellectual disability is often used independently from the other disorders to replace the condition previously known as mental retardation. Nevertheless, unless otherwise specified, references to intellectual disability used throughout this chapter will mean cognitive disabilities and related impairments.

As Leslie Francis asserts, intellectual disabilities are complex and multi-faceted, and their attendant impairments vary significantly from person to person.[143] Some children with intellectual disabilities may have difficulty with abstract reasoning and impulse control. Intellectual disability challenges the child's ability to make right judgment. They often experience problems with social adaptation rendering them gullible and naïve, placing them at risk for victimization, and increasing their dependency on others.[144] Because many intellectual disabilities lack physical manifestations, the child's vulnerability may be invisible, compounding the risk of victimization from the unsuspecting third-party presumption of "normalness."

According to the Centers for Disease Control and Prevention, the prevalence of children diagnosed with any form of developmental disability increased between 2014 and 2016 from 5.76% to 6.99%,[145] respectively, ranging from mild speech and language impairment to more severe intellectual disability and autism.

Specifically, diagnoses of autism, or autism spectrum disorder (ASD), have appreciably increased since 2000; such that today, 1 in 59 children will be diagnosed with one or more of autism's spectrum of pervasive disorders.[146] "The most recent Global Burden of Disease data estimates that in 2015, there were 3.6 million children aged 1-9 years living with autism and more than 15 million living with idiopathic developmental intellectual disability."[147] In addition to learning the reasons why more children than ever are being diagnosed with ASD, there is much more to discover about this complicated disorder specifically, and intellectual disabilities generally. Aside from understanding the causes and risk factors, early and accurate identification and diagnosis of a child's impairment can help to mitigate adverse effects to the child as well as those experienced by family and caregiver stakeholders.

In the wake of Willowbrook, much attention has been paid to protecting children with intellectual disabilities because of their vulnerability.[148] However, bioethicists, researchers, and disability advocates, have argued that excluding persons with intellectual disabilities from research is unfair, may be too stringent, and may be equally harmful to them. For instance, it is widely understood that early detection and evidence-based interventions provide the best opportunities for children with ASD to develop and flourish.[149] Interventions such as speech and occupational therapy, as well as emotional adaptation training allow the plasticity of the young child's brain to change and have a better chance of developing enhanced potential. Denying evidenced-based research opportunities designed to discover effective and customized interventional therapies can thwart these chances. Also, precluding children with intellectual disabilities from participation in research denies family members and caregivers, broader insight and understanding into treatments and interventions that aid them, and aid the child.[150]

Children with cognitive disabilities are contingently vulnerable in that they are dependent upon the authority and control of others. They are also contextually vulnerable to the environment, conditions, and relational experiences unique to them vis-à-vis their disorder. Understanding the contextual world of a child with a cognitive disability is often eclipsed by communication and other sensory barriers. *Participatory research* helps to overcome these barriers. It contends that to fully understand the contextual nature of a child's vulnerability, the child ought to participate in the actual design and execution of the research. There is growing evidence and acceptance of the participatory approach to research with children with intellectual disabilities.[151]

Unpacking this further, participatory research illuminates the goodness-of-fit model of relational ethics. Through collaboration and engagement with the child and their authority figures, healthcare professionals can identify and acknowledge how the child's perspectives are tied to and shaped by their relationship with others. For example, unlike children with HIV, or those who are maltreated, the dependencies of the child with intellectual disability likely did not evolve gradually from the onset of the disorder. Rather, most children with intellectual disability, especially autism, have never experienced any other way of being,[152] or understanding of themselves. Therefore, the way these children see the world and themselves in relation to it, are attitudes and points of reference that must be understood and appreciated to effectuate ethical research on them. In addition, it will help to ensure necessary clinical advances exist to address the population health of this stakeholder community.

Ethical and Legal Strategies for Managing Pediatric Obesity: A Moral Duty

Population health refers to an "understanding of the epidemiology of a particular population and aligning a community's healthcare resources to not only treat illnesses ...but to keep the population healthy."[153] Managing population health, particularly with respect to vulnerable populations, requires accountable leadership who possess a moral commitment to the sustained health and lifelong fulfillment of patients and communities served by the HCO.[154] The remainder of this chapter addresses a specific area of population health. It delves deeply into the ethical and legal strategies for accountable leaders to prevent and mitigate the psychosocial and physiological effects of pediatric obesity on children.

Childhood obesity is a critical public health threat. Solving the problem of pediatric obesity requires a delicate balance between the need for regulated behavior modification, and the respect for the child's individual self-determination. It also sits amidst the competing interests of government and physician intervention, and respect for parental sovereignty in determining what is best for their child physically and psychologically. When obesity creates a degree of harm to a child that is disproportionate to the benefit conferred by the competing interests, and actions or inactions exacerbate and negative consequences of obesity, ethical concerns arise.[155] Something or someone must intercede on the child's behalf. This chapter addresses the moral duty of the ethically accountable HCO to this public health threat and to this vulnerable stakeholder group. It outlines the ethical justification for HCO intervention to address the disproportionate psychosocial and physiological harms of childhood obesity through care ethics, and the invocation of a modified common law doctrine of *parens patriae*.

Pediatric Obesity as a Public Health Threat

Even though one-third of the world's population goes to bed hungry each night, *over-nutrition* – that which occurs when too many calories and excess nutrients and food components are consumed vis-à-vis suboptimal energy expenditures – is rampant in the United States. Barring some intervening metabolic disorder, over-nutrition nearly always results in excess levels of fat tissue and bodyweight. But body fat can vary according to race, sex, and age.[156] And when calculated against an individuals' height, the resulting body mass index (BMI) is the standardized yardstick used to determine whether an individual is obese.

According to the Organization for Economic Co-operation and Development, adult obesity rates in the United States are the highest in the world. Thirty percent of adults and 31% of children in the United States are obese, and by

2030, 47% of the U.S. population will be.[157] Although there is some dispute as to the outer limits of bodyweight or BMI necessary to constitute obesity, it recognized that childhood obesity is a biological reality that has wide-ranging societal implications.[158]

The current state of the obesity crisis in the United States is most obviously measured in raw statistics. Since 1980, childhood obesity rates have tripled to the point that close to one-third of children over age 2 are overweight or are obese.[159] Approximately 6.1% of U.S. children are considered severely obese;[160] a figure which outpaces the number of children with cancer, HIV, cystic fibrosis and juvenile diabetes combined.[161] Even though the numbers associated with childhood obesity can be calculated in various ways, all available data shows a dramatic and accelerated rise. Obesity is a multi-factor disease.[162] It has wide-ranging genetic, societal, and behavioral causes that begin in childhood and left unabated can continue into adulthood. This characteristic renders it a two-stage disease.[163]

One of the most pressing concerns to emerge is the impact that continual rises in childhood obesity will have on the adult disease rate going forward. U.S. statistics show that a child who was obese during the first and second year of life stands an 8% chance of becoming an obese adult, while a child who is obese between the ages of 10 and 14 has a 70% chance. The rates are even higher if the child has at least one obese parent.[164] Because it is a two-stage disease, not only does the physicality of obesity accompany the adult, the adverse medical and psychosocial health outcomes also negatively impact adult lives.

All of this presupposes that the child can even expect to live to adulthood. For the first time since the 1900s, when public health initiatives first began to make significant and measurable improvements in pediatric health, life expectancy for children is eroding because of obesity. According to recent statistics, children can no longer expect to live longer than their parents, due to the effects of adult diseases such as Type II diabetes and other diseases tied to childhood obesity.[165] Childhood obesity has been shown to lead to higher death rates in middle age due to the fourfold increase in risk of heart attack, doubled risk rate from cancer, and more than doubled risk of death from respiratory disease.[166] Moreover, roughly 36% of adults in the United States who are twenty years or older are obese, and 6.3% of them are considered extremely obese. It is estimated that 300,000 deaths annually are linked to obesity.[167]

The societal costs of this obesity explosion are both real and indirect. The real costs are often the most startling and attract wider audience interest because they represent comprehensible dollars and cents. Lifetime medical costs attributed to normal-weight children are approximately $12,900 per child however they are reported to exceed $19,000 in the case of an *obese* child.[168] Many of the direct medical costs are associated with excessive doctor's visits and medication. According to recent study estimates, lifetime medical costs can exceed $14 billion when they are multiplied by the present number of obese 10-year-olds in the United States. A number of these additional real costs will not be realized until much later when the child begins to experience health and behavioral conditions that are tied to childhood obesity.

As such, obesity's impact is so diverse and dramatic that the World Health Organization Consultation on Obesity's prescient report in 1997 determined it to be a highly neglected public health problem with a potential impact as great as that of smoking.[169] Since this conclusion was drawn, obesity as a public health threat has gained the same recognition as anti-tobacco and related legislation, especially with respect to its influence on children's behavior. These ground-breaking regulatory interventions were fueled by, among other things, vocal appeals to change the influences that sustained such harmful behavior.[170]

Children Become What They Eat

There are at least 200 genes known to factor into a person's weight, and although genetics do play a limited role in obesity, researchers and experts adhere to the position that obesity is largely controlled through behavior. With the exception of certain known metabolic conditions for which obesity is a consequence, along with certain inheritable statures and body shapes, the fundamental causes for the obesity epidemic are behaviors and lifestyles, especially diets.[171] Current research suggests that as much as 80% of children in the United States have diets that are considered poor or in drastic need of improvement, amplified by behaviors which are strongly dominated by negative societal influences.[172] As a behavior-induced disease, there are also a number of environmental factors that influence not only the behaviors but the environmental changes within which those behaviors thrive.

One demonstrable way in which negative behaviors thrive in response to their environment is in the super-sizing and over-consumption of unhealthy processed foods. Up to a certain age, children will only eat what they are given, and the growing phenomenon of *food deserts* – places where healthy food options are not readily available – leave little if any healthy, obesity-resistant alternatives.[173] In addition to food deserts, Western culture is programmed to consume unhealthy food quickly, cheaply and in mega quantities with scale-shattering consequences.[174]

Further, Warren and Smalley aptly suggest that decreased levels of physical activity have led to a "lazy-fication" of children. Studies have shown that nearly three-quarters of children have a sedentary lifestyle and do not get the recommended daily amount of exercise. Lazy-fication is amplified by the fact that physical education in public school systems – once an important component of learning – is no longer valued as such.[175] As an obesogenic influence, an inactive child's basic caloric needs have gotten lower without offsetting a corresponding decrease in caloric *intake*.[176]

Technology and child-safety concerns have fortified the lazy-fication and fattening of children. Nielson recently reported that children aged 2 to 5 spend an average of 32 hours per week – the equivalent of a work week – watching television or playing video games. Children are essentially plugged into inactivity.[177] Prolonged television viewing impacts numerous health outcomes through its cumulative impact on diet and exercise including obesity and diabetes. For every extra 2 hours of television watching per day, there are 176 more cases of Type 2 diabetes.[178] Simply put, most children do not move around much anymore. They live in a largely automated society that performs many things for them.

Childhood recreation has shifted from that which used to include sustained physical activity, to sedentary computerized technology and social media providing instant gratification. Add to this the fact that, to protect children from predatory threats, abduction, and other forms of neighborhood violence, parents no longer encourage unsupervised outside play. Eating used to be a way for children to recharge their batteries. Today, however, children no longer must *spend* calories to *get* them.[179] To promote movement away from lazy-fication, it is necessary to first understand environmental and individual factors influencing this phenomenon.

Obesogenic Influences

It is well understood that the socio-cultural environment influences body-size preferences, as well as eating and activity patterns. In the United States in particular, much emphasis is placed on possessing an attractive body. An attractive body in that societal context equates to thinness. As such, the role that culture and social values assume with respect to childhood obesity cannot be overstated.

Cultural influences shape food-related practices in families and broader community settings. Not only is the notion of a well-nurtured body a notion that is culturally shaped, but children are also exposed to a wide continuum of values and expectations from parents and their sibling/peer groups that affect their ideal of body-size as well as appropriate eating and activity practices.[180] These cultural groups and their values undergird the eating choices that result from individual and environmental constructs.

The network of factors leading to obesity is complex and spans many sectors of society including the family, the education system, the food industry, the media, the transport sector, and of course, the government.[181] Despite the temptation to assign blame for the pediatric obesity problem to one factor over another, because of their contextual complexity, it is not possible to do so.

Eating is a social behavior that most often takes place where people spend the most amount of time. At least for children, that place is traditionally the home. And especially for children, who are particularly susceptible to behavioral influences, observing the eating habits of others within the home is a powerful influence on their own preferences and behavior. It is well-established that the home and the activities that take place within it and the family unit, tend to define the child and his or her behaviors and preferences. Children learn what they live. Therefore, it is not surprising that the nutrition behaviors and preferences of children and adolescents are associated with those of their parents and others within the family unit.[182]

Research indicates that children who experience a family-centered and emotionally supportive home life tend to engage in healthier behaviors and eating habits. "A common family value is a shared mealtime."[183] Children who experience structured mealtimes tend to consume a healthier diet and are less likely to be overweight. Mealtime becomes a family-centered activity where eating choices and portion sizes are predetermined, controlled, and supported.[184]

Admittedly there is, however, relatively little documented information concerning parenting practices of overweight children. And it is difficult to know whether the parental behavior or the obesity came first. Nevertheless, family conflict and lower levels of parental warmth and engagement are often associated with poorer adherence to treatments for other pediatric chronic medical conditions; therefore, it is not unreasonable to draw a nexus to childhood obesity.[185] Still, additional environmental, societal, and individual factors bear directly upon obesity in children.

It is well documented that increased rates of childhood obesity coincide with increased numbers of parents participating in the workforce.[186] As such, two-thirds of children under the age of 6 in the United States spend some time in childcare and are likely to experience some if not most of their daily calorie consumption and expenditure in that setting.[187] Childcare centers influence nutrition and eating practices. But as a regulated industry, childcare services are the purview of the state, and recommendations to create positive nutritional environments are largely a matter for the legislators. Nevertheless, day care centers and schools are responsible for children outside of the home and family, and represent another place where children spend a significant portion of their eating time. As obesogenic environments continue to be identified, it is important to understand the long-term consequences of pediatric obesity.

Obesogenic Vulnerability

While long-term medical consequences of pediatric obesity are well-recognized, the less obvious but the most pervasive ones in Western societies, are its psychosocial costs.[188] Because of the stigma, shame, and isolation of obesity that often follow the child into adulthood the psychosocial costs of pediatric obesity are more chronic over a child's lifetime than the physiological.[189] Still, the physiological effects of childhood obesity are often irreversible and can, not only shorten a child's life expectancy, but interfere with their ability to flourish; thereby punctuating the significance of contingent vulnerability, and underscoring the moral duty of the HCO to intervene.

Physiological Harms

Physicians are treating children for many obesity-related adult diseases that have never been seen before in children. Because of a paucity of pediatric research generally, adult diseases present in children are difficult to manage and equally difficult to prevent from accompanying the child to adulthood. Moreover, many pediatricians are not adequately trained nor prepared to treat children for some of these adult-oriented conditions such as cardiovascular disease, sleep apnea, and hypertension.[190] Type II diabetes mellitus – which is often referred to as *adult onset* – presents another such example.

There is no known cure for Type I, or *juvenile diabetes*. It is an autoimmune disease in which the body no longer produces insulin, and survival depends upon a lifetime commitment to strict diet control and insulin dependence. Causes have been linked to genetic predisposition as well as exposure to certain viruses, and while a child with Type I diabetes may become overweight throughout the disease, obesity is not typically a precursor to it. On the other hand, there are many factors that contribute to and increase someone's risk for Type II diabetes, with obesity representing such a significant factor that they have been described as "twin epidemics."[191] With an emphasis on diet and exercise, Type II diabetes is most often both curable and preventable.

The more fatty tissue a person has, the more resistant the person's cells are to the sugar controlling effects of insulin.[192] A team of researchers from the Institute of Molecular and Cell Biology recently revealed that an important protein responsible for regulating insulin in the cells is lacking in obese individuals. The gene code for the NUKE protein is inactive in individuals who have high-fat, calorie-dense diets. The absence of NUKE leads to insulin resistance which impedes the body's ability to regulate glucose effectively which increases blood sugar levels and leads to diabetes. The NUKE protein reappears when high-fat diets are eliminated.[193]

Obese children often experience *cardiovascular adaptation*, which means that the heart must adjust to the differences in body weight, oftentimes by working harder, thereby impacting the way it functions. Pericardial fat can build up around the heart. As such, overweight adolescents have reported decreased heart function because their increased body mass places so much strain on their heart.[194] As the heart is pushed to function harder, high blood pressure places compounding strain on the circulatory system which forces it to work harder thereby adding strain to the body's blood vessels. Plaque builds up in the arteries of overweight children by the time they reach their 20s. The body gradually accumulates all the exposure to the harmful cardiac influences which then sets into motion a cascade of bodily processes and reactions that lead to the development of cardiovascular disease.[195] The omnipresence of these trigger points, suggests that an overweight child with an overburdened cardiovascular system is practically assured of irreversible cardiac disease.

Given the emphasis on weight loss, requests for weight-loss surgeries for children are increasing. And since the average age of a typical bariatric surgery patient is 40-years, these physicians face the same dilemmas as the pediatrician. "Physicians trust that morbidly obese adult patients can put all known risks and complications into perspective before agreeing to a bariatric operation. It is not clear that pediatric patients and their families have the same perspective."[196] Bariatric surgeons are not always trained and adequately prepared for the pediatric patient. Additionally, the long-term consequences of bariatric surgery on young children, such as the need for postoperative lifelong compliance with diet and behavioral modifications, are not well understood.

Understanding the link between obesogenic influences and behaviors and imposing changes to those factors is the moral duty of parents and other sources of authority who can mandate change through control of the environments. These changes can not only prevent obesity-related illness but can help the child's mind consciously or unconsciously adapt, in a healthy way, to its social environment. This psychosocial balance is often threatened by obesity-related consequences such as bullying, victimization, damaged self-esteem, and even depression. To successfully change these environments, these psychosocial factors must be understood first within the family and peer environments and then more closely within the individual's settings.[197]

Psychosocial Harms

Peer relations are central to a child's healthy social and emotional development. Peer acceptance and popularity are often the litmus tests for a child's healthy self-perception. Children who are a typical weight and body size are most often the most popular. Therefore, all children, regardless of their weight and size, are abundantly aware of the importance of bodyweight and are introduced to that preference practically from the moment peer socialization begins, as early as age 5. They see it, discuss it, and ridicule it. They may try to hide their own body if they are at all overweight and draw attention to the size of others' if they are not. But obesity, unlike many other diseases, is impossible to hide. Size is one of the most salient features of a person and is often the basis for premature judgment and dislike.[198]

Not unlike their adult counterparts, non-obese children often view overweight peers as less-disciplined, lazy, self-indulgent, and inherently less popular. Research reveals that one of the most immediate consequences of being overweight is the differential treatment overweight children report receiving from their peers *and* society at large.[199] These consequences are the result of *weight bias*, or "the inclination to form unreasonable judgements based on a person's weight…and stem from negative attitudes and beliefs."[200] Simply stated, the peer environment is not accepting of obesity.[201] Problematic peer interactions are one of the most notable hallmarks of the psychosocial correlate of pediatric obesity. Name-calling, teasing, bullying, and other forms of victimization are significant social problems affecting obese children. They rarely concern non-obese children or adolescents. Differential treatment is both damaging and devastating to a child's self-perception. However, bullying can be the cruelest and most tragic obesity-related consequence.

Nearly 25% of boys and 17% of girls are bullied. These statistics have been tied to increases in victim substance abuse and suicide. In fact, a recent meta-analysis demonstrated that children who are bullied are more than twice as likely to have suicidal ideations and to make suicide attempts as their peers who are not bullied.[202] The most common motivator for bullying is physical appearance – especially body size. Overweight children are 50% more likely to be bullied than typical-weight children. Sadly, many children report being harassed about their weight from their own families.

Bullying generally is a long-term and consistent issue. If a child is bullied once, their chance of continual bullying increases, and the damaging consequences of bullying are compounded and intensified. This unrelenting harm to a child helps to explain why victims of bullying have higher rates of anxiety, bed-wetting, depression, psychosomatic symptoms, eating disorders, lower academic achievement,[203] and of course, fewer friends and more relationship issues.[204] Withdrawal and disassociation are common traits of a bullying victim. As such, children who have been bullied because they are obese, suffer harm from the general effects of being overweight compounded by the humiliation of being bullied. Because of its two-staged characteristic, the duality of consequences associated with persistent obesity-related bullying can lead to life-long struggles with mental illness.

Many, if not all overweight children begin to believe the differential descriptors and preconceptions about themselves. And, although longitudinal studies are necessary, evidence shows that the negative attitudes that obese children hold about themselves and their physical appearance cyclically invite further stigmatization and rejection.[205] The obese child who is bullied perceives themselves as diminished and unworthy, thereby reinforcing the preconception that they are weak and unworthy, which invites and encourages more abuse. Cumulatively, this lays the groundwork for pediatric psychological disorders, and further increases the risk for additional psychological challenges into adulthood.

Perception Becomes Reality: Internalizing the External

Health-related quality of life ratings, or HRQOL, rate the physical, emotional, and social well-being of a person based on their own internal perspectives. Largely because they come to believe and accept the stigma attributed to them through their obesity, children with low HRQOL tend to be those with the highest body weight. Children with low HRQOL most often exhibit internalized symptoms such as depression. Conversely and further validating the argument that obesity is a two-stage disease, obese adolescents who had the highest level of depressive symptoms were shown to persist in their obesity over time.[206]

The relationship between obesity and psychiatric conditions, the current treatments, and related studies point to higher rates of somatoform disorders – those disorders which convert emotional distress into the physical symptoms of an illness. It is now widely held that psychosomatic conditions such as undiagnosed pain and mood and anxiety disorders are attributable to obesity. In addition, most anxiety symptoms are believed to be related to the corrosive negative impact obesity has on a child's self-esteem; another demonstration of the correlation between poor body image and psychiatric comorbidity.[207]

The cyclical characteristic of obesity in which psychosocial and psychosomatic conditions are bolstered and sustained by the obese child's self-image and perception leads to speculation as to whether obesity may result from other currently classified psychiatric disorders. However, many of the psychiatric disorders associated with obesity appear as adaptive responses. Negative coping strategies such as substance abuse, avoiding exercise out of shame or embarrassment and eating in private are mental health consequences closely tied to being overweight.[208] In other words, depressed children and adolescents may eat in response to stress, and those eating patterns and depression-induced inactivity may lead to overconsumption. This overconsumption typically continues long after the depressive disorder has remitted.[209]

Moreover, children with psychiatric conditions are more vulnerable to other social factors that contribute to obesity such as abuse, neglect, and non-family-centered home life. Research has shown that neglected children are nine times more likely to be obese than children who are properly cared for.[210] For children who have suffered some form of trauma or neglect, eating serves as a means of self-affectation and as a compensatory mechanism to cope with neglect and feelings of low self-worth and self-esteem resulting from automatic thoughts about themselves.

Schemas are mental codifications about the way the world works based upon repeated personal experiences beginning with childhood, and they form experiential rule books of life. Schemas result in automatic thoughts that are extensions of the rule book that become so ingrained that those who form them don't even realize they have them. Negative schemas are called upon whenever critical events take place. For example, a child who is continually frightened by a neighbor's ferocious barking dog will likely associate fear with all dogs of that breed, without considering evidence to the contrary. As such, the schemas of overweight children about how the world works may be formed at a time when they are being ridiculed and ostracized.[211] An obese child's negative automatic thoughts can trigger self-deprecating beliefs that they are ugly, unworthy, and un-loveable. These beliefs can trigger harmful coping strategies such as turning to food or harmful substances, thereby renewing the cycle again and again.[212] And, because they are automatic thoughts and beliefs, they do not end after the person loses weight. Negative schemas live on – often it the form of pervasive psychological disorders.

Not all self-esteem issues that befall obese children have such destructive effects. But there are equally pervasive aspects of a child's personality that are negatively affected by being overweight or having been overweight. Shyness, oversensitivity, and becoming easily discouraged when faced with adversity are common personality impacts. Phlegmatic tendencies and adoption of other defensive personality traits such as developing a protective comedic personality – becoming the "jolly fat person" as a protective shield against weight bias – are also common adaptations to the stigma of being obese.[213]

Yet, there is insufficient empirical evidence to understand exactly how growing up obese implicates future personality disorders because obese children have not been longitudinally tracked and should be for 15 or 20 years to produce a meaningful measure. The psychological distress of childhood obesity continue as the child matures, and overweight adults are more likely to end up somewhere in the mental health system than non-overweight adults. In addition, it is not surprising that mental health professions expect that their overweight adult patients will have more psychological problems than their typical weight patients.[214]

Differential treatment and discrimination continue to accompany many obese people. At this writing, there are no anti-discrimination laws protecting obese children or adults from mistreatment and stigma.[215] For some obese victims of stigma and discrimination, recourse may be sought in the United States by pursuing claims under the Americans with Disabilities Act of 1990 (ADA). Even though obesity itself is not a disability, many of the diseases' secondary conditions are. Aggressively defending obese victims, the Equal Employment Opportunity Commission (EEOC) has successfully filed and settled claims against employers.[216] However, the biases that plague obese persons' internal and external personas will most likely continue unabated and proliferate as the numbers of obese children continue to climb. Legal recourse alone will only serve to placate the offense and will not effectuate the root cause – the obesity itself. Effects of obesity-related victimization and bullying, and the negative attitudes and beliefs are so compelling as to demand ethical intervention strategies to protect the vulnerable.

Parens Patriae: Parenting the Community

As a relational notion, vulnerability, according to Mullin means that people are vulnerable *to* others, both to their actions and their inaction when help is needed.[217] She further asserts that children "are particularly vulnerable to acts and omissions of caregivers charged with significant responsibility for keeping them safe and healthy and for aiding in their physical, emotional, intellectual, and moral development."[218] Somebody must take care of those who cannot yet fully take care of themselves in the face of such vulnerability.

It is from the notion of relational care that the authority to act as a parent emerges. With respect to children, a *social parent* is, according to Mullin, "anyone who is charged with such responsibility, whether a child's biological parent or not, whether paid or not…it is understood in the context of their relationship."[219] The social parent is the embodiment of the relationship between the vulnerable child and the one upon whom they depend. Throughout the remainder of this chapter, Mullin's *social parent theory* is presented as an interstitial concept in establishing ethical accountability to those most affected by pediatric obesity and alleviating their harms.

Merely establishing causation is not going to reverse harms from current obesity trends. As demonstrated throughout this chapter, psychosocial harms are socially constructed harms. As such, these profound social costs along with discrimination of all sorts are significant public health risks that warrant community intervention in executing remediation strategies. As an interdependent unit and social parent, it is incumbent upon the HCO to consider its impact on obese children in the face of obesogenic influences, and its duty to protect them. The strategies employed must consider the cultural influences and community values that affect obesity trends.[220]

Private Lives Publicly Held

Individualism, individual choice, and the freedoms associated with them undergird the prevailing ideology in the United States. Consequently, the ideology of individual responsibility is reflected in the pervasive view of obesity generally, that the individual and their choices are to blame for their obesity. A person is believed to be what they eat. It is clear, however, that an effective solution will not come from the obese child alone. The intervention of a higher sort, directly involving the pediatrician on many levels, must occur.[221]

Childhood obesity is not an example of a personal choice alone, but rather a public health and societal problem whose solution is dependent upon resolving value conflicts. Balancing the autonomy of the parent and their right to raise their children their own way, according to their views and values is paramount. Parents have a right to raise their children according to their perceived best interests, and interference against their will is highly controlled and limited to only the most serious cases.[222] However, where the best interest of the child is threatened, and where the choices of the parent endanger a child's life or, in the case of public health, the lives of obese children generally, third-party intervention can be ethically justified.

The polarity between the individual and the collective, or the private and the public view of health is the quintessential tension in public health ethics. Particularly as applied to childhood obesity, it requires a balance between the individual rights and freedoms of the child and their caregivers and the collective needs of the government to promote and sustain a healthy community.[223] This balancing must consider the risks of harm to members of society with and without the intervention, as well as the threat to fundamental rights of people to choose to live unhealthy lifestyles, and the potential for unwarranted intrusion into private lives. Public health ethics must also look beyond the individuals, governments, and communities and consider the unique ethical issues that arise from interventions into obesogenic environments – specifically the family unit, and schools. There are wide-ranging value conflicts.

Understanding and balancing these rights and ethical issues of the child is further nuanced by the considerations of agency and responsibility. Not only must public health advocates and practitioners who are concerned with childhood obesity consider the child, they must determine who has ultimate responsibility for execution of the intervention. Public health ethics considers the moral duties the government owes to the child and their caregivers, and the community.[224]

Several theories dominate discourse in public health ethics. But because public health and childhood obesity are value-laden and subject to various social contexts, public health ethical justification cannot rely upon one single dominant theory. It requires a framework from which the principles of the duty to do good and avoid harm, intersect with the individual rights to be left alone, and the state and HCO's responsibilities to advance the stakeholder community's best interests. This book suggests that a theory of *principled communitarianism* applies the best of all three objectives.

Communitarianism emphasizes the social and interdependent nature of life and undergirds the notion that what is best for the community ought to determine society's moral thinking and it attributes responsibility of execution to the community.[225] The harm principle – which compels forbearance of conduct or behavior that would harm someone other than the actor – is distinctive in that it does not permit mandatory interventions unless the intervention will prevent harm to vulnerable third parties.[226] As applied to public health, the notion of *principled communitarianism* extracts the best of the values of the harm principle and communitarianism in order to adopt the idea that public health interventions are a shared enterprise. A principled communitarian theory should look at, among other factors, quality of life of obese children and determine whether the psychosocial, physiological, and psychological implications are so severe as to impact the child's ability to enjoy a healthy life thereby justifying the intervention.[227]

Moral justification alone does not guarantee successful interventions. Obese-centered public health intervention, like most public health initiatives, will require that people modify their behavior and lifestyles to comport with the intervention, and in many cases abandon previously held beliefs about obesity's causes and effects. The need to educate, sensitize, and reconsider preconceptions about the dignity of the person is essential to reshape the culture and societal contexts of obesity,[228] and help the population of obese children reshape views of themselves. The failure to implement and comply with these interventions will allow the harm from obesogenic influences to survive and thrive. When the community, which includes the children's family and caregivers, fails the child, the state and other social parents must act within their proper authority.

Moral Authority: Social Parents and Care Ethics

With an emphasis on communal goods and services[229] communitarianism affords a look into the world of socio-cultural influences that encourage an obesogenic environment. The focus is on the communities within which the different environments co-exist. Folding in the harm principle's concern for intervention for the sake of avoiding harm, the interdependent community and its constituents are responsible for and accountable to its children who are vulnerable to obesity.

But where the community, including the parents and legal guardians, fail to provide necessary and adequate protection for the child and are negligent by their actions or inactions, the state as a sovereign may become a de facto parent.[230] The fact is that no parental authority, regardless of its intrinsic character, exists independent of the sovereign. In the United States, the federal government has a supreme duty to all its subjects, and the sovereign states have inalienable duties to protect its children.[231] Reflecting that model of authority, Amy Mullin's *social parent*, empowered by its contextual relationships to its vulnerable children, has a moral and legal duty to its obese pediatric populations.

Mullin's care theory, from which the social parent stems, examines the social arrangements that either generate or mitigate vulnerability, and considers "how attention to the different domains of children's relationship with their caregivers" can identify solutions.[232] Although her work is largely directed to the emotional maltreatment of children and its consequences, the multi-factor nature of obesity and its concomitant physical and emotional harms justifies its applicability as an appropriate care theory. By understanding the relational contexts, Mullin's care theory "directs attention to the needs that are the source of children's vulnerability and the role of the caring relationships in meeting those needs."[233] Of the different relational domains responsible for the satisfaction of certain needs, the domain concerned for the child's protection and security most prominently undergird the social parent's moral duty. This moral duty further presumes that the child's best interest is paramount when considering the autonomy and exclusivity of parental responsibility vis-a-vis the best interests of their child.

The best interest of the child is the current legal standard in most jurisdictions; however, care theory looks at the *relational interests* of social parents as well as the child. This potentially puts disproportionate emphasis on the presumed parental love for the child. To that end, Mullin aptly argues that "any version of care theory that attends to vulnerability cannot simply trust parents or assume they will seek help" and must recognize the need for increased state intervention[234] when necessary and appropriate.

Under the common law, states' attorneys general may bring actions against parties who directly or indirectly harm the health or well-being of the citizens of their state. The source of this legal authority is the doctrine of *parens patriae*. Translated literally, it means "parent of the country" and was originally promulgated by the British Crown to protect minors and incompetents; later evolving into a broad sweeping common law theory.[235] To assert *parens patriae*, the state must first have an interest that is separate and apart from the individual interests of those impacted by the harm or threat. It must also have a quasi-sovereign interest in the health, well-being, and economic life of its residents. An example of the exercise of *parens patriae* authority in the United States is the recent litigation brought by attorneys general against the tobacco industry for the inherent harms to the citizens of its states.

Applying the same precedent against the food industry for its role in the obesity epidemic may not be as straightforward as tobacco litigation; although consumer groups concerned with obesity are projecting increasingly active voices against this industry.[236] There is not an easily traceable chain of causation between the conduct of the food industry, the food itself, and obesity, as there is in tobacco-induced health risks.[237] Nevertheless, that disconnect did not deter William Sorrell, during his tenure as Vermont's attorney general, from convening more than 100 food industry stakeholders over a two-year period to successfully focus on obesity prevention legislation and policy changes.[238]

Regulating the food industry, nonetheless, is most appropriately the province of state and federal legislators. However, it is a well-settled law that the state *is* permitted to intervene to protect a child's mental and physical health as in cases of *medical neglect*. As obesity is a medical and psychologically affected condition with far-reaching implications, it logically flows that the state would have similar *parens patriae* legal authority to act in cases of obesity-related neglect of minors.[239]

The community has a legal duty to protect its vulnerable and is particularly responsible to protect its children from harm. Situations of child abuse and medical neglect are most often the purview of state laws addressing domestic relations and child protective services. This includes mandatory reporting obligations of pediatricians and other clinicians. This duty to protect against abuse is clearly articulated within the statutory definition of medical neglect and is expressly conferred upon parents and those who provide care and supervision, and/or control of a child in lieu of parental care.

Medical neglect and abuse are the failures to provide medical or psychological care necessary to prevent or to treat serious physical or emotional injury or illness by someone who is required to provide such care. Such neglect occurs when a parent or other responsible party fails to act[240] or to provide care in an emergency, or to address an acute illness that results in harm or injury to the child. But it also occurs when a parent fails to respond to medical recommendations for conditions that are treatable or when such treatment would prevent a life-threatening condition. Determining whether the presence of persistent obesogenic environments and the failure to remove obesogenic influences constitutes medical neglect on the part of the family or other responsible party requires an intense balancing of interests, harms, benefits, and duties.

Because the family is considered the center of family life for most Americans, its decisions are rarely subject to state challenges except for the most special circumstances which threaten the physical and emotional health of its children.[241] Invoking the doctrine of *parens patriae* can be morally and legally justified when obesity-related conditions are exacerbated by medical neglect. In exercising *parens patriae* through application of medical neglect statutes, the state is essentially challenging the parents' failure to prevent or remediate the physiological and psychosocial harms from obesity. The circumstances warranting state intervention and the gravity of those interventions each fall into three general categories.

U.S. courts have typically held that interventions addressing medical neglect under the doctrine of *parens patriae* look at the degree to which the neglected medical treatment is lifesaving, life-prolonging, or quality-of-life enhancing. State intervention is most strongly advocated when the treatment is lifesaving. Because childhood obesity is often a two-stage disease, interventions that either reverse or prevent obesity before a child reaches adulthood can also be life-prolonging. Courts have also upheld interventions which neither save nor prolong life, but instead improve the quality of the child's life. Proponents of state intervention in such cases argue that it is necessary to protect the child's psychological health and the right to a live a *normal* life.[242]

It has long been held that treatments and interventions intended to improve or enhance quality-of-life or degree of flourishing, are difficult to weigh and measure. Because these objectives are subjective, the state's ability to intervene based upon inconsistent values and competing interests is a challenging task. For example, morbidly obese parents of a moderately obese child may consider her quality-of-life superior to that which they experienced at her age. On the other hand, their present condition may be all that is needed to invigorate the desire to reverse her condition and free her from obesity-related constraints. In either event principled communitarianism looks at the balance between the harms and benefits of the intervention in harmony with the values unique to the community.

Principled communitarianism would consider obesity-related medical neglect as an abrogation of the parent's duty to provide a child with a quality-of-life based upon the minimum quality-of-life threshold that the community's values will tolerate. In other words, most communities would agree that intervention is necessary and appropriate when a child's life is in imminent danger. However, most obese children face consequences that are less imminent. The principled communitarian would consider the risk that such a low standard might create if intrusion into family life were to occur where a child suffers from minor to moderate obesity. In these cases that the community must counter-balance the long-range consequences created by stigma, discrimination, and other factors described throughout this chapter against the continuity of family relations. In addition to its values, the community's appetite for intervention must be respected vis-à-vis its state negligence statutes. Some statutes clearly articulate the degree of harm necessary, but many do not. As such, the state and its communities have a duty to rescue its children from the clutches of known *and* unknown dangers.[243] As members of the community of stakeholders, the HCO and its pediatricians share in this moral and legal duty. Because of the relational dynamics, and consistent with care ethics, the HCO and its clinicians and pediatricians are social parents to their pediatric patients struggling with obesity. Therefore, pediatricians and HCOs, in addition to the state, have the moral authority to intervene on behalf of the child, when conditions warrant, through the doctrine of *parens patriae*.

Intervention as a Shared Moral Duty

Although litigation, as well as the mere threat of it can be a powerful motivator for legislative and public policy changes, some opponents to state intervention aptly argue that coercion alone does not create a strong enough foundation for permanent change.[244] In fact, the fear of a nanny state – a government that is perceived as having an excessive interest in controlling the welfare of its citizens particularly in the enforcement of public health and safety – can be a formidable adversary to state intervention. However, commentary from the Johns Hopkins Berman Institute of Bioethics underscores that government interference into obesity control and prevention does not amount to a nanny state interference. It contends that the health implications for being overweight and the obesity-related disparities create a government duty in the name of social justice.[245] With that, social justice in accordance with principled communitarianism, supports *parens patriae* interventions incorporating notions of fairness, respect for the values of the community and the individuals, and adoption of community-based approaches to policy.[246] True community-based initiatives presuppose collaboration across the various stakeholder and social parent relational groups.

Interventions represent different degrees of intrusion and must be weighed against the community's interests, responsibilities, and convictions. Interventions must respect the parents' interests, as well as the concerns of pediatricians and other healthcare providers, the state, and the children. Interventions range from benign mandates such as public education to increase interest in healthier lifestyles, to interference with family eating habits.[247] For example, many U.S. health insurance providers and hospitals have addressed food insecurity – the uncertain ability to obtain nutritious foods – by identifying food deserts and developing strategies, programs, and tools to bring healthy foods to their food-insecure stakeholders.[248] Whether they impact legislation, public policy or social norms, all obesity-related interventions will involve some degree of modifying and even restricting individuals and community behavior.

Although they are not the only target for change, parental behavior and habits play a significant role in childhood obesity. Parents will receive a citation if their child is not snapped into a seatbelt while they drive, but there is, to date, no penalty for feeding kids to death. Children have a right to be protected against unhealthy influences, and even the most caring families may be letting their children down in that regard.[249] Nevertheless, in accordance with principled communitarianism, the chosen method of intervention must be in proportion to the gravity of the obesity in harmony with community values. For example, a child with a BMI of 28 should not be removed from the parents' home in the absence of another more threatening situation. In addition, when introducing interventions that modify parental behavior, the community must guard against the slippery slope suggesting that if one intrusive measure is good, more must be better. Excessive intrusion may infringe upon autonomy eventually resulting in total government control.[250]

Consider how, in 2000, the New Mexico Children, Youth and Families Department (CYFD) exercised *parens patriae* authority and removed three-year-old Anamarie Martinez-Regino from her home and the custody of her parents. She was taken from her parents on the grounds that they repeatedly failed to comply with medical orders to correct the present and long-term health effects of her morbid obesity.[251] At the age of three, Anamarie stood less than four-feet tall and weighed 131 pounds. She was hospitalized several times for extended periods and for various obesity-related conditions – losing weight during each hospital stay – but experiencing significant weight gain soon after returning home. The family physician was alarmed and took his concerns to the CYFD. The state held that they had probable cause to remove the child – a clear victim of medical neglect.

This case gained notoriety and created a groundswell of divisive camps within the community; many believed the government had overstepped its authority. The medical community supported intervention based on threats to Anamarie's long and short-term health. Many feared removing Anamarie from the home was the first slippery step toward allowing the state to take draconian measures against parents anytime parental conduct was called into question. In the final analysis, Anamarie's parents reached a sealed court-approved agreement with the state allowing the child to return home.[252]

The Martinez-Regino case illustrates how the doctrine of *parens patriae,* in its most extreme form, illuminates the injustices suffered by obese children, the need for balanced intervention, and how core community values that can be polarizing. A shared cultural model of core values does not presuppose that everyone agrees with every decision made according to the model, but rather, the community agrees with the values that support the decision.[253] The instant case further evinces how, a community of interdependent people, share in the responsibility of ensuring that a child's personal dignity is preserved by the community itself and the social network it creates. The community may disagree as to the outcome, as the case of Martinez-Regino suggests but it did not disagree with the direness of the concern, and the physician's affirmative duty to report.

Not all *parens patriae* interventions are as severe an Anamarie's experience. However, even in non-threatening interventions, the government's police power to intervene cannot be arbitrary. It must be rationally related to the public health protections targeted and reasonably designed to correct a situation impacting public health.[254] As such, interventions should be developed within an integrated chronic disease prevention model resident within the community and home settings.[255] For example, the U.S. Institute of Medicine suggests that interventions for obesity prevention target nutrition and physical activity, behavioral treatment, decreasing the prevalence of sedentary activities, and social and psychological support involving families.[256] Hassink goes so far as to suggest that intervention into childhood obesity begin before birth as fetal life and intrauterine environment factors are influenced by maternal obesity to the extent that it may render a child more likely to develop childhood obesity.[257] These interventions require environmental and individual behavior modifications which are necessarily supported by the interplay of families and the medical community.

The pediatrician's duty as a social parent is not unprecedented as they are concerned about the health and growth of the children they treat practically from the moment the children are born. The correlation between good nutrition and optimal baby growth, weight and development are foundational principles of pediatric medicine. Identifying failure to thrive, and weight or height accelerations and decelerations have long been considered early warning signs of significant illness.[258] Since the late nineteenth and early twentieth centuries, pediatric medicine's concern for good food and nutrition consumption underscored efforts to promote breastfeeding, safe milk supplies, remediate vitamin deficiencies, and even advocating healthy school lunches. Moreover, the development of premature infants as well as those children who are vulnerable to the effects of certain chronic conditions remain integral concerns of pediatric practice.[259]

Despite this, some primary care pediatric practitioners contend that universal obesity prevention and management is an inappropriate use of their time and is best left to the parents and family. They further argue that the sanctity of physician-patient relationship would be compromised by discussing this sensitive and stigmatizing topic. They want to minimize judgment repugnance.[260] Fortunately, however, there are those who do consider secondary or selective prevention – that which seeks to mitigate or reverse *existing* obesity – as an opportunity to responsibly collaborate with parents and unify the effort, even if they do see parental involvement as a significant barrier.[261] However, many parents are not comfortable discussing the child's weight with the child for fear that the efforts are fruitless or attention will undergird the stigma and further erode self-esteem.[262] They expect the pediatrician to address the child's weight if it's a problem.

Consider that almost all childhood obesity prevention and management programs recommended by practitioners require calculating and charting BMI once-a-year during well-child visits, including emphasizing healthy nutritional guidelines and encouraging physical activity. But, despite the efforts of the practitioners, there is extraordinarily little evidence of monitoring or accountability of the parents or family once the recommendation is made. An example of a public policy adhering to the theory of principled communitarianism would be one that supports mandatory reporting of all children whose obesity remains unchecked and unaffected for a period of more than 12 months. This reporting would be transmitted via a database registry that would be validated during each well-child visit. The physician's duty to report parental noncompliance would be mandated as a duty to report under appropriate state statutes and professional codes of conduct.[263]

Regardless of which view prevails, a proper relationship with food and the interplay of physical activity must be taught to children, because it will be very difficult for the child to change the way they view food once they reach adulthood.[264] Family-based treatment interventions that promote and teach self-management of healthy eating can positively alter parent and child behaviors and thought patterns in order to also combat negative psychosocial consequences.[265]

By exercising *parens patriae* authority, the government can promote such self-management interventions linking physicians and families to culturally tailored and competent programs[266] in order to support healthy nutrition and lifestyles.[267] Providing tax subsidies for weight loss, finding a community champion,[268] increasing provider reimbursements for improved outcomes from obesity management, and limiting foods that can be purchased with government-sponsored food stamps, are rationally-related and ethically justified government interventions.[269] And, as activist child health experts, pediatricians should exercise their authority as social parents by leading community coalitions and legislative endeavors to take healthy eating lifestyles beyond the clinic walls.[270]

Conclusion

Ethically accountable healthcare organizations have a moral duty to create opportunities for the communities of stakeholders they serve. Their obligation to the common good includes empowering the most vulnerable within those stakeholder communities, specifically pediatric populations. Throughout history, children represent a highly vulnerable stakeholder group whose dignity and integrity have been defiled. They have been exploited and harmed, oftentimes during efforts to protect them, such as excluding them from clinical research. The need to empower children and the importance of research to understand the pathology of diseases and disorders involving them is compelling. This is particularly evident when understanding children infected with HIV, those who are victims of abuse, and those with cognitive disabilities.

Children with illnesses and disorders are contingently and contextually vulnerable vis-a-vis the cultural and environmental influences within which they live. Additionally, their vulnerability is magnified by those who wield power and authority over them. It is that power and authority that establishes the moral duty of the HCO, and its moral agents to understand and respect the humanness of these children. To that end, physicians, and researchers, who are often the same person are obligated to adhere to ethical principles of autonomy, beneficence, and fairness throughout the ethical research process. Adherence to these principles entails an understanding beyond the intrinsic characteristics of the child and their special needs. It requires examination of their experiential and conjectural perspectives.

Because healthcare and clinical research are relational, the importance of the child's interpersonal and social relationships with authority figures such as researchers, physicians, and caregivers, underscores the relevance of relational ethics. Specifically, the goodness-of-fit model of relational ethics assesses all aspects of clinical treatment and research, against the child's capacity to understand, their relationship with those upon whom they are dependent, and the cultural and personal values that shape their world.

The collaboration between asymmetrical stakeholders such as the physician, researcher, child, and even the broader community undergirds the moral accountability to vulnerable pediatric populations. Their moral obligation and responsibility to better understand population health to mitigate and prevent the psychosocial and physiological effects of pediatric obesity includes executing their social parent duties. A social parent embodies the relationship between the vulnerable child, the need which gives rise to their vulnerability, and the ones upon whom they depend. The authority of interdependent social parents, and their attendant duties to protect obese children in the face of obesogenic influences, is akin to the legal doctrine of *parens patriae*.

By exercising this authority, self-management of healthy eating habits and culturally tailored programs linking parents and physicians will improve outcomes for obese children specifically, and public health obesity management generally. The challenges facing children with HIV, those who are maltreated, those with intellectual disability, and children living with obesity rarely improve with age or maturity. As such, the practical and ethical considerations for this vulnerable population create ongoing opportunities for HCOs to enable ethical accountability, social responsibility, and collaboration with communities of stakeholders across the child's life continuum.

Notes

1. David M. Gallagher, "The Common Good," in *Catholic Health Care Ethics. A Manual for Practitioners*, ed. Edward J. Furton, Peter Cataldo and Albert S. Moraczewski (Philadelphia, PA: The National Catholic Bioethics Center, 2009), 29.
2. Catriona MacKenzie, Wendy Rogers, and Susan Dodds, eds., "What is Vulnerability, and Why Does it Matter for Moral Theory?" in *Vulnerability. New Essays in Ethics and Feminist Philosophy*. (New York, NY: Oxford University Press, 2014), 4.
3. Paul Oliver, *The Student's Guide to Research Ethics*," (Berkshire, England: McGraw Hill Education. Open University Press, 2010).

4. Rosamond Rhodes, "When is Participation in Research a Moral Duty?" in *The Journal of Law, Medicine & Ethics* 45 (2017), 322.
5. Celia B. Fisher, Miriam R. Arbeit, and Tiffany Chenneville, "Goodness-of-Fit Ethics for Practice and Research Involving Children and Adolescents with HIV," in *A Clinical Guide to Pediatric HIV*. (Cham: Springer International Publishing, AG, 2016), 229–258.
6. Alexandra A. Brewis, *Obesity, Cultural and Biocultural Perspectives*, (Piscataway, NJ: Rutgers University Press, 2011), 4–6.
7. Amy Mullin, "Children, Vulnerability, and Emotional Harm." in *Vulnerability. New Essays in Ethics and Feminine Philosophy*. (New York, NY: Oxford University Press, 2014), 266–287.
8. John Cottingham, Robert Stoothoff and Dugald Murdoch, trans. *The Philosophical Writings of Descartes*, vol 2, (New York, NY: Cambridge University Press, 1984), 18–19.
9. Daniel Callahan, "What Price Better Health. Hazards of the Research Imperative," (Los Angeles, CA: The University of California Press, 2003), 13.
10. Wendy Rogers, "Vulnerability and Bioethics," in *Vulnerability. New Essays in Ethics and Feminine Philosophy*, ed. Catriona Mackenzie, Wendy Rogers, and Susan Dodds (New York, NY: Oxford University Press, 2014), 68–69.
11. Stephen J. Teach and Joseph W. St. Geme, "The Indirect Effects of COVID-19 on Pediatric Research, *Pediatric Research* (2021), https:doi.org/10.1038/s41390-021-01563-x.
12. Priscilla Alderson and Virginia Morrow, *The Ethics of Research with Children and Young People. A Practical Handbook*, (Los Angeles, CA: SAGE, 2011), 132.
13. Mackenzie, Rogers, and Dodds, "What is Vulnerability and Why Does it Matter for Moral Theory?" 2,4.
14. Mackenzie, Rogers, Dodds, "What is Vulnerability and Why Does it Matter for Moral Theory?" 6.
15. Amy Mullin, "Children, Vulnerability, and Emotional Harm," 267.
16. Wendy Rogers, "Vulnerability and Bioethics," 60.
17. Agomoni Ganguli-Mitra and Nikola Biller-Andorno, "Vulnerability in Healthcare and Research Ethics," in *The SAGE Handbook of Healthcare Ethics: Core and Emerging Issues*, ed. Ruth Chadwick, Henk ten Have, and Eric M. Meslin, (London, UK: SAGE Publications, Inc., 2011), 240.
18. Jan Helge Solbakk, "Vulnerability: A Futile or Useful Principle in Healthcare Ethics?" in *The Sage Handbook of Health Care Ethics*, ed. Ruth Chadwick, Henk ten Have, and Erick Meslin, (London, UK: SAGE Publications, Inc., 2011), 232–233.
19. Solbakk, "Vulnerability: A Futile or Useful Principle in Healthcare Ethics?" 233–234.
20. MacKenzie, Rogers, and Dodds, "What is Vulnerability, and Why Does it Matter for Moral Theory?" 10.
21. Mackenzie, Rogers, and Dodds, "What is Vulnerability, and Why Does it Matter for Moral Theory?" 13.
22. Steven Joffe and Robert D. Truog, "Equipoise and Randomization," In *The Oxford Textbook of Clinical Research Ethics*, edited by Ezekiel J. Emanuel, Christine Grady, Robert A. Crouch, Reidar K. Lie, Franklin G. Miller, and David Wendler (Oxford, UK: Oxford University Press, 2008), 245; Levine, Robert J.,"The Nature, Scope, and Justification of Clinical Research," in *The Oxford Textbook of Clinical Research Ethics*, edited by Ezekiel J. Emanuel, Christine Grady, Robert A. Crouch, Reidar K. Lie, Franklin G. Miller, and David Wendler (Oxford, UK: Oxford University Press, 2008), 216; Alexander M. Capron, "Legal and Regulatory Standards of Informed Consent in Research," In *The Oxford Textbook of Clinical Research Ethics*, edited by Ezekiel J. Emanuel, Christine Grady, Robert A. Crouch, Reidar K. Lie, Franklin G. Miller, and David Wendler (Oxford, UK: Oxford University Press, 2008), 613.

23. Daniel Callahan, *What Price Better Health? Hazards of the Research Imperative*, 88–91.
24. Levine, Robert J., "The Nature, Scope, and Justification of Clinical Research," 211.
25. Levine, "The Nature, Scope, and Justification of Clinical Research," 211, 214.
26. Paul J. Weindling, "The Nazi Medical Experiments," in *The Oxford Textbook of Clinical Research Ethics*, ed. Ezekiel J. Emanuel, Christine Grady, Robert A, Crouch, Reider K. Lie, Franklin G. Miller, and David Wendler, (Oxford, UK: Oxford University Press, 2008), 20, 24–25.
27. Weindling, "The Nazi Medical Experiments," 25.
28. Paul Ndebele, "Research Ethics," in *The SAGE Handbook of Health Care Ethics: Core and Emerging Issues*, ed. Ruth Chadwick, Henk ten Have, and Eric M. Meslin (London, UK: SAGE Publications, Inc., 2011), 306.
29. George J. Anna, Michael A. Grodin, "The Nuremberg Code," in *The Oxford Textbook of Clinical Research Ethics*, Ezekiel J. Emanuel, Christine Grady, Robert A. Crouch, Reider K. Lie, Franklin G. Miller, and David Wendler, (Oxford, UK: Oxford University Press, 2008), 136–139.
30. Ndebele, "Research Ethics," 310.
31. James H. Jones, "The Tuskegee Syphilis Experiment," in *The Oxford Textbook of Clinical Research Ethics*. ed. Ezekiel J. Emanuel, Christine Grady, Robert A. Crouch, Reidar K. Lie, Franklin G. Miller, and David Wendler (Oxford, UK: Oxford University Press, 2008), 86–96.
32. Ndebele, "Research Ethics," 312–313.
33. Alderson and Morrow, *The Ethics of Research with Children and Young People. A Practical Handbook*, 15, 50; Laine Friedman Ross, *Children in Medical Research. Access versus Protection*, (New York, NY: Oxford University Press, 2006), 1.
34. Alderson and Morrow, *The Ethics of Research with Children and Young People*, 50–51.
35. Friedman Ross, *Children in Medical Research. Access versus Protection*, 12.
36. Freidman Ross, *Children in Medical Research. Access versus Protection*, 15.
37. Walter M. Robinson and Brandon T. Unruh, "The Hepatitis Experiment at Willowbrook State School," in *The Oxford Textbook of Clinical Research Ethics*. ed. Ezekiel J. Emanuel, Christine Grady, Robert A. Crouch, Reidar K. Lie, Franklin G. Miller, and David Wendler (Oxford, UK: Oxford University Press, 2008), 80–81.
38. Freidman Ross, *Children in Medical Research. Access versus Protection*, 44.
39. Alderson and Morrow, *The Ethics of Research with Children and Young People*, 15–16.
40. Tom L. Beauchamp, "The Belmont Report," in *The Oxford Textbook of Clinical Research Ethics*. ed. Ezekiel J. Emanuel, Christine Grady, Robert A. Crouch, Reidar K. Lie, Franklin G. Miller, and David Wendler (Oxford, UK: Oxford University Press, 2008), 149–151.
41. U.S. Department of Health and Human Services. *Additional Protections for Children Involved as Human Subjects in Research*, 45 CFR 46 Subpart D.
42. Charles R. McCarthy, "The Origins and Policies that Govern Institutional Review Boards," in *The Oxford Textbook of Clinical Research Ethics*. ed. Ezekiel J. Emanuel, Christine Grady, Robert A. Crouch, Reidar K. Lie, Franklin G. Miller, and David Wendler (Oxford, UK: Oxford University Press, 2008), 550.
43. Friedman Ross, *Children in Medical Research. Access versus Protection*, 66–71.
44. Julie Samuel, Bartha Maris Knoppers, and Denise Avard, "Medical Research Involving Children: A Review of International Policy Statements," in *The SAGE Handbook of Health Care Ethics* ed. Ruth Chadwick, Henk ten Have, and Eric M. Meslin (London, UK: SAGE Publications, Inc., 2011), 265–266.
45. Samuel, Knoppers, and Avard, "Medical Research Involving Children: A Review of International Policy Statements," 261.
46. Ann Farrell, *Ethical Research with Children*. (Berkshire, UK: Open University Press, 2005), 6.

47. Sheila Greene and Diane Hogan, *Researching Children's Experience.* (London, UK: Sage Publications, 2012) 64.
48. Alan R. Fleischman and Laure K. Collagen, "Research with Children," in *The Oxford Textbook of Clinical Research Ethics.* ed. Ezekiel J. Emanuel, Christine Grady, Robert A. Crouch, Reidar K. Lie, Franklin G. Miller, and David Wendler (Oxford, UK: Oxford University Press, 2008), 449.
49. Sheila Greene and Diane Hogan, *Researching Children's Experience,* 61–62.
50. Robinson and Unrul, "The Hepatitis Experiments at Willowbrook State School," 80–85.
51. U.S. Food & Drug Administration, accessed July 21, 2019, http://fda.gov/drugs/drug-information-consumers/drug-research-and-children.
52. Charles Schmidt, "Pediatric Predicament," In *Scientific American* (September 2017) vol. 317, no. 3. 24–25.
53. Duke University, "Prospect of Direct Benefit in Pediatric Clinical Trials," *Margolis Center for Health Policy* (March 29, 2019), 1.
54. Rosamond Rhodes "When is Participation in Research a Moral Duty?" 320.
55. Rhodes, "When is Participation in Research a Moral Duty," 322–324.
56. Mark Yarborough, "Why There is No Obligation to Participate in Clinical Research," in *The Journal of Law, Medicine and Ethics* 45 (2017), 327.
57. Yarborough, "Why There is No Obligation to Participate in Clinical Research," 328.
58. Yarborough, "Why There is No Obligation to Participate in Clinical Research," 328, 331.
59. Fleischman and Collagen, "Research with Children," 448.
60. Fleischman and Collagen, "Research with Children," 448.
61. Fleischman and Collagen, "Research with Children," 449.
62. Samuel, Knoppers, and Avard, "Medical Research Involving Children: A Review of International Policy Statements," 263.
63. The National Commission for the Protection of Human Subjects of Biomedical and Behavioral Research. *The Belmont Report. Ethical Principles and Guidelines for the Protection of Human Subjects of Research,* (April 18, 1979) 44 Fed Reg. 23191 (1979).
64. Samuel, Knoppers, and Avard, "Medical Research Involving Children: A Review of International Policy Statements," 264.
65. Teach and St. Geme, "The Indirect Effects of COVID-19 on Pediatric Research."
66. Institute of Medicine, *Ethical Conduct of Clinical Research Involving Children,* (Washington, D.C.: The National Academies Press, 2004), 56.
67. Samuel, Knoppers, and Avard, "Medical Research Involving Children: A Review of International Policy Statements," 267.
68. Tom L. Beauchamp and James F. Childress, *Principles of Biomedical Ethics,* 7th edition (New York, N: Oxford University Press, 2013), 106–108, 120–124.
69. Rebecca Dresser, "The Reasonable Person Standard for Research Disclosure: A Reasonable Addition to the Common Rule," in *The Journal of Law, Medicine and Ethics,* 47 (2019), 195.
70. Federal Policy for the Protection of Human Subjects, 82 Federal Register 7149, 7265 (final rule, January 19, 2017).
71. Dresser, "The Reasonable Person Standard for Research Disclosure: A Reasonable Addition to the Common Rule," 197.
72. Joan P. Porter and Greg Koski, "Regulations for the Protection of Humans in Research in the United States, in *The Oxford Textbook of Clinical Research Ethics,* ed. Ezekiel J. Emanuel, Christine Grady, Robert A. Crouch, Reidar K. Lie, Franklin G. Miller, and David Wendler (Oxford, UK: Oxford University Press, 2008), 156–158,.
73. Erika Blacksher and Jonathan D. Moreno, "History of Informed Consent in Clinical Research," in *The Oxford Textbook of Clinical Research Ethics,* ed. Ezekiel J. Emanuel, Christine Grady, Robert A. Crouch, Reidar K. Lie, Franklin G. Miller, and David

Wendler (Oxford, UK: Oxford University Press, 2008), 591, 607–611; Vilhajalmur Arnason, Hongwen Li, and Yali Cong "Informed Consent," in *The SAGE Handbook of Health Care Ethics*, ed. Ruth Chadwick and Henk ten Have, (London, UK: SAGE Publications, Inc. 2010), 109.

74. Arnason, Li, and Cong, "Informed Consent," 111.

75. Jonathon Sargeant and Deborah Harcourt, *Doing Ethical Research with Children*, (Maidenhead, UK: McGraw Hill/Open University, 2012), 7–9; Alderson and Morrow, *The Ethics of Research with Children and Young People*, 1, 12–13, 120–122.

76. Friedman Ross, *Children in Medical Research. Access versus Protection*, 131–136.

77. Erici G.Yan and Kerim M. Munir, "Regulatory and Ethical Principles in Research Involving Children and Individuals with Developmental Delay,"in *Ethics Behav*. 14 (2004): 39.

78. Laine Friedman Ross, *Children in Medical Research. Access versus Protection*, 88.

79. Donald L. Rosenstein and Franklin G. Miller, "Research Involving Those at Risk for Impaired Decision-making Capacity," in *The Oxford Textbook of Clinical Research Ethics*, ed. by Ezekiel J Emanuel, Christine Grady, Robert A. Crouch, Reider K. Lie, Franklin G. Miller, and David Wendler, (Oxford, UK: Oxford University Press, 2008), 440.

80. Vilhajalmur Arnason, Hongwen Li, and Yali Cong," Informed Consent," 112.

81. Arnason, Li, and Cong, "Informed Consent," 112.

82. Michael Cook, "Consent language can be too complicated for patients," in *BioEdge. Bioethics News from Around the World*. 18 August 2019, https://www.bioedge.org/bioethics/consent-language-can-be-too-complicated-for patients.

83. The National Commission for the Protection of Human Subjects of Biomedical and Behavioral Research, *The Belmont Report. Ethical Principles and Guidelines for the Protection of Human Subjects of Research*.

84. Samuel, Knoppers, and Avard, "Medical Research Involving Children: A Review of International Policy Statements," 270.

85. Alexander Friedman, Emily Robbins, and David Wendler, "Which Benefits of Research Participations Count as 'Direct'"? in *Bioethics*, 26(2), (2012), 60.

86. E. Keyserlingk, K. Glass, S. Kogan and S. Gauthier, "Proposed Guidelines for the Participation of Persons with Dementia as Research Subjects," in *Perspectives in Biology and Medicine*, 38 (1995): 319–361.

87. Institute of Medicine, *Ethical Conduct of Clinical Research Involving Children*, 132.

88. Nancy King, "Defining and Describing Benefit Appropriately in Clinical Trials," In *Journal of Law Medicine and Ethics* 28 (2000), 332.

89. Alexander Friedman, Emily Robbins, and David Wendler, "Which Benefits of Research Participation Count as Direct?" 60.

90. Friedman, Robbins and Wendler, "Which Benefits of Research Participation Count as Direct?" 60–67.

91. The National Commission for the Protection of Human Subjects of Biomedical and Behavioral Research, *The Belmont Report. Ethical Principles and Guidelines for the Protection of Human Subjects of Research*, 8.

92. The National Commission for the Protection of Human Subjects of Biomedical and Behavioral Research, *The Belmont Report. Ethical Principles and Guidelines for the Protection of Human Subjects of Research*, 8.

93. 45 CFR §46.303.

94. Friedman Ross, *Children in Medical Research. Access versus Protection*, 75–83.

95. Alderson and Morrow, *The Ethics of Research with Children and Young People. A Practical Handbook*, 24–28, 79; Friedman-Ross, *Children in Medical Research. Access versus Protection*, 125.

96. Nancy M.P. King, "Key Information in the New Common Rule: Can It Save Research Consent?", 207.

97. Mullin, "Children, Vulnerability, and Emotional Harm," 266.

98. Agomoni Ganguli-Mitra, and Nikola Biller-Andono, "Vulnerability in Healthcare and Research Ethics," 242.

99. James M Dubois, *Ethics in Mental Health Research. Principles, Guidance and Cases.* (New York, NY: Oxford University Press, 2008), 112.

100. Gangul-Mitra and Biller-Andono, "Vulnerability in Healthcare and Research Ethics," 241.

101. U.S. Department of Health and Human Services, Centers for Disease Control and Prevention, Division of HIV/AIDS Prevention, National Center for HIV/AIDS (August 14, 2019). http://www.cdc.gov/hiv/basics/whatishiv.html.

102. Karine Dube, Laurie Sylia, Lynda Dee, Jeff Taylor, David Evans, Carl Dean Burton, et al., "Research on HIV Cure: Mapping the Ethics Landscape," in *PLOS Med* 14(12): e1002470. (2017) https://doi.org/10.1371/journal.pmed. 1002470.

103. UNAIDS. AIDS by the numbers, accessed September 29, 2019. http://www.unaids.org/sites/default/files/media. (2019).

104. Susan L. Gillespie, "Epidemiology of Pediatric HIV Infection," In *A Clinical Guide to Pediatric HIV. Bridging the Gaps Between Research and Practice*, ed. Tiffany Chenneville. (Cham, Switzerland: Springer International Publishing, 2016), 1.

105. Gillespie, "Epidemiology of Pediatric HIV Infection," 2.

106. Karine Dube, et al.,"Research on HIV Cure: Mapping the Ethics Landscape," 1.

107. Lori Wiener, Claude Ann Mellins, Stephanie Marhefka and Haven B. Battles, "Disclosure of an HIV Diagnosis to Children: History, Current Research, and Future Directions," in *Journal of Developmental and Behavioral Pediatrics.* 28 (2) (2007): 155.

108. Jamie N. Albright, Cynthia D. Fair, and Christy Newman, "Psychosocial Considerations for Children and Adolescents with HIV," in *A Clinical Guide to Pediatric HIV. Bridging the Gaps Between Research and Practice*, ed. by Tiffany Chenneville (Cham, Switzerland: Springer International Publishing, 2016), 75.

109. Jamie N. Albright, Cynthia D. Fair, and Christy Newman, "Psychosocial Considerations for Children and Adolescents with HIV," 73.

110. Wiener, Mellins, Marhefka and Battles, "Disclosure of an HIV Diagnosis to Children: History, Current Research and Future Directions," 163.

111. Wiener. Mellins, Marhefka and Battles, "Disclosure of HIV Diagnosis to Children: History, Current Research and Future Directions," 164.

112. Sabhyta Sabharwal, Jason W. Mitchell, and Victoria Y. Fan, "Should There Be a Disclosure Mandate for Physicians Caring for Perinatally Infected Adolescents Who Don't Know Their HIV Serostatus?" in *AMA Journal of Ethics* 20 no. 8 (August 2018): E745.

113. Stephanie L. Marhefka, DeAnne E. Turner, and Tiffany Chenneville, "HIV Disclosure in Pediatric Populations: Who, What, When to Tell, and then What?" in *A Clinical Guide to Pediatric HIV. Bridging the Gaps Between Research and Practice*, edited by Tiffany Chenneville (Cham: Switzerland: Springer International Publishing, 2016), 189.

114. Celia B. Fisher, Miriam R. Arbeit, and Tiffany Chenneville, "Goodness-of-Fit Ethics for Practice and Research Involving Children and Adolescents with HIV," 230–231.

115. Fisher, Arbeit, and Chenneville, "Goodness-of-Fit Ethics for Practice and Research Involving Children and Adolescents with HIV," 236.

116. Fisher, Arbeit, and Chenneville, "Goodness-of-Fit Ethics for Practice and Research Involving Children and Adolescents with HIV," 248.

117. Guitele J. Rahill, Manisha Joshi, and Celia M. Lescano, "Cultural Considerations for Pediatric HIV Research and Practice," in *A Clinical Guide to Pediatric HIV. Bridging the Gaps Between Research and Practice*, edited by Tiffany Chenneville. (Cham: Springer International Publishing, 2016), 267.

118. Katherine Guttman, Michelle Shouldice, Alex V. Levin, *Ethical Issues in Child Abuse Research*, (Cham: Springer Nature Switzerland AG, 2019), 1–2.

119. Richard D. Krugman, "The More We Learn, the Less We Know: A Brief History of the Field of Child Abuse and Neglect," in *The APSAC Handbook on Child Maltreatment*, ed. J. Bark Klika and Jon R. Conte. (Los Angeles, CA: SAGE Publications, Inc., 2018), 3.

120. Krugman, "The More We Learn, the Less We Know: A Brief History of the Field of Child Abuse and Neglect," 4–9.

121. Brett Drake and Melissa Jonson-Reid, "Defining and Estimating Child Maltreatment," in *The ASPAC Handbook on Child Maltreatment*, edited by J. Bark Klika and Jon R. Conte. (Los Angeles, CA: SAGE Publications, Inc., 2018), 14.

122. Christine Walsh and Harriet MacMillan, "Conducting Research in Child Maltreatment: Problems and Prospects." In *Ethical Issues in Community-Based Research with Children and Youth*, ed. Bonnie Leadbeater, Elizabeth Baniser, Celcila Benoit, Mikael Jansson, Anne Marshall, and Ted Riccken. (Toronto, Canada: University of Toronto Press, 2006), 190.

123. Rebecca Leeb, *Research and Practices in Child Maltreatment Prevention*. vol i, *Definitions of Abuse and Prevention*, edited by Randell Alexander (St. Louis, MO: STM Learning, Inc., 2017), 5.

124. Brett Drake and Melissa Jonson-Reid, "Defining and Estimating Child Maltreatment," 15.

125. Elizabeth J. Susman, Jennie G. Noll, and Karen Appleyard Carmody, "The Contribution of Penelope K. Trickett to the Study of Child Maltreatment," in *Child Maltreatment, Research, Policy and Practice. Contributions of Penelope K. Trickett*, ed. Sonya Negriff. (Los Angeles, CA: Springer, 2018), 1, 2, 5.

126. Kristen L. Berg and Michael E. Msall, "The Prevention of Maltreatment Among Children with Disabilities Through Early Identification and Comprehensive Provision of Services," in *Research and Practices in Child Maltreatment Prevention. Societal, Organizational, and International Approaches*, vol. ii., ed. Randell Alexander (St Louis, MO: STM Learning, Inc. 2017), 263.

127. Berg and Msall, "The Prevention of Maltreatment Among Children with Disabilities Through Early Identification and Comprehensive Provision of Services," 264.

128. Melissa K. Peckins, Sonya Negriff, Jonathan M. Reader, and Elizabeth J. Susman, "Perception of Maltreatment: Gender-Specific Mental Health Outcomes Associated with Maltreatment as Most Upsetting Experience," 27.

129. Melissa K. Peckins, Sonya Negriff, Jonathan M. Reader, and Elizabeth Susman, "Perception of Maltreatment: Gender-Specific Mental Health Outcomes Associated with Maltreatment as Most Upsetting Experience," 27.

130. US. Department of Health and Human Services, Child Welfare Information Gateway, *Child Maltreatment 2019: Summary of Key Findings. Numbers and Trends*, (April 2021). http://www/childwelfare.gov/pubs/factsheets/canstats/.

131. Guttman, Shouldice, Levin, *Ethical Issues in Child Abuse Research*, 16.

132. Walsh and MacMillan, "Conducting Research in Child Maltreatment: Problems and Prospects," 193.

133. National Research Council, *Understanding Child Abuse and Neglect*, (Washington, D.C.: National Academies Press, 1993), 324.

134. Guttman, Shouldice, Levin, *Ethical Issues in Child Abuse Research*, 10–11, 16, 30.

135. Guttman, Shouldice, Levine, *Ethical Issues in Child Abuse Research*, 3–5.

136. Lisa Aronson Fontes, "Child Maltreatment Services for Culturally Diverse Families," in *The APSAC Handbook on Child Maltreatment*. ed. J. Bark Klika and Jon R. Conte. (Los Angeles, CA: SAGE Publications, Inc., 2018), 366.

137. Carol Plummer, "Cultural Considerations in Prevention of Child Abuse and Neglect," in *Research and Practices in Child Maltreatment Prevention. Societal, Organizational, and International Approaches*, ed. Ramdell Alexander. (St Louis, MO: STM Learning, Inc., 2017), 286.

138. Lisa Aronson Fontes, "Child Maltreatment Services for Culturally Diverse Families," 368.
139. Fontes, "Child Maltreatment Services for Culturally Diverse Families," 369–370.
140. Eric G. Yan, Kerim M Munir, "Regulatory and Ethical Principles in Research Involving Children and Individuals with Developmental Disabilities," 31.
141. American Association on Intellectual and Developmental Disabilities, "Frequently Asked Questions on Intellectual Disability." Accessed October 30, 2019. http://www.aidd.org/intellectual-diability/definition/faqs-in-intellectual-disability.
142. Licia Carlson, "Research Ethics and Intellectual Disability: Broadening the Debates," in *Yale Journal of Biology and Medicine* 86 (2013), 304.
143. Leslie P. Francis, "Understanding Autonomy in Light of Intellectual Disability," in *Disability and Disadvantage*, ed. Kimberly Brownless and Adam Cureton. (Oxford, UK: Oxford University Press, 2009), 203.
144. Leslie P. Francis, "Understanding Autonomy in Light of Intellectual Disability," 204.
145. U.S. Department of Health and Human Services, Centers for Disease Control and Prevention, "Estimated Prevalence of Children with Diagnosed Disabilities in the United States, 2014–2016," NCHS Data Brief No. 291. (November 2017), 2.
146. U.S. Department of Health and Human Services, Centers for Disease Control and Prevention, "Data & Statistics on Autism Spectrum Disorder," (September 3, 2019), 1.
147. Pamela Y. Collins, Beverly Pringle, Charlee Alexander, Gary L. Darmstadt, Jody Heymann, Gillam Huebner, Vesna Kutlesic, Cheryl Polk, Lorraine Sherr, Andy Shih, Dragana Sretenov, Mariana Zindell, "Global Services and Support for Children with Developmental Delays and Disabilities: Bridging Research and Policy Gaps," in *PLoS Medicine* 14 (9): e1002393. (2017) DOA: 10.1371/journal.pmed.1002393.
148. Licia Carlson, "Research Ethics and Intellectual Disability: Broadening the Debates," 304.
149. Lonnie Zwaigenbaum, Margaret L. Bauman, Roula Choueiri, Connie Kasari, Alice Carter, Dorren Granpeesheh, "Early Intervention for Children with Autism Spectrum Disorder Under 3 Years of Age: Recommendations for Practice and Research," in *Pediatrics* 136 (October 2015), S61.
150. Carlson, "Research Ethics and Intellectual Disability: Broadening the Debates," 305.
151. Monica Cuskelly, "Ethical Inclusion of Children with Disabilities in Research," in *Ethical Research with Children*, edited by Ann Farrell. (Berkshire, UK: Open University Press, 2005), 103.
152. Deborah R. Barnbaum, *The Ethics of Autism, Among Them, But Not of Them,* Bloomington, IN: Indiana University Press, 2008), 199.
153. Alan T. Belasen, Barry Eisenberg and John W. Huppertz, *Mastering Leadership. A Vital Resource for Health Care Organizations.* (Burlington, MA: Jones and Bartlett Learning, 2016), 243.
154. Carrie R. Rich, J Knox Singleton, and Seema S. Wadhwa, "An Introduction to Environmental and Sustainability Issues in Healthcare Management," in *Managerial Ethics in Healthcare. A New Perspective*, ed. Gary J. Filerman, Ann E. Mills, and Paul M. Schyve. (Chicago, IL: Health Administration Press, 2014), 199.
155. Connie S. Lewis. "Childhood Obesity: Physiologic and Psychological Implications and Ethical Responsibilities," in *Online Journal of Health Ethics* 13 (1). http://dx.doi.org/10.18785/ojje.1301.5.
156. Cheryl D. Fryar, Margaret D. Carroll, and Joseph Afful, "Prevalence of Overweight, Obesity and Severe Obesity Among Children and Adolescents Aged 2–19 Years: United States, 1963-1965 through 2017-2018." NCHS Health E-Stats. 2020.
157. OECD, *Obesity Update 2017.* http://www.oecd.org/health/obesity-update.htm.

158. Brewis, *Obesity, Cultural and Biocultural Perspectives*, 11, 23–29, 31–33.
159. Institute of Medicine, *Legal Strategies in Childhood Obesity Prevention Workshop Summary*. (Washington, D.C.: The National Academies Press, 2011), 1.
160. Fryar, Carroll, and Afful, "Prevalence of Overweight, Obesity and Severe Obesity Among Children and Adolescents Aged 2–19 Years.
161. Mandy L. Perryman and Kara A. Sidoti, "Ethical Considerations in the Treatment of Obesity." in *Medicolegal and Bioethics* 5 (2015): 17.
162. Andrew Pollack, A.M.A. *Recognizes Obesity as a Disease*, The New York Times, June, 19, 2013 B1.
163. Vicki L Collie-Akers and Stephen B. Fawcett, "Preventing Childhood Obesity through Collaborative Public Health Action Communities." In *Handbook of Childhood and Adolescent Obesity*, ed. Elissa Jelalian and Ric G. Steele, (New York, NY: Springer, 2008, 351.
164. Tim Lobstein, Louise A. Bauer, and Rachel Jackson-Leach, "The Childhood Obesity Epidemic," in *Preventing Childhood Obesity: Evidence, Policy and Practice*, ed. Elizabeth Walters, Boyd Swindburn, Jacob Seidell, and Ricardo Uauy, (West Sussex, UK: Blackwell Publishing, Ltd., 2010) 8.
165. Jacob C. Warren and K. Bryant Smalley, *Always the Fat Kid. The Truth About the Enduring Effects of Childhood Obesity*, (New York, NY: Palgrave Macmillan, 2013) 26–27.
166. Warren and Smalley, *Always the Fat Kid*, 87.
167. John B. Hoke, Note, *Parens Patriae: A Flawed Strategy for State-Initiated Obesity Litigation*, 54 Wm & Mary Law Rev. 1753, 1755 (2013).
168. Michelle Healy, "Price Tag for Childhood Obesity: $19,000 per kid," USA Today, April 7, 2014, http://www.usatoday.com/story/news/nation/2014/04/07/childhood-obesity-costs/7298461/.
169. Shireen Arani, Comment, *State Intervention in Cases of Obesity-Related Medical Neglect: A Comment on In re Martinez* 82. B.U.L.Rev. 889.
170. Edieth Y. Wu, *McFat – Obesity, Parens Patriae, and the Children*, 20 Okla. City U.L. Rev. 569.
171. Arani, *State Intervention in Cases of Obesity-Related Medical Neglect*, 891.
172. Marieke ten Have, Ines de Beaufort and Soren Holm, *"No Country for Fat Children? Ethical questions concerning community-based programs to prevent obesity."* In Preventing Childhood Obesity: Evidence Policy and Practice, Elizabeth Walters et al., eds., (West Sussex, UK: Blackwell Publishing, Ltd., 2010) 33.
173. Warren and Smalley, *Always the Fat Kid*, 38–45; Brewis, *Obesity, Cultural and Biocultural Perspectives*, 2–37.
174. Jordan Ninkovich, *Epidemic: Obesity. Harrassment. Bullying. A Survivor's Story*. (Lincoln, NE: iUniverse. 2006), 7.
175. Perryman and Sidoti, "Ethical Considerations in the Treatment of Obesity," 18.
176. Warren and Smalley, *Always the Fat Kid*, 54.
177. Warren and Smalley, *Always the Fat Kid*, 55.
178. Warren and Smalley, *Always the Fat Kid*, 58.
179. Warren and Smalley, *Always the Fat Kid*, 58–59.
180. Helen Mavoa, Shiriki Kumanyuja and Andre Renzaho, "Socio-cultural issues and body image," In *Preventing Childhood Obesity: Evidence Policy and Practice*, ed. Elizabeth Waters et al., (West Sussex, UK: Blackwell Publishing, Ltd., 2010) 140–141.
181. Lobstein, Bauer, and Jackson-Leach, "The Childhood Obesity Epidemic" 8. 32.
182. Johannes Brug, Saskia te Velde, Ilse DeBourdeaudhuij and Stef Kremers, "Evidence of the Influence of the Home and Family Environment," in *Preventing Childhood Obesity: Evidence, Policy and Practice*. Elizabeth Waters et al., eds. (West Sussex, UK: Blackwell Publishing, Ltd., 2010) 64–65.
183. Perryman and Sidoti, "Ethical considerations in the Treatment of Obesity," 19.

184. Meg Zeller and Avani C. Modi, "Psychosocial Factors Related to Obesity in Children and Adolescents," in *Issues in Clinical Childhood Psychology. Handbook of Childhood and Adolescent Obesity*, ed. Elissa Jelalian and Ric G. Steele (New York: Springer, 2008). 27.
185. Zeller and Modi, *"Psychosocial Factors Related to Obesity in Children and Adolescents."* 28–29.
186. Lewis, "Childhood Obesity: Physiological and Psychological Implications and Ethical Responsibilities." 2.
187. Institute of Medicine of the National Academies, *Legal Strategies in Childhood Obesity Prevention. Workshop Summary.* (Washington, DC.: The National Academies Press, 2011).
188. Arani, *State Intervention in Cases of Obesity-Related Medical Neglect*, 888–889; Lobstein et al *"The Childhood Obesity Epidemic."* 9.
189. Brewis, *Obesity. Cultural and Biocultural Perspectives*, 84–90.
190. Warren and Smalley, *Always the Fat Kid.*70.
191. Alvin Powell, "Obesity? Diabetes? We've been set up." In *The Harvard Gazette*, March 7, 2012. news.harvard.edu/gazette/story/2012/03/the-big-setup.
192. Warren and Smalley, *Always the Fat Kid.* 72.
193. Catherine Paddock, "Obesity Linked to Type 2 Diabetes by an Absent Protein." *Medical News Today*, July 7, 2014. http://www.medicalnewstoday.com/articles/279129.php.
194. Warren and Smalley, *Always the Fat Kid.* 74.
195. Warren and Smalley, *Always the Fat Kid.* 88, 95.
196. D.A. Caniano. *Ethical Issue in Pediatric Bariatric Surgery.* Semin Pediatr Surgery, 2009; doi: 10.1053/j.sempedsurg.2009.04.009.
197. Zeller and Modi, "Psychosocial Factors Related to Obesity in Children and Adolescents," 25.
198. Warren and Smalley, *Always the Fat Kid. The Truth About the Enduring Effects of Childhood Obesity.* 97.
199. Warren and Smalley, *Always the Fat Kid. The Truth About the Enduring Effects of Childhood Obesity.* 99.
200. Lewis, "Childhood Obesity: Physiological and Psychological Implications and Ethical Responsibilities," 4.
201. Zeller and Mondi, "Psychosocial Factors Related to Obesity in Children and Adolescents," 30.
202. Mitch van Geel, Paul Vedder and Jerry Tamilon, "Relationship Between Peer Victimization, Cyberbullying and Suicide in Children and Adolescents, A Meta-Analysis," JAMA Pediatrics, http://www.jamanetwork.com/journals/jamapediatrics/fullarticle/184020; Warren and Smalley, *Always the Fat Kid. The Truth About the Enduring Effects of Childhood Obesity.* 101.
203. Lobstein et al, *The Childhood Obesity Epidemic*," 11.
204. Warren and Smalley, *Always the Fat Kid. The Truth About the Enduring Effects of Childhood Obesity.* 103.
205. Zeller and Mondi, "Psychosocial Factors Related to Obesity in Children and Adolescents,"31.
206. Zeller and Mondi, "Psychosocial Factors Related to Obesity in Children and Adolescents," 33.
207. Alan Zametikin, Alanna Jacobs, and Jessica Parrish, "Treatment of Children and Adolescents with Obesity and Comorbid Psychiatric Conditions," in *Issues in Clinical Childhood Psychology. Handbook of Childhood and Adolescent Obesity.* New York: Springer, 2008. 426.
208. Warren and Smalley, *Always the Fat Kid. The Truth About the Enduring Effects of Childhood Obesity.* 117–118.

209. Zametiken, Jacobs, and Parrish, "Treatment of Children and Adolescents with Obesity and Comorbid Psychiatric Conditions," 428.
210. Zametitken, Jacobs, and Parrish, "Treatment of Children and Adolescents with Obesity and Comorbid Psychiatric Conditions, In Issues in Clinical Childhood Psychology," 428.
211. Warren and Smalley, *Always the Fat Kid. The Truth About the Enduring Effects of Childhood Obesity, 119–120.*
212. Warren and Smalley, *Always the Fat Kid. The Truth About the Enduring Effects of Childhood Obesity, 122.*
213. Warren and Smalley, *Always the Fat Kid. The Truth About the Enduring Effects of Childhood Obesity, 141–144, 147.*
214. Danielle Barry and Nancy M. Petry, "Obesity and Psychiatric Disorders," *Psychiatric Times* (Dec. 5, 2009): 2 http://www.psychiatricimes.com/anxiety/obesity-and-psychiatric-disorders.
215. Warren and Smalley, *Always the Fat Kid. The Truth About the Enduring Effects of Childhood Obesity, 148–152.*
216. U.S. Equal Employment Opportunity Commission, "Resources for Human Development Settles EEOC Disability Suit for $125,000," (April 10, 2012), http://www.eeoc.gov/eeoc/newsroom/release/4-10-12a.cfm.
217. Mullin, "Children, Vulnerability, and Emotional Harm," 267.
218. Mullin, "Children, Vulnerability, and Emotional Harm," 272.
219. Mullin, "Children, Vulnerability, and Emotional Harm," 272.
220. Brewis, *Obesity. Cultural and Biocultural Perspectives*, 24, 77.
221. Sandra Hassink, *Pediatric Obesity. Prevention, Intervention, and Treatment Strategies for Primary Care*, 2nd edition, (Elk Grove Village, IL: American Academy of Pediatrics, 2014), 93.
222. ten Have, de Beaufort and Holm, "No Country for Fat Children? Ethical questions concerning community-based programs to prevent obesity," 36.
223. Stephen Peckham and Alison Hann, *Public Health Ethics and Practice*, (Bristol UK: The Policy Press, 2010), 4; Alan Cribb, "What kind of ethics for public health?" in *Public Health Ethics and Practice*, ed. Stephen Peckham and Alison Hann, (Bristol UK: The Policy Press, 2010) 22, 27; Stephen Holland, "Public health ethics: What is it and how to do it," in *Public Health Ethics and Practice*, edited by Stephen Peckham and Alison Hann, (Bristol UK: The Policy Press, 2010) 33.
224. Alan Cribb, "What kind of ethics for public health?" in *Public Health Ethics and Practice*, 19–21.
225. Stephen Holland, *Public Health Ethics*, (Cambridge, UK: Polity Press, 2007), 41.
226. Holland, *Public Health Ethics*, 52–54; The Nuffield Council on Bioethics, *Public Health: Ethical Issues*, (London UK: Nuffield Council on Bioethics, 2007), 16.
227. Arani, *State Intervention in Cases of Obesity-Related Medical Neglect*, 893.
228. Alexandra Brewis, *Obesity: Cultural and Biocultural Perspectives*, 75.
229. Holland, *Public Health Ethics*, 4.
230. Mark Lawrence and Boyd Swinburn, "The Role of Policy in Preventing Childhood Obesity," in *Preventing Childhood Obesity. Evidence, Policy and Practice*, ed. Elizabeth Waters, Boyd Swindburn, Jacob Seidell, and Ricardo Uauy, (West Sussex, UK: Blackwell Publishing, Ltd., 2010), 203–204.
231. Wu, *McFat—Obesity, Parens Patriae, and the Children*, 577.
232. Amy Mullin, "Children, Vulnerability and Emotional Harm," 267.
233. Amy Mullin, "Children, Vulnerability and Emotional Harm," 269.
234. Mullin, "Children, Vulnerability and Emotional Harm," 280.
235. Hoke, *Parens Patriae: A Flawed Strategy for State-Related Obesity Litigation*, 1759; Henry Campbell Black, Black's Law Dictionary, 6th edition, (St. Paul, Minnesota: West Publishing, 1990), 1114.
236. Wu, *McFat – Obesity, Parens Patriae, and the Children*, 573–574, 576.

237. Hoke, *Parens Patriae: A Flawed Strategy for State-Related Obesity Litigation*, 1767.
238. Institute of Medicine, *Legal Strategies in Childhood Obesity Prevention. Workshop Summary*, (Washington, D.C.: The National Academies Press, 2011), 65.
239. Hoke, *Parens Patriae: A Flawed Strategy for State-Related Obesity Litigation*, N26.
240. 55 Pa. Code §3490.4.
241. Arani, *State Intervention in Cases of Obesity-Related Medical Neglect*, 876.
242. Arani, *State Intervention in Cases of Obesity-Related Medical Neglect*, 886.
243. Wu, *McFat – Obesity, Parens Patriae and the Children*, 577.
244. Institute of Medicine, *Legal Strategies in Childhood Obesity Prevention*, 51–58.
245. Johns Hopkins Berman Institute of Bioethics. "*Is the Nanny State Ethical When Policing Obesity?*" Science Daily, 19 March, 2014. www.sciencedaily.com/releases/2014/03/14031943738.htm.
246. Patricia B. Crawford, Gail Woodward-Lopez, Suzanne Rauzon, Lorrene Ritchie, and May C. Wang. "The Role of Public Policy in Addressing the Pediatric Obesity Epidemic," in *Issues in Clinical Child Psychology: Handbook of Childhood and Adolescent Obesity*, ed. Elissa Jelalian and Ric G. Steele, (New York: Springer, 2008) 371.
247. ten Have, de Beaufort, and Holm, "No Country for Fat Children: Ethical Questions Concerning Community-Based Programs to Prevent Obesity," 31.
248. AHIP, *Access to Healthy Foods: Social Determinants of Health. Issue Brief.* (May 2018). http://www.ahip.org/access-to-healthy-foods-social-determinants-of-health.
249. ten Have, de Beaufort, and Holm, "No Country for Fat Children: Ethical Questions Concerning Community Based Programs to Prevent Obesity," 32.
250. ten Have, de Beaurfort, and Holm, "No Country for Fat Children: Ethical Questions Concerning Community Based Programs to Prevent Obesity," 34–37.
251. Arani, *State Intervention in Cases of Obesity-Related Medical Neglect*, 875.
252. Patrick Armijo, "State Says Details Hurt Girl," *Albuquerque J.*, (Nov. 10, 2000): B1.
253. Brewis, *Obesity, Cultural and Biocultural Perspectives*, 120.
254. Institute of Medicine, *Legal Strategies in Childhood Obesity Prevention, Workshop Summary*, (Washington, D.C.: The National Academies Press, 2011), 43.
255. Andrea M. d Silve-Sanigorski and Christina Economos, "Evidence of Multi-Setting Approaches for Obesity Prevention: Translation to Best Practices," in *Preventing Childhood Obesity: Evidence, Policy and Practice*, ed. Elizabeth Waters, Boyd Swindburn, Jacob Seidell, and Ricardo Uauy, (West Sussex, UK: Blackwell Publishing, Ltd., 2010), 61.
256. Karen Lock and Rebecca Hillier, "The Prevention of Childhood Obesity in Primary Care Settings: Evidence and Practice," in *Preventing Childhood Obesity: Evidence, Policy and Practice*, ed. Elizabeth Walters, Boyd Swindburn, Jacob Seidell, and Ricardo Uauy, (West Sussex, UK: Blackwell Publishing, Ltd., 2010), 96.
257. Hassink, *Pediatric Obesity. Prevention, Intervention and Treatment Strategies for Primary Care*, 17.
258. Hassink, *Pediatric Obesity. Prevention, Intervention, and Treatment Strategies for Primary Care*, 7.
259. Hassink, *Pediatric Obesity. Preventions, Intervention and Treatment Strategies for Primary Care*, 7.
260. Warren and Smalley, *Always the Fat Kid. The Truth About the Enduring Effects of Childhood Obesity*. 17.
261. Lock and Hillier, "The Prevention of Childhood Obesity in Primary Care Settings," 102.
262. Alan Zametikin, Alanna Jacobs, and Jessica Parrish, *Treatment of Children and Adolescents with Obesity and Comorbid Psychiatric Conditions*, 429.
263. Lock and Hillier, "The Prevention of Childhood Obesity in Primary Care Settings: Evidence and Practice," 101.

264. Warren and Smalley, *Always the Fat Kid. The Truth About the Enduring Effects of Childhood Obesity*. 50.
265. Perryman and Sidoti, "Ethical considerations in the treatment of obesity," 20–21.
266. Mavoa, Kumanyuja and Renzaho, *"Socio-Cultural Issues and Body Image,"* 142–143.
267. Lobstein, et al, *"The Childhood Obesity Epidemic,"* 12.
268. Crawford, et al, "The Role of Public Policy in Addressing the Pediatric Obesity Epidemic," 382–384.
269. Institute of Medicine of the National Academies, *Legal Strategies in Childhood Obesity Prevention. Workshop Summary*, 24–25.
270. Hassink, *Pediatric Obesity. Prevention, Intervention and Treatment*, 104.

5 Community Stakeholders in Healthcare

Older Adults and Persons With Disabilities

Introduction

As a condition of human life, vulnerability impacts stakeholder populations when consequences and conditions render them susceptible to physical, emotional, economic, and social harm or disadvantage. People are also vulnerable to social biases that have less to do with their actual condition and more to do with social perceptions and preconceptions about them. Biases disadvantage, discriminate, and disempower and are innately evolutionary. Humankind's earliest ancestors needed to quickly decide based upon their perceptions, whether a person, situation, or animal was likely to threaten their survival.[1] They characterized such encounters and made judgments accordingly. Today, older people and persons with disabilities are often judged quickly according to perceptions and are victimized by biases.

For example, at some point in the life continuum, older people face a culture that treats them differently from youth, buoyed with the presumptive undercurrent that the future is less relevant for them as they have lived a good life already.[2] Youth represents beauty and promise, whereas old age reflects the transient nature of life and the death that is certain for everyone.[3] Similarly, persons with disabilities often face biases that render them the "other" in dehumanizing ways; these biases often suggest that they represent a "counterpoint to normality."[4] For both of these stakeholder groups, biases can intensify vulnerability and present assaults to their dignity. Propagation of such biases without substantiation also unfairly and unjustly denies opportunities to those who very often need them the most. Since an HCO is obliged to serve the common good for the sake of many[5] it is, therefore, a moral duty of the ethically accountable HCO to provide for the most vulnerable normative stakeholders across the life continuum. This chapter examines that duty through the lens of to the last of the three vulnerable stakeholder categories highlighted in this book: older persons, and persons with disabilities.

Aging is an ambivalent reality. Presumably, most people hope to live a long life, however, few will delight in the prospect of growing older. Hardly anyone can admit a willingness to embrace and welcome the physical, emotional, and oftentimes economic challenges that can accompany physical maturity. Yet, the reality that "aging, or just living life does entail inevitable change"[6] is uncontroverted and begins the moment one is born. Although the process of aging as a stage of

DOI: 10.4324/9781003229957-5

human development can be positive, living a long life can present challenges to the vulnerable older person, and to the communities within which they live. Nowhere are these challenges more visible than in the resource allocation and mechanisms that provide access to long-term healthcare services to the aged.

This chapter begins with a view of the demographic profile of today's aged stakeholder populations, and their contextual vulnerability vis-à-vis ageism biases and their unique health needs. It then explores the current public policy trends for addressing their needs, including a short summary of age-based rationing and the different propositions advanced by Daniel Callahan, Norman Daniels, Paul Menzel, and John Kilner. This thesis then presents a justification for revised public policy to address the unmet long-term informal care from an ethics of care model that relies upon the interconnectedness of people.[7] It then illustrates how caregiver and provider advocacy supports person-focused, compassionate long-term care through the musings of Tellis-Nayak and Muriel Gillick.

Progression across the life continuum to old age practically guarantees people will become dependent and at risk of severe illness and disability.[8] For some, however, disability is not a progressive old age event, but rather some permanent consequence of war, injury, illness, or genetic precondition. According to the World Health Organization, "disability is part of the human condition."[9] Because concern for the human condition is at the heart of healthcare, promoting the dignity of persons with disabilities is a moral duty of the ethically accountable healthcare organization. The remainder of this chapter focuses on the healthcare profession's obligation to enhance the lives of those with disabilities by creating enabling environments within which they can flourish.

It begins with the definition and demographic of human disability. It then explores the relationship between disability and human dignity, what it means to be human, to flourish, and to have a good life. Relevant evolutionary and religious interpretations of the human condition of disability, including those by Celia Deanne-Drummond, William May, and Hans Reinders are introduced. Specifically, they investigate humankind's desire to improve the human condition of disability through genetic intervention. The argument for ethical accountability to this stakeholder community further unfolds to assert justification for creating enabling opportunities that eliminate barriers to flourishing, reverse ableism biases and their effects, and impart a culture of disability ethics. It explores these matters through thought-leaders such as Michael Oliver, Alicia Ouellette, Jackie Leach Scully, and Eva Feder Kittay. Underscored by care ethics, this chapter concludes that all of humanity moves "in and out of relationships of dependence through different life stages and conditions of health,"[10] and that care as a virtue is essential to understanding another's needs.[11]

The Older Population – The Cared for and the Caregiver

The term "elderly" often conjures images of a frail and fragile person. Mindful of the distortions of this imagery, the social sciences more positively refer to the population of individuals 65 and older as "older adults."[12] This book adopts a clear preference for the latter image. Any appearance of "elderly" throughout indicates the word choice of the source cited. To that end, attempts to address the needs of older persons must emerge from an understanding of what it means to belong to this stakeholder community, by examining a few of the notable definitions. Traditionally, "'elderly' has been defined as a chronological age of 65 years old or older, while those from 65 through 74 years old are referred to as 'early elderly' and those over 75 years old as 'late elderly.'"[13] Its origins are attributed to the German Empire more than a century ago when 65 was the age by which persons were eligible to receive national pension plan benefits.[14] Patterning itself after the European nations' establishment of chronological eligibility for old-age insurance programs, in 1935 the United States determined age 65 as the benchmark retirement age through the adoption of the Social Security Act.[15]

Today, 65 is hardly considered old age as people are living well past that milestone into their 90s, and beyond. In 2016, the number of people over age 65 in the United States was 49.2 million, representing 15.2% of the population.[16] Persons over 85 account for about 6.4 million people, 52 times more than there were in 1900. In 2016, there were 81,896 people over the age of 100 in the United States,[17] more than double the 32,194 reported in 1980. It is vitally important, however, that older persons represent more than mere census statistics. They are a heterogeneous population of persons who once were parents, teachers, veterans, laborers, physicians, and most often caregivers themselves. They represent the human condition in transition.

Living with Unmet Needs

Aging is an individualized process. Individuals age differently and have highly diverse needs, often influenced by their chronological age. Some demographers contend that these differences and the sheer size and proportion of the population considered "old age" points to a need to establish age groups to differentiate the "young old" from the "oldest old." Some argue for applying a four-age-group model breaking society into young people, working people, younger retired people, and the oldest people. While others suggest adoption of an "oldest old" based on two groups the 50–74-year-old group, and the 85+ group.[18] Despite the need for differentiation, there are some generalities within each of these age groupings that medicine and science explore to objectively meet the unmet long-term healthcare needs of older persons.

From the Greek *geras* meaning "old age" and *iatrikos* meaning "physician," geriatric medicine is one of several groups of specialties defined by the patient's stage of human development, such as pediatrics and neonatology, rather than by organ systems, such as cardiology and neurology.[19] Geriatrics is concerned with disease and health problems specific older adults.[20] Accordingly, the benchmarks of geriatric medicine rely upon the age of the patient. Because it is unlike most other specialties which look primarily to the physical and biological aspects of illness, geriatrics by design pigeonholes its patients according to where they are on the life continuum. As such geriatrics is innately predisposed to the unconscious or conscious biases of the healthcare professional, according to their preconceptions of "elderly." There are inherent risks to such biases. Using stereotypes during care can result in, among other things, premature, and/or missed diagnosis "when clinicians fail to see their patients as more than their perceived demographic characteristics."[21]

Coined in 1968 by geriatric medicine pioneer Robert Butler, *ageism* is "a systematic stereotyping of and discrimination against people because they are old."[22] It can be conscious (explicit), or unconscious (implicit), and is not the exclusive province of healthcare. It is an attitude that is influenced by cultural ideologies and practices.[23] Throughout history in less industrialize societies, older adults have been valued for their wisdom of counsel and serve as inspiring role models to the younger members of society.[24] In the United States, however, society tends to presume that old age renders people unable to make good decisions because intellect, wisdom, and decision-making capabilities are compromised by age.[25]

Ageism can be subtle; for example, when healthcare professionals bypass direct communication with the older adult and address younger family members first.[26] Ageism can also be overt as reflected in a survey of Johns Hopkins medical students revealing that 80% would aggressively treat pneumonia in a 10-year-old girl, while only 56% would do the same for an 85–year-old woman.[27] In either case, assumptions and ideologies, including those that suggest that all older persons are mentally infirm, lead to treating them in authoritative and dismissive ways.[28]

Stereotypes, prejudice, and discrimination can present obstacles to health equality, not only in terms of quantity but quality of care. A recent U.S. study evidenced "age-related treatment of heart attacks relative to national treatment guidelines, with older patients less likely to receive standard diagnostic procedures and recommended treatment."[29] And unlike other forms of discrimination that rely upon immutable biological characteristics such as sexism and racism, ageism will affect anyone who lives long enough.[30] Although ageist tendencies can penetrate the entire healthcare system, this book concentrates primarily on its impact on vulnerability in the clinical setting, and to long-term care policy.

When older persons can no longer provide for their basic needs, and/or they are denied dignified methods of dealing with their functional decline, their dependency on other caregivers renders them particularly vulnerable. They are subject to threats or events that have the power to advance them toward adverse and harmful outcomes.[31] Understanding the nature of vulnerability entails examining contingencies, threats and risks, and the extent to which they are defenseless against them. According to Schroder-Butterfill and Marianti, vulnerability in this context of older persons is a probabilistic concept that has incremental outcomes based upon their proximity to harm. "A person's risk of suffering harm – her vulnerability – is the incremental outcome of a set of distinct but related risks."[32] Probabilities are aligned to the exposure to a threat, the materialization of the threat, and the ability to cope or defend against the threat. This is a particularly useful framework for understanding the aged who must consider proximity to and accumulation of risk exposure across the lifetime. There is an incremental reality to the dynamic process of aging. The probabilities of risk are best addressed when those with moral authority recognize their interrelationships with older persons and their collective obligations to them,[33] enabling them to live their best lives according to what matters to them.

Medical advances and technology have made it possible to prolong healthy human life. These advances naturally include prolonging the lives of those with complex, chronic, disabling conditions, and functional disabilities. The aged represent some of the most acutely sick persons requiring some of the costliest and protracted care. The top four leading causes of death – heart disease, cancer, cerebrovascular disease, and Alzheimer's – are nearly all accompanied by prolonged periods of functional decline, disability, and high rates of health services preceding death.[34] According to the 2017 International Health Policy survey, more than one in three people (36%) of adults over the age of 65 in the United States had multiple chronic conditions.[35]

Women are more likely than men to suffer from multiple chronic conditions such as diabetes, hypertension, migraines, digestive problems, and other orthopedic maladies that are not necessarily imminently life-threatening; although they generally result in limitations to mobility, physical, and social activities.[36] Stroke, heart attack, and cancer are more common in men[37] who utilize more in-patient hospital services – reimbursable by Medicare – whereas women use more prescription and custodial care services. The net result is that Medicare covers a smaller portion of women's healthcare needs.

Ironically, women outlive men despite being disproportionately impacted by chronic healthcare and access issues.[38] In 2016, there were 27.5 million women over age 65 compared with 21.8 million men, or a ratio of 126 women for every 100 men. Beyond age 85, the ratio increased to 187 women for every 100 men.[39] Because women tend to marry men who are older than themselves, they are less likely to share their later life with a spouse. This fact helps to explain why 75% of nursing home residents are single women.

Marital status is also attributed to economic, physical, and emotional measurements of well-being as a person's age. Older married persons typically have higher household incomes, better health, and lower incidences of depression than their unmarried counterparts. Further, they experience reduced risks of institutionalization as spouses tend to be the primary caregivers for their frail and disabled partners.[40] Statistically, in 2017, 70% of men over the age of 65 were married, compared to only 46% of women; of the unmarried women, 33% were widows.[41]

Historically there has been a pervasive and strong societal dependency on family as primary and even sole caregiver for older adults. The presence of family caregivers is a key factor in keeping older people out of nursing homes. Fifty percent of older people with long-term care needs who do not have family caregivers are in nursing homes, while only 7% who have a family member to care for them are placed in long-term care institutions.[42] Stalled population growth and the imbalance between the population of young and older persons means that fewer offspring and other family members will be available to care for older loved ones. The fact that couples and unmarried offspring have more parents to care for than they have children to assist in that care negatively draws on the human capital available to provide informal care to the aged.[43] Because of upward trends in the age composition of older adults, and the fertility histories of women who will be retiring, the shortage, and the need for long-term care solutions will be much greater.[44]

Long-Term Care

Long-term care refers to the services and support relied upon by those who need daily help to function day-to-day. Such help includes a wide array of services including personal care, assistive technologies, care coordination, home modification, transportation, and rehabilitation. Assistance may be needed regularly or intermittently, for periods of months, years, or for the remainder of a person's life.[45] The need for such care is measured according to the person's ability to perform daily activities and tasks.

The notion of long-term care incorporates formal (paid) and informal (typically unpaid) services. Persons over the age of 65 account for approximately 75% of formal long-term care spending in the United States.[46] Specific examples of formal long-term care services are adult day care, in-home care services, care provided in residential facilities, and intermediate and skilled nursing facilities.

In comparison to high-technology healthcare for the acutely ill, for which there is a strong preference in the United States, long-term care services are considered "low-technology" low-cost care. Nancy Jecker states that most of the healthcare dollars spent in the United States are spent on acute care, high-technology medicine centered on intensive, short-term, crisis-driven healthcare.[47] Yet, those who generally need long-term care are those whose care is chronic and continual rather than acute and episodic.

Chronic health conditions most often restrict the ability to perform activities of daily living (ADLs) such as dressing, bathing, and eating as well as instrumental activities (IADLs) such as meal preparation and housekeeping. Because these chronic conditions and the accompanying limitations require continual rather than episodic care, the need for long-term care is most often permanent. A great percentage of the oldest old living in community settings face ADL challenges. Over 25% of older these older adults require assistance bathing and showering, 40% have difficulty walking without assistance and 10% need assistance with toileting. A sizeable proportion of the oldest old also report difficulties with IADLs. It is estimated that 17% need help to use the telephone, 24% cannot do light housework without assistance, and 23% cannot prepare meals alone.[48] Formal long-term care services most commonly include skilled nursing and other personal care home settings. Informal long-term care options are most desirable and appropriate for many older adults with ADL and IADL limitations who desire to remain in their home setting.

Home care is an informal outpost of the healthcare system by which services are brought to patients in a setting that reinforces autonomy and self-respect, social integrity, familiarity, safety, and low cost.[49] Providing supplemental services to people in their homes most often provides a cost-effective alternative to a nursing home and other forms of long-term formal care. In addition, it provides them with a sense of continuity and safety in their comfortable setting, allowing them to "age in place" near family and community networks.[50] Older adults frequently associate living in their own home with independence as it provides evidence of their ability to make decisions for themselves.[51] It remains the one place where they can be themselves – and be free from their "sick" identity and be more at home with their changing bodies.[52]

Despite the need and the benefits of informal long-term care, current policy trends, ageism, and age-based rationing and allocation can obstruct access to these vital services. Such attitudes advocate for providing them to only those who are perceived to have the direst, means-tested needs while denying them to those persons on the fringes. Equally significant is the public ignorance, dogma, and stigma that influence the social figments associated with formal long-term care, particularly the negative connotation of nursing homes.[53] Such attitudes widen the chasm of unmet needs, and further punctuate the imperative for policy change.

Public Policy and Age-Based Allocation and Rationing

The purpose of public policies is to articulate how governments distribute resources, influence behaviors, and help to ensure the security of its constituents. They also reflect common consensus about values, and tell a story about people, history, and what is important to the populace. Policies try to solve problems or support core beliefs.[54] Throughout the past several decades, certain core beliefs concerning the rationing of healthcare needs of older adults have dominated policymaking thinking in this space. Policy concerning care for them is shaped and influenced by perceptions of what it means to be aged, and how the human lifespan is viewed in the United States.

Older people are generally viewed as a homogenous and undifferentiated constituency, and the human lifespan is typically considered to be a lifespan of production, spanning a pre-work, work, and post-work life continuum. Those who have surpassed the age of 65 are seen as all belonging to the same spot on the lifespan and therefore sharing the same undifferentiated needs. This thinking sparked many of the federal programs designed to provide healthcare for older Americans – chiefly Medicare. While these programs reflect compassion toward the aged, many of them encourage a view that they are weak, inferior, and fragile. This ageist ideology coupled with the need to control rising healthcare costs and expenditures, while improving access to care, established the basis for allocation and rationing.[55]

Allocation and rationing are methods of addressing the distribution of scarce of resources. As a public policy measure, *allocation* of healthcare resources considers what resources ought to be committed to a particular program and is typically assessed at a macro level considering only statistical lives. For example, determining the appropriate number of beds allocated to a particular hospital unit is an example of allocation. In contrast, *rationing* occurs when resource assessments consider the impact at the micro-level of identifiable lives.[56] Since it is widely recognized, this book adopts the definition of *rationing* adopted by the Catholic Health Association as "the withholding of potentially beneficial services because policies and practices establish limits on the resources available for health care."[57] Determining which patients occupy scarce critical care beds during a pandemic is an example of rationing. Because governments and HCOs encounter older adults at the macro and micro levels, they regularly make decisions that involve both allocation and rationing. The following highlights the predominant views of age-based rationing and allocation to demonstrate how applying ethics of care, as the moral alternative to purely age-based considerations, supports the provision of dignified long-term care services.

The antiquated belief that older adults were a bottomless pit of needs and that meeting those needs disproportionately stressed overly burdened financial resources undergirded much of public policy forming the basis for age-based rationing.[58] The scarcity of medical resources is a reality, and as such there is no longer a debate about whether healthcare should be rationed but rather how to do it equitably.[59] Influential scholars and bioethicists have shaped the course of public policy with respect to rationing, and their range of thinking spans a continuum from rationing of services based on a perceived natural lifespan, to a care-oriented approach with "care" as the core principle.

Perspectives on Age-Based Rationing

Daniel Callahan's original communitarian model is the most extreme call for age-based rationing of healthcare for the elderly. He argues that patients over 80-years-old ought to be considered to have lived a natural life span, and for the sake of the good of the community, they should not receive certain life-saving procedures and services but merely accept a tolerable death.[60] His expectation is that older people will consider the value of their remaining lives in relation to the larger intergenerational community, and because of their advanced age, they should prepare themselves to pass the torch of life to subsequent generations.[61]

According to Callahan, the elderly experience a meaningful life when they serve the young, and that they serve as models of morality when they surrender medical services in favor of the young. One way to ensure that they comply with this moral expectation is to compel them through age-rationing measures.[62] Callahan's myopic model misses the richness of experiential reasoning and thought that older persons bring to the intergenerational community of younger people. It caters to a "youth-oriented culture" demeaning the status of older people.[63] Moreover, he fails to consider that the life plans of older adults do not end at a prescribed age, but rather remain an inseparable part of their optimal functioning, relative to their condition and capabilities.

Norman Daniels proposes his Prudential Lifespan Account of rationing. According to Daniels, the just distribution of limited healthcare resources between the young and the old entails varying the health services provided through the different stages of life. A distribution supported by stable policies at each stage. He argues that providing different levels of services – essentially, treating people differently based upon their life stage – does not breed inequality if *everyone* in the same life stage is treated the same way all the time. This means that society would treat the young one way as a matter of policy, and the aged another, and this is done over their whole lives and the net result is that all persons are treated equally.[64]

In contrast to Callahan, Daniels contends that it is necessary to provide healthcare to older persons to help them maintain their own degree of functioning and a fair opportunity to enjoy their life plans. Unlike Callahan, Daniels does not assume that one stage of life is more valuable than life at another stage, but rather the Prudential Life model turns on the judgments that people would make concerning their care at each of the different stages of life, according to an agreed upon principle.[65] As such, Daniels argues that providing public long-term care services ought to be incorporated into the life of the prudent planner.

Incorporating vestiges of Daniels' argument, Paul Menzel's Prudent Consent model of rationing works from peoples' rational and prudent self-interest based upon the needs and goals of their lives. It is not an age-based model, but one that is more "age-influenced," based upon the quality of life that the individual anticipates. This model allows persons to choose the beneficial care that they want now and what they anticipate wanting in later years, thereby placing the rationing determination squarely in their hands. It respects autonomy and the integrity of self-determination.[66]

A significant challenge for U.S. policymaking is that universally very little attention and planning takes place until the need for care arises. Menzel's model foresees a proactive rather than reactive system of rationing influenced only by the characteristic of age rather than the age itself. The Prudent Consent approach encourages persons to self-manage their lives and their resources and to take accountability for long-range needs based on how they want to live their lives.

Expressing his alarm at the utilitarian culture that seeks to maximize the good for the greatest number of younger citizens at the expense of adequate care for the vulnerable aged, John Kilner questions the wisdom of age-based rationing entirely.[67] Kilner examines the standard age-based argument that as healthcare for older persons is costing more, and their population is rising faster than any other population, it is necessary to cut back on all health resources available to them including long-term, low-technology care. His position argues instead for a standard of policy making that considers the person first before other economic and social considerations.

Kilner presents a person-first approach. That is, the person needing long-term care is a *person who is older*, not an "older person." And their needs are examined through economic, cultural, social, and political lenses. He concludes that one of the primary reasons that society considers cutting back health services for the aged is the cultural preoccupation with youth. He describes what he observes as the increasingly utilitarian view in the United States that actions should produce the greatest benefits for the greatest number of people. Coupled with the general bias toward favoring those who are most productive within the market-driven U.S. economy, the net result encourages the view that the aged are nonproductive and subject to rationed services.[68]

Kilner advances several strong arguments contending that such age-based rationale guiding current policy trends are not ethically justified. He attacks the economic argument on several fronts. Rising healthcare costs are due to many other factors that have no direct relationship to the elderly, and that other countries with similar trends include the economic impacts of other dependent groups – such as children – into the cost allocation equation. He further questions the wisdom of a society seeking to ration available healthcare resources rather than controlling other aspects of rampant spending in an excessive consumption-driven economy.[69] But most germane to the issue of long-term care is his contention that the most needed form of care for persons who are older demands the least economic impact.

Most healthcare rationing focuses on lifesaving care, yet a very small proportion of services for the elderly are of a lifesaving nature.[70] Most elderly need informal "life-sustaining" care. Moreover, even if lifesaving care is necessary, Kilner agrees that those incidences and the likelihood of repeat episodes can be lessened by providing basic low-technology, preventive care – such as in-home medication management and assistance with ADLs and IADLs. Reformulating the national policy on equitable resource distribution necessarily begins with an understanding of current policy trends and implications.

Current Policy and Trends

Society's frail and aged have a variety of unmet needs. Policymakers, as well as ethically accountable healthcare organizations, must understand better how current cultural and economic contexts coupled with the healthcare system's reimbursement payment structure, fail to adequately provide for these needs. As an example, Medicaid and Medicare programs were constructed as entitlement programs designed to assist low-income beneficiaries and serve as primary insurance for persons over 65, respectively. However, even though they were intended to help the disadvantaged and needy, they represent indirect forms of rationing as Medicaid's restrictive eligibility requirements more often than not limit individual enrollment, and Medicare's reimbursement rates and coverage limitations often fail to provide needed services after the acute episode has passed.[71]

Since its inception in 1965, the central focus of Medicare has been to pay for medical services for acute and life-threatening conditions, not chronic, disabling conditions. Although it is widely accepted as old-age insurance, historically it was more accurate to characterize it as a funding mechanism for hospitals and professional providers. However, recent cost-containment initiatives and payment methodologies have lowered hospital reimbursements such that the elderly are being discharged sooner thereby going home "quicker and sicker."[72] Ironically, post-discharge events, which frequently lead to readmissions, often exacerbate the unmet needs of older chronically ill persons.

From discharge – the point at which acute care is no longer provided – older adults and their family are most often left to go it alone without access to necessary life-sustaining services. Current policy trends do not sufficiently consider the total-care delivery package which considers a comprehensive view of the older patient's needs before, during, and after acute care treatment. Many of the decisions that determine which needs to satisfy depend upon who or what bears the financial burden of paying for what is needed. These needs most often include social services. As healthcare for older adults should not be considered independent of the social services required to support them when their capabilities begin to decline.[73]

Although Medicare is the primary funding source for home healthcare, nearly three-quarters of the nation's older American's pay for these services out-of-pocket. One reason for this is that many beneficiaries pay out-of-pocket for deductibles, copayments, and coinsurance premiums.[74] Another reason is that even though Medicare reimburses for home care, it does so on the condition that the services are skilled versus informal and that they be hands-on, short-term illness resolution services such as occupational and physical therapy modalities. Moreover, they are reimbursed on a payment-per-visit basis and terminate as soon as the fiscal intermediary administrator determines that the skilled services are no longer medically necessary and reimbursable. As such, Medicare home care services do not fully meet many of the post-discharge home needs of older persons but appear to be a substitute for extended hospitalization leaving much of the residual of necessary services up to the patient to purchase.

Part of the reason why Congress, when it passed Medicare in 1965, opted not to cover informal long-term care services had to do with the prevailing assumption in the United States that the needs of older persons are solely the purview of the family. As such, exclusion of these services was supported by the fear that if a public benefit was available for family caregivers, the inducement for fraud would have alleged family caregivers coming from everywhere. This remains an outdated and cynical view of family caregivers, as today most caregivers want respite, not remuneration or replacement.[75]

In the United States, there is a compelling interest in keeping older adults out of skilled nursing facilities for as long as possible, yet there are few if any informal care communities prepared to care for them as they transfer out of acute care facilities.[76] Societal needs have significantly changed since social welfare programs were initially designed in 1935. At that time, such programs responded to family arrangements that are no longer operative today, and to a vastly different population composition. The social programs available today have not kept pace with this changed demographic.[77]

The economic cost of informal caregiving services is staggering and has steadily increased since the beginning of this century. "At $470 billion in 2013, the value of unpaid caregiving exceeded the value of paid home care and total Medicaid spending in the same year, and nearly matched the value of the sales of the world's largest company, Wal-Mart ($477 billion)."[78] In 2014, approximately $217 billion of the value of unpaid care was attributed to care for persons with Alzheimer's or other dementias. Contrast this to the $613 billion in total 2014 Medicare expenditures[79] and it becomes apparent that the mere presence of informal caregivers is a vital part of Medicare cost-containment and deserves the attention of policymakers. Caregiver needs are important and policy trends must be attentive to the crucial role they play.

Throughout the U.S. healthcare system, more generous attention is paid to high-technology, high reimbursement procedures and services rather than those that are low-cost, low-technology. One reason for the proliferation of costly technology is that cost-effectiveness is not a Medicare criterion for determining whether to reimburse manufactures for new technologies. There is little incentive for manufacturers to invest in low-cost alternatives.[80]

Hence, the United States system pays more for short-lived, costly procedures and relatively little for low-cost, high-yield cognitive and other informal care services. The low-technology needs of frail older persons are as much a part of their illness/pathology as those of the acutely ill. Nevertheless, decisions of who is entitled to receive them are based on seemingly arbitrary assessments examined against standardized guidelines. Public policy supports not paying for low-technology informal care whenever an assessment model is conducted without regard for the delivery of care, or the facts and circumstances unique to each person's illness-related need.

Enacted in 1965 as a health benefit program to assist certain disadvantaged segments of society – primarily low-income beneficiaries – Medicaid is a means-based, state-run entitlement program. Medicaid authorizes states to include home-based services and waiver programs intending to keep people at home and in the community and out of nursing homes.[81] However, the majority of states have set the coverage and eligibility limits at or below the federal poverty guidelines,[82] which means that less than one-third of the chronically ill and disabled older persons can qualify.

Because eligibility for Medicaid services is means-tested, many older adults are forced to draw down and significantly dilute their assets to become sufficiently impoverished to qualify for needed care. In the Commonwealth of Pennsylvania, for example, a chronically ill older person who has anything more than $8000 in assets[83] would have to spend the excess on qualified expenses to be eligible for assistance. The mere process of forcing a person to relinquish assets that likely represent the net sum of a lifetime of productive achievement and accomplishments can be, in many ways, more painful than the chronic condition. It also runs afoul of the very market-driven economy and policy trends that support self-determination and autonomy.[84]

The U.S. system of long-term care is a residualist model whereby the government provides resources only after informal attempts have failed – either through resource depletion or other failures. This model ensures that every claim for care becomes a needs-based claim that is structured more on the perceived failings or inabilities of family, or other caregivers, to take care of their own. These needs-based claims can become catalysts for mobilizing shame, guilt, and embarrassment for everyone – including the older person.[85] Society must move away from providing care to only what is left of a person's health and dignity and move toward long-term care services that view caregiving as a collective societal concern, not merely a private matter.

Reshaping Public Policy Through Ethics of Care and Compassion

Families and other informal caregivers must be empowered to discharge their duties to care for their older loved ones. Through sound policy, society must also be able to sufficiently meet the healthcare needs of their most vulnerable citizens. The ethically accountable healthcare organization has a moral duty to respond to the needs of these normative stakeholders and provide later-life experiences that preserve human dignity and self-respect. The HCO is uniquely empowered with authority to effectuate the change necessary to fulfill these needs. To that end, it is necessary for them to engage and work to reshape public policy to better target benefits to those with the greatest needs. As Weber suggests "[h]ealthcare organizations are major stakeholders in public health policy...through either their own government affairs offices or the efforts of advocacy organizations such as the American Hospital Association, the American Medical Association, and the American College of Emergency Physicians."[86] They are powerful influencers, and the value of their voice to serve this community of stakeholders cannot be overstated.

With the patient at the center, the delivery of appropriate, affordable, and quality care depends upon the relationships between the HCO and encircling and interconnected communities of normative stakeholders. These communities include family, professional and facility providers, social workers, and therapists, as well as many derivative stakeholder groups and strategic partners not typically aligned with healthcare systems.[87] Examples of these groups, include facility administrators, state, local and federal governments, and professional associations who establish standards of care, transportation agencies, as well as third-party payers. In addition, certain extenders such as religious communities, social and civic organizations, and volunteer agencies can be collateral caregivers and are integral to this model.

Acknowledging this interrelatedness, Holstein, Parks, and Waymack advocate for an ethic of interconnectedness in policymaking.[88] They argue that policies that consider individuals as solely independent and autonomous persons do not have the gravity and effectiveness of policies that purport to serve most of the population. The interconnectedness of the individuals to their groups is bound together by the values and ethics of the group.

Since prehistoric times, humankind's survival relied upon collective team cohesion and support against life-threatening elements. That reliance is amplified today, as societies are more interconnected, specialized, and complex, rendering connection a prerequisite for survival physically and emotionally.[89] HCOs and policymakers can more readily effectuate policy changes to expand access to long-term care once they acknowledge the need for such access and understand the interconnected community values and experiences attributed to it. Interconnectedness requires that policies represent a commitment to what Holstein, Parks, and Waymack refer to as "intergenerational solidarity" and a rejection of the view that individuals and families can address the economic and social difficulties of caring for their older family alone.[90] They depend upon resources and support from the wider community.

However, ethical healthcare policy-making, and specifically long-term care, is not just about allocation of limited resources. Ethics, according to Smith, "[i]s an unparalleled regulator of value selection and must therefore be factored into the formulation of a national elderly healthcare policy."[91] It is about compassion, and understanding the voices of those in need, their values and what matters most to them, the ethical principles guiding decision-making, and the care that undergirds those decisions.

The Ethics of Care

"Everyone who reaches adulthood does so because someone else cared for her or him."[92] The simple truth of Groenhout's account illuminates the reality that care is an emotion involved in providing for the needs of another and is indispensable for human life.[93] Caring is not theoretical. It is an empirical reality that begins before birth in the form of a primitive caring relation, and the survival of the infant is wholly dependent upon continuation of that relation.[94] Such caring, for Carol Gilligan, entails "paying attention to seeing, listening, and responding with respect… it is a relational ethic grounded in a premise of interdependence."[95] Hence, as a normative theory of ethics, ethics of care arrives at moral decisions and actions from the understanding that is acquired from interpersonal relationships.

For Virginia Held, "care has many forms, and as the ethics of care evolves, so should our understanding of what care is."[96] Nel Noddings espouses that caring "[i]nvolves attention, empathetic response and a commitment to responding to legitimate needs. It is sometimes referred to as an attitude, but it is more than that. It is a set of dispositions to respond positively to in interpersonal relations."[97] She further argues that it "[i]s not merely a fuzzy feeling, nor is it a prescription for how all cared-fors must be treated. It is a moral response to expressed needs."[98] The moral response is relational at its core. Although needs are expressed individualistically, the response must be collective.

Addressing collective responsibility, Vanlaer and Gastmans define care as "practices of responsibility in which the different persons involved take responsibility in a process of reacting to vulnerability."[99] According to their personalist approach, "the dynamics and content of care are determined by the proper nature and origin of the relationship between these persons, the vulnerability of the persons, and the context within which the care takes place."[100] The most consequential common denominator to all of these perspectives for health *care* is the human relationship that binds stakeholders, and the ethics of care model that guides actions and decisions.

Healthcare is about interconnected human relationships. The traditional medical model approach to care recognizes the interdependent interactions between clinician, patient, and third-party payers for the purpose of diagnosis and treatment of disease or conditions, and payment for services. However, many more stakeholder concerns, relationships, and factors affect care for vulnerable older persons

There are also social determinants that can significantly impact their care, quality of life, and health, such as proximity to children, access to food and nutrition requirements, adequacy of clothing and shelter, social isolation, and access to healthcare services generally.[101] Although they are increasingly recognized as necessary to understand the public health needs of communities, these factors are not always apparent or made available to the provider of services under the traditional medical model of care and are often not considered in the care plan. Adherence to the ethics of care model brings these additional factors to the conversation because it supports a collective and communal, rather than a purely individualistic approach to care.

This communal care ethic does not vitiate the liberal notion of living freely and autonomously, but rather reinforces the connectedness and sameness that makes people who they are and fortifies them; it is, in many ways the ethics of empathy. The ethics of care balance individual rights, freedom, and human connections. It affords people the ability and opportunity to develop and maintain nurturing relationships. To enjoy what matters most to them. To that end, moral leaders must not forget that humankind will cease to exist when people stop caring with, for, and about one another; and "without carefully developed and nourished relationships of care, human life cannot be lived to the fullest."[102]

Thereupon, it is worth considering how most religious traditions perceive the human lifespan as encompassing a lifetime of dynamic mutual giving and receiving. Parents sacrifice for their children who then sacrifice for them.[103] Catholic traditions also teach the exercise of responsible stewardship at every stage of life.[104] When policymakers and healthcare leaders imbed these virtues into policy and practice, the moral justification for public support of long-term care communities becomes self-evident. Stewardship promotes the authentic good of human beings and human society, and preserves human dignity and self-respect; with particularity, it benefits the aged and their caregivers.[105] Importantly, human dignity transcends a person's age, condition, gender health, religion, or stage of development. The inherent dignity and sacredness of all human life is paramount.[106]

In applying the ethics of care, a transparent dialogue must also include the voices of the professional providers and practitioners who have direct or indirect treating relationships with chronically ill older persons. The policies they follow must also consider the challenges they encounter as formal caregivers, as well as their ethical obligations prescribed by their profession. At the core of this book is the recognition that few relationships are more sacred than the relationship between a physician and her patient. Therefore, in support of ethical long-term care policymaking, professional and facility providers have a moral duty to work collaboratively[107] and in relation with other stakeholders, to advocate for older persons who are chronically ill.

The traditional view of the physician's duty to her patient has been that the patient's vulnerability, illness, impairment, and even ignorance created strong duties of fidelity and personal commitment to the patient. To assuage the assertions that the imbalance of power between the physician and patient unfairly compromised the patient's decision-making capabilities, the principle of autonomy permitted the patient to decide themselves, free from controlling influences.[108] However, as older patients encounter increased challenges to their self-determination, applying the principled approach alone to ethical advocacy will be insufficient.

The values of independence and autonomy fit best within the acute care setting and have been overemphasized within the context of older person policy.[109] In long-term care, the decision-making does not typically center on single matters such as consenting to a particular treatment or course of care. It is dynamic and nearly always implicates others and their resources.[110] As suggested by Ludwick and Silva, "facilitating autonomous decision-making for patients would be very straightforward if healthcare professionals could simply designate patients as competent or incompetent to make decisions. However, decision-making is more nuanced."[111]

By adopting an ethics of care, the ethically accountable physician and HCO will see their roles vis-à-vis the older patient differently. The ethics of care asks that healthcare providers accept that they are "self-in relation" with the older patient.[112] It demands a degree of attentiveness that implies having sufficient knowledge of what to look for and taking responsibility for care.[113] In adopting an ethics of care, the provider will "strive to find solutions that reinforce relationship and uphold values of caring, empathy and integrity."[114] The provider must relate and respond to what matters most to the person. Providers are compelled to give a voice to the older patient, advise them of alternative care settings, and even facilitate the provision of services by administering outreach to ancillary services.

Established in 2017, the Age Friendly Health System was developed to address the complexities of caring for older adults in health systems across the United States. This collaboration between The John A. Hartford Foundation, the Institute for Healthcare Improvement, the American Hospital Association, and the Catholic Health Association of the United States set a bold vision to provide age-friendly care to older adults. Their 3-step vision for age-friendly care provides that: care follows a set of evidence-based practices, it does not cause harm and aligns with what matters most to the older person and their caregivers.[115]

The evidenced-based practices apply an ethics of care and consist of elements of high-quality care known as the "4Ms." The 4Ms – What Matters, Medication, Mentation, and Mobility – help to organize and manage care for older adults based on their strengths, preferences, and abilities, rather than their illness. Applying elements of what matters to a person, considering how their medications may affect what matters to them, addressing dementia and depression across settings of care, and ensuring that their mobility aligns with what matters drive all care decisions implicating the older adult.[116] Incorporating this framework and the 4Ms into plans of care help to ensure that what matters to the older patient is prominent in every encounter. The 4Ms also help to imbed the healthcare professional more deeply into care.

A healthcare professional who becomes so embedded in an older person's care contributes to their dignity and self-respect. The ethically accountable provider who embraces the ethics of care, will begin to see her role in relation to the interconnectedness of the larger community and understand the values and norms that will reshape public policy for older adults. She will have a clearer insight into the impact of decisions on other relationships and points of view that are important to the patient.[117] When compassion effectuates positive change for her patient through the ethics of care, this change will help reshape the norms and values for all physicians, health *care* practitioners, and policymakers. According to Tellis-Nayak, her expression of compassion is "the most noble of human relations which lets us into the personal world of the other and shares the other's pain and trouble."[118] Such person-centeredness can transform the culture of long-term elder care for the patient, the caregiver, and the community.

Caregiver and Community-Based Person-Centered Care

Because communities care together for the well-being of their members,[119] the collective responsibility for older persons must also include addressing the needs of children, in-laws, spouses, and other informal family caregivers. This should include access to human, economic, and spiritual resources. Collective responsibility must also consider the needs of the changing family structure, find ways to support mutual caring activities, and challenge dangerous caregiver assumptions, particularly those that ignore the needs of women caregivers.

Caregiving by women is the unspoken foundation of contemporary long-term care policy. That is not a surprise, as Gilligan holds, that "[w]omen not only define themselves in a context of human relationship, but also judge themselves in terms of their ability to care."[120] According to the U.S. Census Bureau findings, in 2017 56.4% of the 51 million providers of informal eldercare were women; 43.8% of them were between the ages of 45–64.[121] Roughly 36% of unpaid caregiving to all older Americans is provided by daughters and daughters-in-law, and sons and sons-in-law account for another 16%. Such caregiving typically lasts 4 years.[122]

Most often, women caregivers are multigenerational[123] and hold other primary caregiver roles – that of mother, wife, and daughter. The children of female primary caregivers are often collaterally impacted by the efforts of their mother to care for and sustain their older grandparents and/or parents. While family neglect, either real or perceived, is generally unintentional, it is quite often a natural consequence of family caregiving. Additionally, feelings of stress, sadness, and fatigue are commonly reported by caregivers and other members of the affected family.[124]

An ethics of care-based system of long-term care policies and programs will help to situate older people in the context of home, family, and community without exploiting others who care for them. It must ensure that proportionate attention is paid to the voices of the recipients and the caregivers to ensure that reciprocal care is morally responsive care. Understanding individual voices and relationships are essential to HCO's in executing their responsibility to disrupt and be a moral change agent for the good of the vulnerable older persons. Gilligan contends that voices are instruments of resistance that bolster transformative change.[125] The power of voice to effectuate change is particularly evident when holistic, person-centered, and compassionate care ethic is the objective.

According to Muriel Gillick, one way to consider long-term care holistically is to reorient the single-minded thinking about the patient as only an individual and consider them in relation to their caregivers, their home environment, and their wider community. She contends that physicians ought to be the architect of plans that consider their homes and community design.[126] The effects of these environments can determine the extent to which a person's health thrives or fails.[127] Providing older adults with technically competent and compassionate person-centered care that considers their health state, what they value most, and is achievable within their unique environments[128] is not merely aspirational. Noteworthy examples of person-centered compassionate care models inspired by physicians to change the culture of aging are providing long-term care that is life-affirming, humane, and meaningful for all affected stakeholders.

As a resource created by long-term care professionals advocating for culture change in all models of care services for the aged, the Pioneer Network was formed in 1997.[129] Its mission is to change the culture of aging in American by encouraging communication, networking, and learning opportunities to create residential environments for the elderly that are person-directed.[130] As the antidote to institutionalization, the Pioneer Network advocates for caring communities for older adults to live in.[131] The Network espouses movement away from provider and staff directed long-term care toward care that is person-centered; where individual preferences and past patterns form the basis for staff decisions making. Ultimately, the goal of the Pioneer Network community is to go beyond person-centered to person-directed care where the aging make their own decisions about their routines, and the staff align patterns to meet their preferences.[132]

Community-based long-term care for older persons interconnects the caregiver and the patient to an environment that focuses on flourishing rather than illness. Thereupon, the Eden Alternative, an international non-profit organization was founded in 1991 by Dr. Bill Thomas, to "create a life worth living for elders in their care."[133] Its founding mission is to transform the way elder care is provided throughout the world. As of 2019, the Eden Alternative Philosophy has positively impacted more than 111,000 elder care organizations globally, through education, training, and provider partnerships.[134]

According to Thomas, the bulk of elder suffering is due to the three plagues of loneliness, helplessness, and boredom.[135] The Eden Alternative antidote to these plagues is a reciprocal caregiving environment that includes plants, animals, and children. As an elder-centered community, the Eden Alternative Philosophy creates opportunities for the aged to give *and* receive care. It de-emphasizes top-down bureaucratic care decisions and places the maximum decision-making authority in the hands of the residents themselves or into those closest to them.[136] Medical treatment, according to this model, is subordinate to genuine human caring.

Also founded by Dr. Thomas, The Green House Project opened its first elder home in Tupelo, Mississippi in 2003. Thomas, a self-described nursing home abolitionist, began tearing down nursing homes and building in their stead small home-like settings designed for ten to twelve residents.[137] These small homes provide private rooms and bathrooms, bright, open kitchens, and intimate dining settings resembling single-family dwellings. Without long hospital-like corridors and communal meal rooms, they are designed to closely resemble the familiar way that many of the residents lived their independent lives. In addition, because of the small, family-like atmosphere, older residents interact with staff and other residents on more personal levels, forming deeper relationships.

Their organizational structure is different from traditional nursing homes. Green Houses practice consistent assignments. This means that the same aides routinely care for the same few residents. This helps to promote relationship. In addition, the staffs are cross trained to work in a variety of different roles from laundry to helping prepare meals. More consistent contact also helps the staff become aware of subtle changes in residents' conditions which help them spot potential health concerns early.[138] To that end, research from the Robert Wood Johnson Foundation concluded that the Green House model is a preferable model of care.[139] The study demonstrated that hospitalizations and readmissions were lower than traditional nursing homes, 38% of residents were less likely to have pressure ulcers, and 45% less likely to have catheters. All of which suggests that emphasizing quality of life did not necessitate sacrificing quality of care.[140] These models, rooted in philosophies promoting person-directed, relationship-based care, are changing the culture of care for vulnerable persons. The ability and capacity to care for, and to be cared for is united to the concept of human dignity.[141]

The Dignity of Disability

In 2019, the Centers for Disease Control and Prevention reported that 1 in 4 adults in the United States had some form of disability. According to that report, they were mostly seen in adults over the age of 65.[142] Despite the statistical reporting and demographics, it is difficult to measure the number of persons with disabilities, as it is not a single state, but rather a multidimensional human condition.[143] Understanding disability as a human condition is a complicated and dynamic endeavor.

Akin to aging, disability is a condition that resides on the human life continuum. The positive and negative effects of disability can wax and wane in a variety of forms over time, affecting the ability of the person with a disability to flourish. Some conditions exhibit periods of long stability, some disabilities are characterized by steadily increasing impairment, and some, particularly those that originate from injury, may even improve.[144]

According to the International Classification of Functioning, Disability and Health (ICF), disability is an umbrella term defining the negative aspects of impairments, activity limitations, and participation restrictions affecting an individual with a particular condition, and that individual's contextual factors.[145]

Defined in this matter, disability refers to the challenges associated with specific areas of functioning, and not the underlying condition itself. Specifically, it looks at impairments to physical or mental functioning, activity limitations such as walking, or eating, and participation restrictions such as employment, transportation, or access to social settings.[146]

The ICF characterization of disability is concerned with the interaction between the person and their environment, which is most often where impediments to flourishing are found. As normative stakeholders, persons with disabilities are entitled to the dignity to live with their disability identity in right relationship with their environment.[147] The moral duty of the ethically accountable healthcare organization is to improve the human condition and the dignity of persons with disabilities and palliate vulnerability by creating environments enabling them to flourish. Like the aged, persons with disabilities are a heterogeneous group representing the human condition.

Understanding the Human Condition

Protagoras observed that "of all things the measure is Man; of the things that are, that they are, of the things that are not, that they are not."[148] Accordingly, man was the reference point from which all things of the world were known – including what it meant to be human. Granting sovereignty to man to determine the terms of human existence was bold and daunting. So much so that more than two-thousand years after Protagoras espoused this ethical relativism, humanity has proven unable to universally define and measure what it means to be human.

Understanding the nature of humanity, what it means to be human, and to possess those characteristics and traits that are uniquely and typically human, has been the object of attention for philosophers, anthropologists, politicians, and theologians practically since the beginning of time. Humanity's ongoing search to define itself is further complicated by its unending desire to improve itself through technology,[149] biomedicine, and genetics. In its quest to improve the human condition, humanity wrestles with reconciling the attraction of eliminating all unacceptable characteristics and traits not deemed typically human, against those held to be ideal. To profess that someone is disabled presupposes that there exist criteria for what it means to be *non-disabled*: to be ideally human. To say that a being possesses ideal human characteristics is largely a social construct.

From an evolutionary perspective, humans and their embodied nature are distinguished from other animals. They are studied according to how they live in relation to tensions within their environment, as well as in terms of human biology and characteristics.[150] They continually strive to change and break from the forces of nature. These continual changes are driven by the human reflective capacities of knowledge and intelligence. Reflective capacities alone cannot explain humanness. According to Allen Buchanan's observations, a human nature possesses good and bad characteristics and dispositions that are impervious to change and external influences,[151] such as the ability to make moral decisions and engage one another socially. According to this view, without these and other impervious and constant characteristics, a being would not be human.[152]

Religious traditions have greatly influenced western thought on the question of humanness. Most hold that what makes human animals *human* is the fact that they are made in the image and likeness of God. Sharing the fact that they bear God's image – that is, a divine presence which remains within all created humans – human beings are in a special relationship with God and serve as co-creators and stewards for humanity. As stewards, humans have divinely bestowed dominion and are responsible for overseeing things produced for the good of humanity as well for the persons producing them.[153] This dominion presupposes the duty to change and improve life for the rest of humanity. What separates humans and distinguishes them from being mirror images of God is their sinful nature. For example, in the Christian tradition, the incarnation of Jesus Christ gave humanity a model to emulate and an opportunity to restore unity, to transform, and emerge from sinfulness.[154]

Both the evolutionary and theological perspectives of what it means to be human prescribe the need for humans to change and to improve. Evolutionary humans measure humanity's physical and intellectual fitness against the chances of survival and elimination of death in a hostile environment, and religious traditions measure human sinfulness against the pursuit of redemption from an evil world. Both scientific and religious traditions agree that a fundamental human characteristic is an aspiration to become transformed into healthier, more grace-filled, productive, and enlightened beings. Even with these characteristics, humanity does not provide normative rules dictating when and which parts of human beings can be changed or even destroyed in their pursuit of self-improvement. What is clear is that human life is challenged by a host of complex variables, including theological concepts, physical parameters, limitations, and even its genetic framework, which can all affect human life. These variables implicate what Walter Doefler refers to as *conditio human* or *the human condition*.[155]

Whether it is viewed theologically or scientifically, the human condition – the endeavor to move humanity through these challenges and variables – strives to eliminate human limitations, alleviate suffering, and improve the quality of human life and human fulfillment. Understanding the depth to which humanity may dive as it pursues elimination of limitations, particularly those perceived limitations associated with human disability, requires examination of the good life. What constitutes a good life, and the quest to select the qualities of human nature which ought to be preserved, is as old as humanity itself. This book adopts Glover's perspective that the measurement of a good life is one that promotes and allows for human flourishing.[156]

Human Flourishing: Abilities and Attitudes

As Jonathan Glover examines human flourishing, he rightly states that what constitutes a flourishing life, is not the same for all humans. Much of human flourishing relies upon the innate differences attributed to each human and their unique circumstances and environments. In addition, the good and flourishing life is only observable based on life as we know it; it does not consider things untried.[157] Further, there is no universal notion of normalcy with respect to the good and flourishing life. It is "how life seems to the person who lives it."[158]

To that end, and with respect to human disability, Glover contends that while all human disabilities involve some functional limitations, the mere presence of a functional limitation does not create a disability; and a disability does not necessarily impede flourishing. A person with a disability enjoys a good life in the same way a person without one can be miserable. The real measurement of a disabling quality is found in the impairments or obstacles to human flourishing. To that end, much of the ability to flourish depends upon the person's reactions and responses to the circumstances and settings that confront them.[159] Those reactions and responses extend beyond what the person with the disability can control, and include things attributed to the wider communities and environments within which they live. In sum, a flourishing life is not devoid of flaws or limitations but is rather one which respects those limits and learns to live alongside rather than beneath them.

What constitutes flourishing is dependent largely on a person's preferences. A disability that renders someone unable to engage in a particular activity may not be a disability at all if the person would not value that activity or want to engage in it even if they could.[160] That is one reason why most persons with disabilities, their families and loved ones express a sincere appreciation for the lives they live according to their preferences. The joy that someone with a disability experiences in the ordinary course of their lives – the joy *they* appreciate – can be markedly different from that which the able-bodied experience; hence, the experiences are often misunderstood or ignored altogether. The inability or unwillingness, of those upon whom persons with disabilities depend, to identify those preferences, will impede flourishing.

Deficient societal settings and distorted perceptions of reality concerning persons with disabilities also inhibit flourishing. For example, the absence of wheelchair ramps, poorly designed transportation systems, and the paucity of education on how to interact with persons with functional limitations impairs human flourishing oftentimes more than the limitation itself. The ability to flourish is further hampered by cultural assumptions of what is *normal,* and society's frequent intolerance, discriminatory practices, and preconceived opinions about persons with disabilities and their limitations.[161]

It is the way that normalcy is constructed that creates problems for those with disabilities.[162] Such constructs and preconceptions presume an understanding of what persons with disabilities experience. Because most people rarely talk about the positive, relational life experiences of persons with disabilities, such experiences are not generally associated with their flourishing. Furthermore, the scarcity of shared experiences results in more distorted preconceptions. It is for this reason that the presence of biases toward persons with disabilities creates real barriers to their flourishing on many societal levels, including the delivery of healthcare.

The same way that ageist tendencies discriminate and disadvantage the older persons, implicit and conscious biases toward the idea of disability as well as those *with* disabilities reinforce stereotypes, obfuscate flourishing and adversely affect the good life. Implicit, or unconscious biases associate attitudes and stereotypes toward categories of people without conscious awareness. Because they happen automatically, they are hard to control or suppress.[163] They are generally formed by personal experiences, attitudes, and culture, and develop and take shape over the course of a lifetime.

While they are not consciously offensive, implicit biases reflect and reinforce stereotypes when they are directed at members of marginalized groups such as persons with disabilities. Implicit biases about persons with disabilities are pervasive.[164] They are typically subtle and not overtly offensive. However, they can offend. For example, when someone addresses questions meant for a visually impaired person to their companion, the message sent is that the person who is blind cannot think and respond independently. These micro-aggressions reinforce negative stereotypes.[165] To attack the roots of biases against persons with disabilities, society must develop, through relational encounters, greater understanding of the experiences and attitudes of persons within disability communities. Human flourishing and the good life rely upon the gravity of human relationships and the experiences emanating from them.

Martina Holder-Franz warns that society must guard against creating a myth of normality that values people merely for their biological characteristics and qualities. With great insight, she contends that life is vulnerable and relational, and persons with disabilities ought not to be judged by their *ability* but rather by their *availability* for relationships.[166] The relationships between persons with disabilities and their families, friends, and the communities within which they live can enhance and enrich the ability to flourish beyond any biological characteristic or quality.[167]

Studies show that persons with disabilities generally show warmth toward their own communities and peers. And the more visible the disability – such as using walker or other assistive device, the stronger the positive attitude toward the disability community.[168] When persons with disabilities are introduced to others according to what they enjoy doing, and the friends they have rather than what they cannot do, others will naturally discover commonality with them. Hence, the desire to create relationships with them that makes life rewarding for everyone involved.[169] Relationships are necessary for human flourishing. "The flourishing of every person, whether disabled or not, is dependent upon others, on the support of our families, friends, communities, and social structures, as well as the cultures given to us by religious and national traditions."[170] Personhood is sustained by relationship, and what sustains relationship is love.[171]

Religious tradition teaches that humans are to live in communion with each other, to share with one another, and to serve one another. The Greatest Commandment is about humans and their loving relationship to their neighbor.[172] Human flourishing requires loving relationships that promote dignity, friendship, and caring. Rather than adhering to attitudinal barriers which create roadblocks to flourishing, humans should be motivated by a belief in the goodness of creation and the image of a God that is present in everyone as a pathway to God's grace.

Grace allows humanity to witness the reality that each person is limited and broken in some manner and is in need of others. This dependency enables all persons, particularly those with disabilities, to live what Matt Edmonds calls a *graceful life*.[173] This togetherness promotes interdependence which welcomes the presence of God and helps to eliminate the fear that often pervades the willingness to get to know a person with a disability. For example, Christian interdependence honors the value of all individuals, despite their limitations, not by what they can or cannot do, but by simply being who they are.[174] Interdependence means persons are dependent upon God and each other, but it also acknowledges God's *dependence* upon everyone to be moral agents for God's healing throughout the world.[175] Healing and cure are seminal objectives often sought when justifying improvements to the human condition, particularly when such improvements seek to eliminate disease and suffering associated with perceived disabilities.

Improving the Human Condition of Disability

A fact of the human condition is that disability exists within a social context that privileges some bodies and minds over others. Thus, it creates a world allowing some capacities to flourish while others do not.[176] Implicit biases against persons with disabilities are also propagated because the social world is largely designed for and supportive of able-bodied people, often stigmatizing those who are not.[177] It is as if societies and their cultures were designed and formed around the presupposition that everything, including people, is to work and be productive according to a preconceived design plan.

To that end, ableism emerged as the social prejudice in favor of persons who are able-bodied. In its most fundamental state, ableism contends that the able body is better than the dis-abled, and anything other than a fully able body is considered broken. Ableist thinking conflates disability with disease, illness, and pain, and can adversely influence improvements to the human condition. According to Reynolds, ableism has been a central and unquestioned part of medicine across its history.[178]

The Medical Model: In Search of a Cure

Throughout most of history, the idea of disability has been a medical one. Whether the objective criteria of illness or injury resulted in rehabilitation or institutionalization for persons who were blind, deaf, or mentally ill, the biological explanation of the condition defined the person. Today, classifications of diseases become the labels attached to persons with conditions or disorders. For example, a person possessing the clinical characteristics of autism is considered autistic, just as one experiencing seizures from epilepsy is branded an epileptic. Such characterizations dehumanize, as they place the disorder ahead of the person. Inquiry into the person becomes not a question of who, but rather *what* they are. The description of the disorder presupposes the person's needs, their abilities, disabilities,[179] and values.

Because the *medical model* of disability views disability as a problem of the person directly caused by disease, trauma, or other health condition, addressing such biologic matters instinctively suggests medical care. According to Iezzoni and O'Day, the medical model relies on two assumptions. The first assumes that individuals will strive to *overcome* their disabilities, and the second presupposes clinicians know what is best for their patients.[180] This model of disability relies upon objective diagnostic criteria and observations that, per se, are not demeaning to the person. However, a person's needs are linearly connected to a clinically identified abnormality, which in the spirit of medicine, must be normalized.[181] When definition and diagnoses become synonymous with disabilities, we confront what Edmonds refers to as the "tyranny of normality."[182] In that regard, the medical model of disability is flawed in that the association of disease or disorder suggests that there is something wrong with the person that needs to be fixed, or cured.

Still and all, medicine has enabled significant breakthroughs in the treatment of conditions affecting individuals with disabilities, many of which have extended their lifespan. Advances in medical technology, including devices, pharmaceuticals, surgery, and the creation of new clinical care pathways have added years to lives. For example, due to multiple medical advances, the life expectancy of a person with Down syndrome has increased from 20 years in the 1980s to more than 60 years today.[183] Because of developments in cardiology, people with Becker muscular dystrophy are living decades longer in the twenty-first century.[184] Such life-extending advances improve with a clinical understanding of disease as well as diagnostic and therapeutic successes.[185] Nevertheless, the World Health Organization cautions that adding "years to life" is devoid of benefit without adding "life to years."[186] Lengthening life-expectancy without mitigating vulnerability and enabling flourishing merely transitions the person with a disability from one vulnerable stakeholder community to another.

Embodiment is the crux of the medical model. It defines the disability as a physical property of an individual that requires medical intervention, according to Tobin Siebers.[187] In essence, this model proposes a superficial distinction between disability and ability. Chiefly that disability is a medical matter, while ability concerns one's natural gifts, physical prowess, imagination, and the capacity and desire to strive, which is the essence of the human spirit.[188] Because the medicalization of disability holds that something is wrong with persons with disabilities, this model generally regards that they are the source of their own problem.[189] To the extent that they are underserved because they compete with other groups for resources, it is often because they are perceived as lacking ability.

This perception of inability materializes and very often translates into reality within the care environment. As a delivery mechanism for medicine, the healthcare setting according to disability advocate Alicia Oullette is "a dangerous and difficult place" from the perspective of disability.[190] Those with mobility limitations may have difficulty entering exam rooms, using physical examination tables, or mammography and other imaging equipment.[191] Communication issues are also associated with general access issues, but also relate to the ability or inability of the care provider to recognize the person's capacity to hear or understand what is being said.[192]

Oullette further contends that bioethicists perpetuate the problem by applying decision-making frameworks that legitimate biases, especially when determining appropriateness of medical technology to promote health and maintain life. She argues that they rely on assessments of health, medical appropriateness, quality of life, and familial best interests to justify decision-making for persons with disabilities. Factors which ignore the unique cultural, social, and personal aspects of the disability.[193] They are often assessed from the paternalistic perspective of the non-disabled bioethicist, clinician, or physician, supported by the medical model undercurrent that the defect must be cured if the person is to achieve full capacity as a human being.[194]

The distinction between cure and healing is frequently blurred. When the word *cure* appears in the English language, it typically refers to the elimination of a disease and its symptoms.[195] A cure is sought in order that a person may be restored to the same health and physical condition as before the disease appeared, or as if it had not appeared at all. If a cure seeks to eliminate disease and suffering, it must be distinguished from *healing* which, as Nancy Lane asserts, is a *process* of integration and wholeness and not simply being free from illness and is not necessarily a physical manifestation. According to Lane, healing is letting go of false and unrealistic expectations. Healing allows one to live with a disability rather than suffer from it.[196] Healing brings about grace, peace, and well-being and often involves finding a sense of meaning and purpose – a spiritual wholeness, but not necessarily a cure.[197] Accordingly, a healing may or may not include a cure, and a cure clearly does not ensure a healing.

Because society traditionally perceives healing very narrowly and typically recognizes it only in the physical improvements and manifestations of those persons with an easily detectable disorder or disability, its inclination is to follow only the physical effects of the healing or cure. This tendency severely limits how society ought to see the collateral, life-affirming, impact to the able-bodied as well as disabled persons who are spiritually healed, even in the absence of a cure. To find a cure, society turns to the medical arts. Spiritual and religious traditions espouse the view that humans can intervene as stewards of the faith and co-creators of life to cure *and* heal, seeing medical professionals as God's agents on earth.[198]

It is in society's best interest to place a high value on health and well-being, to value good health over ill-health, and to reduce morbidity and improve overall health. However, as Wilkinson argues, placing a high value on good health, should not conclude that those who are ill or live with a disability are valued less. The value of health cannot mean that less value is accorded to those who are impaired. Important to this is the objective reality that one who is disabled is not necessarily unhealthy. A particular impairment may be unassociated with any disease pathology. While presumably most people would prefer being able-bodied to being disabled, and healthy rather than unhealthy, the reality is that much of what is considered *normal* and *able*, and the attitudes about certain illnesses are subject to normative belief.[199]

The medical model provides truly little, if any, understanding of the descriptive realities of disability, and there is little incentive to investigate beyond what it takes to fix the impairment. Moreover, the medical model misses the universality of disability. Failing to see the ubiquity of disability is incongruous with the reality that even the most robust members of society are only temporarily able; in time, all are broken to some degree.[200] So, a principle issue for contemporary society seeking to improve the human condition is whether it is right to judge what it means to be healthy, normal, and able; and in particular to determine the state of any future person by eliminating disability through genetic intervention.

Genetic Interventions: A Search for
Perfection or Path to Flourishing?

Cultural and societal attitudes shape which human characteristics are considered *normal* and *abnormal*. However, applying a medical model that relies on the human genetic code can prescribe a predictable baseline of what are considered *healthy* genetic characteristics. Influenced by the principles of beneficence and autonomy genetic technology and medicine undergird the duty to improve the human condition by preventing mortality, morbidity, and disability.[201] This is so because genetic technology has the capacity to fundamentally change human nature by preventing the birth of certain persons who may have a disease or disorder for which there is no cure.[202] Understanding the societal impacts and the human practices that result from genetic technology[203] is an imperative that must begin by examining its deep roots in the evolution of eugenics.

The term *eugenic* was coined in the late nineteenth century by Sir Francis Galton to refer to those who were *well-born* and was applied to the study of heredity.[204] For Galton, Charles Darwin's cousin, heredity centered on discovering ways to improve the genetic makeup of the human race by removing undesirable individuals from the societal gene pool. These early studies and well-funded eugenic movements in the United States clearly did not reflect the American principle that all men are created equal. Yet, the U.S. Supreme Court decision in 1927 upholding the eradication all "imbeciles" through forced sterilization bolstered and fortified this movement.[205] Henceforth, it became an obligation and reproductive duty of all good citizens who were the "right type," to leave behind their blood in the world through procreation, and to prevent the "wrong type" of person from reproducing. Forced sterilization laws mandated prisoners, residents of mental facilities and paupers – those deemed manifestly unfit – be irreversibly prohibited from reproducing. [206]

It was not until Hitler's perverse world of eugenics, genocide, and mass murder resulted in the systematic execution of those persons classified as "defective" that the American eugenics movement began to die. Eventually, any association with Nazi eugenics was shunned. However today, eugenic-like conduct has been reintroduced into American culture. In contemporary times, eugenics is typically characterized as a study of the conditions under which the human condition or the biological character of humans can be improved. For Wilkinson, it is not whether eugenics expressed in this manner is intrinsically wrong, but rather, whether a particular form of eugenics is morally acceptable or not.[207]

Often influenced by political and social controls, *positive eugenics* occurs when the goal of a eugenic activity is to produce humans of high quality by increasing the good gene pool – to enhance the human condition. And *negative eugenics* seeks to reduce undesirable genes that cause disease and disability – to prevent harm to humanity by minimizing the number of sick babies born.[208] The dichotomy of eugenics and the motivating factors each type determines whether disability is seen as a defect requiring enhancement or elimination, a condition that seeks healing, or as an illness seeking a cure.

Mahowald contends that negative eugenics under the guise of genetic advances appear largely through prenatal testing, the killing of embryos, and abortion of fetuses with genetic disorders. This is evidenced in the way that the presence of the single trait of Down syndrome or other chromosomal anomaly has come to define the whole person in utero without ever getting to know the rest of the person.[209] To that end, Jeffrey Bishop contends that the objectifying tools of medicine – ultrasounds, prenatal testing, and screenings – reduce the disabled fetus to a faceless object in the womb.[210] It is in this sense that modern medicine, in its endeavor to prevent the coming of a person, leans toward negative eugenics. It is also in this way that the person born with a genetic anomaly and functional disability is vulnerable to becoming a dehumanized dysfunctional object.[211]

For some opponents like Joseph, prenatal testing is a form of backdoor eugenics, and for others like David Wasserman, genetic technology could be used irresponsibly to deliberately create children with disabilities.[212] Such selective impairment is controversial and uncommon, but not fictional or imaginary, as shown by the McCullough and Duchesneau case involving an American deaf lesbian couple who deliberately selected a congenitally deaf sperm donor to successfully give birth to a deaf daughter.[213] Wasserman also maintains that preconception and prenatal selection are incompatible with the unconditional welcome that parents should exhibit toward their unborn child.[214] Ethicists who argue against eliminating disability aptly contend that genetically screening out and deselecting disability, or even attempting to correct characteristics of disability in the absence of a diagnosis, advances the view that the objectified person is unfit. Such beliefs may be projected onto the persons themselves. And even ethicists who support negative eugenics admit that continued efforts to reduce the number of sick babies will increase the list of unfit characteristics, qualities, and conditions to be eliminated, further propagating discriminatory ableism.

Contemporary eugenics, particularly selective reproductive techniques such as preimplantation genetic diagnosis (PGD) emboldens preconceived notions about what kind of life is desirable versus those that are less meaningful, have less purpose, and deemed unworthy to live.[215] For Wilkinson, the notion that deselecting embryos that are believed to carry a disabling condition to avoid creating a low-quality life is unacceptable. He asserts that the happiest person with a disability will likely experience a better quality of life than the most miserable able-bodied person.[216] Wilkinson further contends that selective reproduction such as PGD and prenatal testing accompanied by selective termination presents the risk children are commodified, discarded, and replaced with a more desirable variety.[217] Similarly, Paul Ramsey considers all forms of genetic control unethical arguing that positive eugenics suffers from cultural influences determining normalcy and defect. Instead, he favors limited negative eugenics through voluntary childlessness and avoiding pregnancy altogether if a known genetic predisposition existed. Taken further, some ethicists see eugenics as genetics in the absence of religious thought.[218] On balance, however, not all efforts to improve the human condition through genetic interventions carry the indicia of negative eugenics.

Although it is possible to improve the human condition and create opportunities for people to flourish in the absence of biological interventions, disease avoidance typically involves some physical interventions. Properly administered screening techniques, to preemptively identify conditions to determine the probability of having a child with a hereditary condition can improve the lives of children with certain conditions.[219]

Newborn screenings detect and provide early intervention health benefits and treatments for more than 30 genetic diseases and abnormalities. Pre-symptomatic identification and diagnosis can help to establish early intervention treatments and can avoid a diagnostic odyssey once actual symptoms present.[220] To that end, newborn screening provides a mechanism for human flourishing which serves to avoid needless suffering for newborn children and their families to improve the human condition without controversy. They also help shape parents' future reproductive decisions.

As partners in care, and because they wield enormous power over the care and treatment of persons with disabilities[221] ethically accountable healthcare organizations and their clinician leadership play a crucial role in these decisions. Their influence on the human condition extends beyond the constraints imposed by the medical model of disability. As such, their influence and actions should be shaped by adopting ethics of care and disability ethics frameworks to enable flourishing lives.

Creating Enabling Environments Through Ethics of Care and Disability Ethics

Joel Reynolds attributes negative health outcomes, ill-conceived state and federal policies, oppression, discrimination, and stigmatization of persons with disabilities to clinician misunderstanding of disability and the resultant miscommunication between them. He argues that anyone who wants to improve their understanding as well as improve health outcomes must first reflect upon "the meaning of disability and the moral obligation and responsibilities owed to communities of disabilities."[222] The medical model of disability, with its reliance on medical description and labeling, is largely responsible for much this knowledge gap. Pathology alone does not prepare the healthcare professional to contribute to a flourishing life for patients with disabilities. Transforming healthcare leadership in this milieu begins by examining its moral obligation through the lens of ethics of care and disability ethics.

For Jackie Leach Scully, there are two ways to consider disability in terms of ethics. She distinguishes the ethics of disability from disability ethics. For Scully, the *ethics of disability* reflects upon the morally correct way to behave toward persons with disabilities in everyday interactions such as employment policy, law, and healthcare.[223] An example of the ethics of disability is ensuring that restrooms are outfitted with automated entrances to accommodate employees using wheelchairs. The ethics of disability implicates normative moral behavior based on what has been determined necessary and appropriate for persons with a disability. It derives its normative standards from the medicalized view that disability is a nominative pathology; that is, a deficit that is determined by reference to a norm of physical or mental function.[224]

Offering a differentiating view, Scully refers to *disability ethics* as "the particular moral understandings that are generated through the experience of disability."[225] That is to say, it is a form of ethical analysis that is "consciously and conscientiously attentive to the experience of being/having a 'different' embodiment… disability ethics looks at the embodied effects of impairment." [226] In contrast to the earlier example, disability ethics considers the experiences of the employee who uses a wheelchair to make certain that social settings are configured to allow them to converse at eye-level with others rather than being looked down upon. Understanding disability through the experience of one with a disability provides insight into the judgments of the moral issues in disability communities.

Scully advocates undertaking a phenomenological approach to understanding the embodied experiences of persons with disabilities.[227] Unless and until ethical analysis moves beyond merely understanding the features of disability, and toward the perceptions and understanding of the world of disability, Reynolds' gap of understanding and attendant biases will persist. Assimilating the experiences of persons with disabilities into a culture of disability ethics entails starting from a collective perspective on the giftedness and of every person, explicitly those persons with disabilities.

The Gift of a Flourishing Life

To live and thrive within an optimal range of functioning does not require physical or cognitive perfection. It first entails embracing all life as a gift through acceptance, tolerance, and stewardship that capacitates a good and flourishing human life. A good life that enables human flourishing is measured and enriched by the experiences, opportunities, and even the choices available to that person. Hans Reinders asserts that what accounts for having a good life is not whether a person would choose to live their life again, if given the choice. But rather, such account is found in the recognition that their life is good because merely *being* is in itself good.[228]

Most religious traditions espouse that life is good because it is given with divine intentionality, and cannot, therefore, be anything but good. The goodness of life is a gift of divine goodness – a *donum*; a gift and giftedness that has a divine purpose.[229] Life as a gift is received from God who intended it to be good and is grounded extrinsically in God's act of giving.[230] The goodness of life, therefore, is preordained because of its giftedness.

The goodness of human life turns to humanity's willingness to learn how to acknowledge giftedness and find peace with it. God's gift of life cannot be returned if it isn't exactly what was desired or doesn't quite align with normative beliefs. Gracious recipients of gifts know that the highest compliment a person can pay the giver is to show gratitude, and to love, protect, and care for the gift. This good and great gift of human life was created by God and given to humanity to guard and protect, and to be its stewards.[231] And so it is that the highest expression of gratitude a human can give God is to thoroughly respect and care for their good life,[232] and empower it to thrive.

Recognition of giftedness is empowering to persons with disabilities. Scarlet fever left Helen Keller deaf and blind at 19 months-of-age. Yet her life story is "a paragon of several key virtues…that commonly constitute a good life: courage, strength, resiliency, self-knowledge, compassion, and wisdom."[233] Despite immeasurable odds, her life's triumphs included achieving academic excellence at the most prestigious universities. Empowered by her experiences as a woman with disabilities, she established the American Civil Liberties Union, and exemplified a life of advocacy and inspiration. Her life was not something to be judged against the idealized norm of a life typically stifled by such debilitating limitations. That is, Keller did not flourish as a disabled woman. She flourished as a person first. It was the context of her disability – its giftedness – that made her flourishing what it was.[234]

Autism is not a barrier to flourishing for William Stillman. An award-winning author and internationally recognized autism support advocate, Stillman is the founder of the Pennsylvania Autism Self-Advocacy Coalition. He has educated state and federal government leaders and program sponsors, as well as families and caregivers, on the giftedness of persons with autism. As a writer with Asperger's Syndrome, his works have illuminated the giftedness of persons with autism by telling their stories of extraordinary spirituality and sensory capacities that very often exceed those of persons not on the autism spectrum.[235] He describes how an inability to produce verbal speech is not a barrier to communication for persons with autism who may understand dormant telepathic intuitions by merely observing the verbally communicative world.[236] Keller and Stillman's lives exemplify the giftedness that is made manifest through disability. Their victories, in harmony with their giftedness, afford communities the opportunity to celebrate and embrace them as such.

As all of humanity are called to be co-creators with God, the duty to respect and care for the giftedness of the good lives of others is obligatory. The faithful recognize their duty to be stewards for Creation and improve the human condition through activities that demonstrate a continual respect for human life. In the context of disability, it is a communal imperative that calls everyone to accept the giftedness of the disability "without resentment, receiving and giving love as companions together in God's time."[237] Improving the human condition of disability by receiving the gift of life in this way involves the collective willingness of persons and groups. It calls upon the receptivity of the person with the disability, the community in which they live, and those who care for them. Illustrated this way, acknowledging the giftedness of life is triune as it is interdependent on the presence of God within each of those three bodies of persons.

William May further illustrates this unity of persons as one centered on proclaiming the Gospel of Life by caring for others for whom God has made humanity responsible.[238] To proclaim the Gospel of Life in this way requires communities to enter into a relationship with and empower and support people who suffer or are otherwise vulnerable; particularly in this context, persons with disabilities. In confronting the moral duty of the HCO, May contends that "a unique responsibility belongs to health-care personnel: doctors, pharmacists, nurses, chaplains… administrators and volunteers" and those in relation, to build a new culture of life that considers the inviolable worth of every human life.[239]

For Eva Feder Kittay, persons with disabilities should remain associated with those connections and relationships that have infused their life with value. In the same way, others in relationship with persons with disabilities should not see themselves as separate from them. The carer and cared-for coexist within an inextricable bond that defines and nurtures the dignity of the persons.[240] Moreover, whether care is given or received, is an indispensable and central good. And for Kittay, it is impossible to have a life of dignity without care – it is an expression of a person's dignity.[241]

Disability draws forth the reality of mutual dependency – or *interdependency* – between the carer and the cared-for. Just as the ethically accountable HCO is an interdependent construct, its normative stakeholders are also interdependent and rely upon the relational quality of their human interactions with providers of care. To that end, care and interdependency undergird the ethics of care in disability. As Kittay beautifully portrays, "giving care to another infuses the other with the worth of the one who does the caring – to do damage to the cared-for is also to violate the caring individual."[242]

By its very nature then, the ethical accountability of HCO leadership, specifically concerning its clinicians, researchers, and providers of care, must see themselves as "selves-in-relation" to their patients and other stakeholders with disabilities. These providers of care must come to understand that their sense of well-being is also tied to the care and well-being of another.[243] Over and above the imperative of interdependency, the moral duty to protect and care for the vulnerable rests with those who are most empowered, and especially those to whom a person is most vulnerable.[244] For Kittay, authority and power to care for the vulnerable is paramount because "providers of care…have to co-exist with the individuals they care for…they exert direct control over the minutiae of the life of their charge."[245] Hence, their moral duty to enable flourishing and effectuate change in the lives of persons with disabilities is unequivocal.

Ethics and Removing Disabling Barriers

Persons with disabilities, as part of the human condition, are contextually vulnerable. They are so in part because they are the "product of a social response to embodied difference, not just as an individual pathology."[246] This social response is the central point of the *social model of disability*. In contrast to the medical model, the social model "shifts attention from a medical description of a person to a consideration of how the environment creates obstacles for people who have disabilities." It purports that society's social, political, and physical arrangements need fixed, not the person with the disability. [247] For Scully, the social model suggests that disability is a product of the interaction, at both personal and structural levels, between the physical or mental impairment and the social world in which the affected person lives.[248] To illustrate simply, it is not the mobility impairment that prevents the person in a wheelchair from entering a doctor's office for care; it is the absence of wheelchair ramps. Even more significantly, it is the gap in understanding the experiences and preferences of that person. It is the absence of knowing what matters most. And to that end, the social model of disability anticipates a commitment from society and its accountable members to promote mutual understanding and effectuate change.

According to Tobin Siebers' perspective of the social model, disability is not reduced to a physical or mental defect but is rather a cultural and minority identity. For Siebers, to refer to disability as an identity means that it is "an elastic social category both subject to social control and capable of effectuating change."[249] That is to say, that the cultural and minority identity of disability is powered by a force and a voice that can either be effective and audible, or stifled and disempowered. As with other minority identities, disability suffers from negative connotations, such as ableism. Healthcare leaders have a moral obligation to comprehend the effects of the social model of disability on the community of persons with disabilities they serve, and to reverse these negative connotations through their actions, and by innovating for change.

Michael Oliver posits a most determined social model argument, asserting that illness may be caused by disease, and impairment by some injury or condition, but disability is caused by social organization.[250] According to this analysis of the social model, social organizations create disability and disadvantageous conditions when they discriminate through ignorance, exclusion, and isolation. The inability to participate in mainstream social activities is deemed the fault of society, culture, and the environment; not that of the underlying condition or impairment.[251] Oliver's assessment of the social model does not ignore the significance of impairment on the fulfillment of human flourishing and does not diminish the importance of medicine or therapeutics. On the contrary, this model acknowledges that the disabling condition is in many ways due to the lack of medical and related services[252] that ought to be provided through social constructs, and by persons with authority to further a culture of life.

Building a culture of life must consider other impediments to flourishing that can be influenced and even deconstructed by those with authority. For example, just as social determinants of health contribute to disparities in access to healthcare, they can also impact access to employment, education, and other aspects of life. Wilkinson submits that social determinants of health such as poverty, poor schooling, and environmental causes can particularly impede flourishing for those with disabilities.[253]

Statistics show that individuals with disabilities are more likely to have trouble securing employment, receive preventive healthcare services, and gain access to and use health information technology, compared to those without disabilities.[254] These determinants coupled with environmental conditions and barriers, amplify the disparities, and compound the negative impact to flourishing. The World Health Organization established recommended principles to address key issues to achieve health equity among persons with disabilities and to mitigate impediments to flourishing. These include the need for better health data to inform program development concerning critical issues of health disparity. The issues also include the need for evidence-based health and wellness programs that can be transferred from clinical settings to community-based programs to promote greater access; and the need to improve facility/environmental designs and public and private infrastructures.[255] Instituting these principles to serve as a catalyst for change involves the explicit and affirmative obligation of ethically accountable healthcare professionals.

Given the interdependency that is inherent in the relationship between the provider of healthcare and the person with disabilities, the effectiveness of that relationship first calls for reconciliation between the experiences of the disability community, and awareness of its healthcare providers. For Oullette, establishing an informed *disability-conscious* requires that the healthcare community engage in civil discourse with disability scholars, advocates, and experts to understand the cultural and social dimension of disability.[256] Although Oullette's work centers specifically on disability-consciousness in bioethics, the framework she suggests for developing disability-consciousness is adaptable to the care provider and social communities. She contends that carers ought to incorporate principles such as respect for inherent dignity in all decision and action points, including, for example, avoiding language and terminology that offends such as "abnormal" and "normal."[257]

Clinicians also have responsibilities to develop what Reynolds refers to as a *disability humility*. Such humility is directed to learning about the experiences, cultures, and history of disabilities. It also entails a willingness to admit that understanding the dynamic condition of disability will never be complete.[258] Studies show that physicians may be poorly prepared to meet the medical and psychosocial needs of this community that are required to create environments that support good care and positive experiences[259] because they lack formal training. The absence of life span perspective on care is particularly evident when patients with disabilities transition from pediatric care to adult care physicians. Moreover, "clinicians and members of society at large have a responsibility to educate themselves about disability and actively work against the effects of ableism that have long undermined the justice and effectiveness of health care delivery."[260] This responsibility mirrors the cultural humility required to understand the pediatric and older adult communities.

Embracing disability humility, clinicians will improve their ability to communicate more effectively with their patients with disabilities. Their deference to the disability perspective will also enhance their willingness and ability to listen.

And they will come to appreciate and respect the authority of those with disabilities as experts about their own lives and community experiences.[261] Disability humility will help to lift the voices of those with disabilities far above the barriers that very often silence them.

Removing the barriers to flourishing is a matter of collaboration. It calls for initiating enabling environments that respect the identity of disability, reverse negative thinking and ableism, understand the culture of disability, and promote access to care that is dignified and welcomed. In the traditional model of care, the relationship between clinicians and patients promotes clinicians as experts in what is best for their patients, and patients as passive to their direction. This paternalistic posture intensifies the vulnerability of patients with disabilities. The collaborative care model, however, departs from this traditional view.[262]

According to this model, clinicians and patients share their expertise. Clinicians are experts in diseases and conditions, and patients are experts concerning their own lives and preferences.[263] Together they identify problems, issues, and health management matters and collaboratively set goals that are jointly managed. They share responsibility and work interdependently, however, clinicians teach patients how do self-manage their worlds to help them flourish independently, as much as possible.[264] Collaboration in this way not only unleashes the voices of persons with disabilities, but it also admits to their rights and responsibilities, their individual and collective identities, and their capacity to flourish in right relationship with their environment.

Conclusion

While vulnerability is an ontological condition that impacts all beings across the human life continuum, consequences and conditions render certain stakeholder populations more susceptible to physical, social, emotional, and economic harms. Vulnerability is amplified by aggravating influences such as biases, negative public policy trends, societal and cultural pressures, and barriers to flourishing within certain environments. The healthcare setting is one such environment that, very often, intensifies human vulnerability. Because individuals and organizations with authority and power to impact the lives of at-risk populations have a moral duty to attend to their interests, improving the human condition for vulnerable stakeholders is a moral imperative of the ethically accountable healthcare organization.

Older adults and persons with disabilities are particularly vulnerable normative stakeholders who are often victimized by disempowering and discriminatory biases that threaten their dignity, deny them needed healthcare and services, and prevent them from flourishing. Cultural, political, and medical models can bolster and promote ageist and ableist tendencies that adversely influence opportunities to meet the unmet long-term care needs of older persons and create barriers for persons with disabilities. While medical advances and technologies have made it possible for both stakeholder groups to add years to their lives, the challenge for accountable healthcare professionals is to ensure that those years are filled with lives that flourish.

To enable and empower these vulnerable individuals to experience a life that preserves human dignity, autonomy, and respect for the giftedness of all human life, policymakers and healthcare communities must focus on the interdependency and interconnectedness of care. To that end, ethically justified care for older persons must shift its focus to community-based interdependent relationships. Relationships that support low-technology, informal care standards based on the ethic of care.

Improving the human condition for persons with disabilities entails recognition that the goodness of human life is not determined by physical or mental perfection, but rather by its giftedness. The giftedness of human life requires acceptance of the responsibilities that all have to one another as stewards in relationships of care. It also requires recognition of the mutual dependency between the one providing care and the one to whom it is provided. The interdependency that is inherent in the relationship between the provider and the person with disabilities calls for the provider community to establish a disability consciousness that is strengthened by disability humility.

Healthcare is about relationships. Relationships which, as they span the life continuum, are comprised of unlimited interactions and care experiences that represent the dependency of all human life upon one another. The objective truth is that no one exists who has not been cared for. For the human condition to continue to evolve and improve, the ethically accountable healthcare organization must remain in relation with its most vulnerable stakeholders to satisfy their needs, and to ensure that their moral response is cloaked in care.

Notes

1. Jasmine R. Marcelin, Dawd S. Siraj, Robert Victor, Shaila Kotadia, and Yvonne Maldonado, "The Impact of Unconscious Bias in Healthcare: How to Recognize It and Mitigate It," in *The Journal of Infectious Disease*, 220 (Suppl. 2), 2019, S63.
2. Karol Charles, *Aging in America. A Cautionary Tale of Wrongful Death in Elder Care*. (Senior Care Publishing, LLC. 2018), 3.
3. V. Tellis-Nayak and Mary Tellis-Nayak, *Return of Compassion to Health Care*. (New York, NY: Cambridge University Press, 2010), 40.
4. Ruth O'Brien, *Crippled Justice. The History of Modern Disability Policy in the Workplace*. (Chicago, IL: The University of Chicago Press, 2001), 1.
5. Joseph W. Weiss, *Business Ethics: A Stakeholder and Issues Management Approach. Cases, Principles and Practices*, 6th edition (San Francisco, CA: Berrett-Koehler Publishers, Inc.), 12.
6. Regula H. Robnett, "The Cognitive and Psychological Changes Associated With Aging," in *Gerontology for the Health Care Professional*. 2nd edition, ed. Regula H. Robnett and Walter C. Chop (Sudbury, MA: Jones and Bartlett Publishers, 2010), 117.
7. Martha B. Holstein, Jennifer A. Parks, and Mark H. Waymack, *Ethics, Aging and Society: The Critical Turn*, (New York, NY: Springer Publishing Company, 2011), 104.
8. Shane Clifton, *Crippled Justice. Disability. Virtue Ethics, and the Good Life*, (Waco, TX: Baylor University Press, 2018), 122.
9. World Health Organization, *World Report on Disability*, 2011, 3.
10. Eva Feder Kittay, "The Ethics of Care, Dependence, and Disability," in *Ratio Juris*. (March 2011) vol. 24, no.1.54.

11. Eva Feder Kittay, "The Ethics of Care, Dependence, and Disability," 52.
12. Nancy Brossoie, "Social Gerontology," in *Gerontology for the Health Care Professional.* 2nd edition, ed. Regula H. Robnett and Walter C. Chop (Sudbury, MA: Jones and Bartlett Publishers, 2010), 21.
13. Hajime Orimo, Hidecki Ito, Takao Suzuki, Atsuchi Araki, Takayuki Hosoi, and Motoji Sawabe, "Reviewing the Definition of "Elderly," in *Geriatrics and Gerontology International,* (February 2006), 149, https://doi:10.111/j.1447–0594.2006.00341.x.
14. Orimo, et al., "Reviewing the Definition of Elderly," 149.
15. Judith G. Gonyea, "The Oldest Old and a Long-Lived Society. Challenges for Public Policy," in *The New Politics of Old Age Policy,* 2nd edition, ed. R. Hudson, (Baltimore, MD: The Johns Hopkins University Press, 2010), 183.
16. U.S. Department of Health and Human Services, Administration for Community Living, 2017 Profile of Older Americans, 2.
17. U.S. Department of Health and Human Services, 2017 Profile of Older Americans, 2.
18. Gonyea, "The Oldest Old and a Long-Lived Society. Challenges for Public Policy, 186–187.
19. Mary Ann Forcia, "History of Medicine. Geriatric Medicine: History of a Young Specialty," in *American Medical Association Journal of Ethics,* May 2014, vol. 16, no. 5 (May 2014): 385–386.
20. Brossoie, "Social Gerontology," in *Gerontology for the Health Care Professional,* 20–21.
21. Marcelin et al, "The Impact of Unconscious Bias in Healthcare: How to Recognize It and Mitigate It," S63.
22. Richard Currey, "Ageism in Healthcare: Time for a Change," in *Aging Well,* vol. 1, no. 1. Winter 2008, 16.
23. Holstein, Parks, and Waymack, *Ethics, Aging and Society,* 175.
24. Brossoie, "Social Gerontology," 21.
25. John F. Kilner, "Why Now? The Growing Interest in Limiting the Lifesaving Health Care Resources Available to Elderly People," in *Choosing Who's to Live. Ethics and Aging,* ed. J.W. Walters. (Chicago, IL: University of Illinois Press, 1996), 140.
26. Mary F. Wyman, Sharon Shiovitz-Ezra, and Jurgen Bengal, "Ageism in the Health Care System: Providers, Patients and Systems," in *Contemporary Perspectives on Ageism,* ed. L. Ayalon, and C. Tesch-Romer, (2018), 199–198, https://doi.org/10.008/978-3-319-73820-8_13.
27. Currey, "Ageism in Healthcare: Time for a Change," 17.
28. Holstein, Parks, and Waymack, *Ethics, Aging and Society. The Critical Turn,* 178.
29. Wyman, Shiovitz-Ezra, and Bengal, "Ageism in the Health Care System: Providers, Patients and Systems," 197.
30. Wyman, Shiovitz-Ezra, and Bengal, "Ageism in the Health Care System: Providers, Patients and Systems," 194.
31. Elisabeth Schroder-Butterfill and Ruly Marianti, "A Framework for Understanding Old-Age Vulnerabilities," in *Aging Society* 26 (1), January 2006:16, doi: 10.1017/S0144686X050044423.
32. Elisabeth Schroder-Butterfill and Ruly Marianti, "A Framework for Understanding Old-Age Vulnerabilities," 11.
33. Catriona Mackenzie, Wendy Rogers, and Susan Dodds, eds. Introduction: What Is Vulnerability, and Why Does It Matter for Moral Theory?" in *Vulnerability. New Essays in Ethics, and Feminist Philosophy,* (New York, NY: Oxford University Press, 2014), 25.
34. Gonyea, "The Oldest Old and a Long-Lived Society," 192, 195.
35. Liz Seegert, "U.S. Ranks Worse in Elder Care vs. Other Wealthy Nations," In *Association of Health Care Journalists. Center for Excellence in Health Care Journalism,* November 15, 2017, 1.

36. Nancy C. Jecker, "Caring for the Disabled Elderly. The Economics and Ethics of Financing Long-Term Care," in *Choosing Who's To Live. Ethics and Aging*, ed. James W. Walters, (Chicago: University of Illinois Press, 1996), 75.
37. Walter C. Chop, "Demographic Trends of an Aging Society," in *Gerontology for the Health Care Professional*, 2nd edition, ed. Regula H. Robnett and Walter C. Chop, (Sudbury, MA: 2010), 7.
38. Jecker, "Caring for the Disabled Elderly: The Economics and Ethics of Financing Long-Term Care," 75–77.
39. U.S. Department of Health and Human Services, 2017 Profile of Older Americans, 2.
40. Gonyea, "The Oldest Old and a Long-Lived Society," 188.
41. U.S. Department of Health and Human Services, 2017 Profile of Older Americans, 4.
42. Holstein, Parks, and Waymack, *Ethics, Aging and Society: The Critical Turn*, 131.
43. Jecker, "Caring for the Disabled Elderly: The Economics and Ethics of Financing Long-Term Care" 77–78.
44. Kilner, "Why Now? The Growing Interest in Limiting the Lifesaving Health Care Resources Available to Elderly People," 127.
45. Ann O'Sullivan and Regula H, Robnett, "Living Options and the Continuum of Care," in *Gerontology for the Health Care Professional*, 2nd edition, ed. Regula H. Robnett and Walter C. Chop (Sudbury, MA: Jones and Bartlett Publishers, 2010), 273.
46. Gonyea, "The Oldest Old and a Long-Lived Society,"195–197.
47. Jecker, "Caring for the Disabled Elderly: The Economics and Ethics of Financing Long-Term Care, 73–76.
48. Gonyea, "The Oldest Old and a Long-Lived Society, 193.
49. Avedis Donabedian, "Quality of Care and the Health Needs of the Elderly Patient," in *Report of a Forum of the Council on Health Care Technology. Care of the Elderly Patient: Policy Issues and Research Opportunities*, ed. J.A. Barondess, D.E. Rodgers, and K.N. Lohr (Washington, DC: National Academy Press, 1989), 11.
50. O'Sullivan and Robnett, "Living Options and the Continuum of Care," 265.
51. O'Sullivan and Regula H. Robnett, "Living Options and the Continuum of Care," 262.
52. Holstein, Parks and Waymack, *Ethics, Aging and Society: The Critical Turn*, 125.
53. David Farrell, Cathie Brady, and Barbara Frank, *Meeting the Leadership Challenge in Long-Term Care. What You Do Matters*, (Baltimore, MD: Health Professions Press, 2011), xvii.
54. Holstein, Parks and Waymack, *Ethics, Aging and Society: The Critical Turn*, 103–105.
55. George P. Smith, *The Elderly and Health Care Rationing*, 7 *Pierce L Rev.* 172 (2009).
56. George P. Smith, "The Elderly and Health Care Rationing," 172.
57. Catholic Health Association, *With Justice for All? The Ethics of Healthcare Rationing*, (St. Louis, MO: Catholic Health Association of the United States, 1991). Ix.
58. Norman Daniels, *Justice Between the Young and the Old: Rationing from an International Perspective* in *Choosing Who's to Live. Ethics and Aging*, ed. J.W. Walters (Chicago: University of Illinois, 1989), x.
59. Smith, "The Elderly and Health Care Rationing," 175.
60. Smith, "The Elderly and Health Care Rationing," 175.
61. Paul T. Menzel, *The Justification and Implications of Age-Based Rationing*, in *Choosing Who's to Live. Ethics and Aging*, ed. J.W. Walters (Chicago, University of Illinois, 1996), 3.
62. Norman Daniels, *Just Health. Meeting Health Needs Fairly*, (New York, NY: Cambridge University Press, 2008), 39.
63. George P. Smith II, "The Elderly and Health Care Rationing," 171.
64. Daniels, *Just Health. Meeting Health Needs Fairly*, 26–34.
65. Daniels, *Just Health. Meeting Health Needs Fairly*, 35.
66. Menzel, *The Justification and Implications of Age-Based Rationing*, xi, 3–4.

67. J.W.Walters, ed., *Choosing Who's to Live. Ethics and Aging,* (Chicago, IL: University of Illinois, 1996), xii.
68. Kilner, "Why Now? The Growing Interest in Limiting the Lifesaving Health Care Resources Available to Elder People," 124–125.
69. Kilner, "Why Now? The Growing Interest in Limiting the Lifesaving Health Care Resources Available to Elder People," 123.
70. Kilner, "Why Now? The Growing Interest in Limiting Lifesaving Health Care Resources Available to Elder People," 124.
71. Catholic Health Association, *With Justice for All? The Ethics of Healthcare Rationing,* 7–9.
72. Jecker, "Caring for the Disabled Elderly: The Economics and Ethics of Financing Long-Term Care," 74.
73. Avedis Donabedian, "Quality of Care and Health Needs of the Elderly Patient," 10.
74. Claire Noel-Miller, "Medicare Beneficiaries' Out-of-Pocket Spending for Health Care," in Insight on the Issues, 151. AARP Public Policy (June 20), 2. https://doi.org/10.26419/ppi.00105.001.
75. Holstein, Parks and Waymack, *Ethics, Aging and Society: The Critical Turn,* 130.
76. Holstein, Parks and Waymack, *Ethics, Aging and Society: The Critical Turn,* 107.
77. Holstein, Parks and Waymack, *Ethics, Aging and Society. The Critical Turn,* 106.
78. Family Caregiver Alliance. National Center on Caregiving. "Caregiver Statistics: Demographics," accessed December 28, 2019. https://www.caregiver.org.
79. "Total Medicare Spending from 1970–2018," accessed December 29, 2019 https://www.statista.com.
80. Muriel Gillick, *Old & Sick in America. The Journey through the Health Care System,* (Chapel Hill, NC: The University of North Carolina Press, 2017), 240.
81. U.S. Department of Health and Human Services, Centers for Medicare and Medicaid Services, (2014) *42 CFR §§ 430–447.*
82. American Council on Aging, "Medicaid and Home Health Care and Non-Medical, In-Home Care, https://www.medicaidplanningassistance.org/in-home-care/. (January 28, 2021).
83. American Council on Aging, https://www.MedicaidPlanningAssistance.org/medicaid-eligibility-pennsylvania.
84. Jecker, "Caring for the Disabled Elderly: The Economics and Ethics of Financing Long-Term Care," 81.
85. Sandra B. Levitsky, "Caregiving and the Construction of Political Claims for Long-Term Care Policy Reform," in *The New Politics of Old Age Policy,* 2nd edition, ed. Robert B. Hudson (Baltimore, MD: Johns Hopkins University Press, 2010), 222–223.
86. Leonard J. Weber "The Healthcare Organization as Employer: The Demands of Fairness and the Healthcare Organization," in *Managerial Ethics in Healthcare: A New Perspective,* edited by G.L. Filerman, A.E. Mills, P.m. Shyve (Chicago, IL: Health Administration Press, 2014), 177.
87. Marice Ashe, Dora Barilla, Eileen Barsi and Stepanie Cihon, "A Systems Thinking Approach to the Social Determinants of Health," in *Stakeholder Health. Insights from New Systems of Health,* ed. Teresa F. Cutts and James R. Cochrane. (Winston-Salem, NC: Stakeholder Health), 2016, 10.
88. Holstein, Parks and Waymack, *Ethics, Aging and Society. The Critical Turn,* 115.
89. C. Tellis-Nayak and Mary Tellis-Nayak, *Return of Compassion to Health Care,* (New York, NY: PAGE Publishing, Inc., 2016), 140.
90. Holstein, Parks and Waymack, *Ethics, Aging and Society,* 118.
91. George P. Smith, "The Elderly and Health Care Rationing," 181.
92. Ruth E. Groenhout, *Interconnected Lives. Human Nature and the Ethics of Care,* (Lanham, MD: Rowman and Littlefield Publishers, Inc., 2004), 24.
93. Ruth E. Groenhout, *Interconnected Lives. Human Nature and the Ethics of Care,* 24.
94. Nel Noddings, *The Maternal Factor. Two Paths to Morality,* (Berkley, CA: University of California, 2010), 28.

95. Carol Gilligan, *Joining the Resistance*, (Cambridge, UK: Polity Press, 2011), 23.
96. Virginia Held, *The Ethics of Care. Personal, Political and Global*, (Oxford, UK: Oxford University Press, 2006), 29.
97. Noddings, *The Maternal Factor: Two Paths to Morality*, 28.
98. Noddings, *The Maternal Factor. Two Paths to Morality*, 130.
99. Linus Vanlaere and Chris Gastmans, "A Personalist Approach to Care Ethics," in *Nurse Ethics* 18 (2011), 169. https://www.doi:10.1177/0969733010388924.
100. Vanlaere and Gastmans, "A Personalist Approach to Care Ethics," 18, 172.
101. Saurabh Ram Bihar Lal Shrivastava, Prateek Saurabh Shrivastava, and Jegadeesh Ramasamy, "Health-care of Elderly: Determinants, Needs and Services," in *International Journal of Preventive Medicine* 10 (October 4, 2013), 1224.
102. Ruth E. Groenhout, *Interconnected Lives. Human Nature and the Ethics of Care*, 24.
103. Kilner, "Why Now? The Growing Interest in Limiting Lifesaving Health Care Resources Available to Elder People," 138.
104. Germain Kopaczynski, O.F. M. "Totality and Integrity," in *Catholic Health Care Ethics: A Manual for Practitioners*, eds. E.J. Furton, P.J. Cataldo, and A.S Moraczewski (Philadelphia: The National Catholic Bioethics Center, 2009) 13.
105. Albert S. Moraczewski, "The Human Person and the Church's Teaching," in *Catholic Health Care Ethics: A Manual for Practitioners* ed. E.J. Furton, P.J. Cataldo, and A.S. Moraczewski (Philadelphia: The National Catholic Bioethics Center, 2009) 6.
106. Moraczewski, "The Human Person and the Church's Teaching,"4.
107. Gillick, *Old & Sick in America. The Journey through the Health Care System*, 17.
108. E. Haavi Morreim, *Balancing Act. The New Medical Ethics of Medicine's New Economics*, 131.
109. Holstein, Parks and Waymack, *Ethics, Aging and Society. The Critical Turn*, 12–14.
110. Holstein, Parks and Waymack, *Ethics, Aging and Society. The Critical Turn*, 15.
111. Ruth Ludwick and Mary Cipriano Silva, "Ethics: Ethical Challenges in the Care of Elderly Persons," in *Online Journal of Issues in Nursing*, (December 19, 2003) vol. 9 no. 1, 4. www.nursingworld.org/MainMenuCategoris/ANAMarketplace/ANA Periodicalss/OJIN/TableofContents/Volume92004/no1Jan04/EthicalChallengnes. aspx.
112. Holstein, Parks and Waymack, *Ethics, Aging and Society. The Critical Turn*, 205–206.
113. Ingegerd Fagerberg and Gabriella Engstrom, "Care of the Old – A Matter of Ethics, Organization, and Relationships," in *International. Journal of Qualitative Studies of Health and Well-Being* (May 8, 2012).
114. Ruth Ludwick and Mary Cipriano Silva, "Ethics: Ethical Challenges in the Care of Elderly Persons," 3.
115. Institute for Healthcare Improvement, *Age-Friendly Health Systems: Guide to Using the 4Ms in the Care of Older Adults*. (July 2020), 4.
116. Institute for Healthcare Improvement, *Age-Friendly Health Systems: Guide to Using the 4Ms in the Care of Older Adults*, 5.
117. Ruth Ludwick and Mary Cipriano Silva, "Ethics: Ethical Challenges in the Care of Elderly Persons," 3.
118. V. Tellis-Nayak and Mary Tellis-Nayak, *Return of Compassion to Health Care*, (New York, NY: PAGE Publishing, Inc., 2016), 17.
119. Virginia Held, *The Ethics of Care. Personal, Political and Global*, 43.
120. Carol Gilligan, *In a Different Voice*, (Cambridge, MA: Harvard University Press, 1982), 17.
121. U.S. Department of Commerce, Economics and Statistics Administration, U.S. Census Bureau. *Population*. June 25, 2018.
122. Richard W. Johnson, "The Strains and Drains of Long-Term Care," in *American Medical Association Journal of Ethics*," (June 2008), vol. 10, no.6, 398.
123. Gretchen Livingston, "More than One-In-Ten U.S. Parents Are Also Caring for an Adult," FACTANK. News in the Numbers. (November 29, 2018).

124. U.S. Department of Commerce, Economics and Statistics Administration, U.S. Census Bureau *Subjective Well-Being of Eldercare Providers: 2012–2013,* Issued February 2018, 8.

125. Carol Gilligan, *Joining the Resistance,* 12–13.

126. Gillick, *Old and Sick in America. The Journey Through the Health Care System,* 235.

127. Marice Ashe, Dora Barilla, Eileen Barsi and Stephanie Cihon, "A Systems Thinking Approach to the Social Determinants of Health," 5.

128. Gillick, *Old and Sick in America. The Journey Through the Health Care System,* 236.

129. The Pioneer Network, *Pioneers in Culture Change and Person Directed Care,* 2. https://www.pioneernetwork.net/about-us/overview/.

130. Tellis Nayak and Tellis Nayak, *Return of Compassion to Health Care,* 150.

131. Tellis Nayak and Tellis Nayak, *Return of Compassion to Health Care,* 150.

132. The Pioneer Network. *Continuum of Person Directed Culture,* 3.

133. Tellis Nayak and Tellis Nayak, *Return of Compassion to Health Care,* 151.

134. The Eden Alternative, *2019 Global Impact Statement.* http://www.edenalt.org

135. The Eden Alternative, *Improving the Lives of Elders* http://www.edenalt.org.

136. Tellis Nayak and Tellis Nayak, *Return of Compassion to Health Care,* 152.

137. Tellis Nayak and Tellis Nayak, *Return of Compassion to Health Care,* 152.

138. Paula Span, "A Nursing Home that Feels, Well, Homey," in *The New York Times* (December 26, 2017):D5.

139. Sheryl Zimmerman, Barbara J. Bowers, Lauren W. Cohen, David C. Grabowski, Susan Horn, and Peter Kemper, "New Evidence on the Green House Model of Nursing Home Care: Synthesis of Findings and Implications for Policy, Practice and Research," in *Health Service,* volume 51, Issue S1, (February 2016), 475–496.

140. Paula Span, "A Nursing Home that Feels, Well, Homey," D5.

141. Eva Feder Kittay, "Equality, Dignity and Disability," in *Perspective on Equality. The Second Seamus Heaney Lectures,* ed. Mary Ann Lyons and Fionnuala Waldron, (Dublin, Ireland: The Liffey Press, 2005). 111.

142. https://www.cdc.gov/ncbdd/disabilityandhealth/infographic-disability-impacts-all-html.

143. World Health Organization, *World Report on Disability,* 2011, 32.

144. Institute of Medicine of the National Academies. *The Future of Disability in America.* (Washington DC: The National Academies Press, 2007), 99.

145. World Health Organization, *World Report on Disability,* 2011, 4.

146. World Health Organization, *World Report on Disability,* 2011, 5.

147. Paul Jewell, *Disability Ethics: A Framework for Practitioners, Professionals and Policy Makers,* (Chicago, IL: Common Ground Publishing, 2010), 164.

148. Joshua J. Mark, "Protagoras of Abdera: Of All Things, Man is the Measure," in *Ancient History Encyclopedia.* (January 18, 2012), https://www.ancient.eu/article/61/.

149. Ted Peters, "Progress and Provolution. Will Transhumanism Leave Sin Behind?" in *Transhumanism and Transcendence. Christian Hope in an Age of Technological Enhancement,* ed. Ronald Cole-Turner, (Washington, DC: Georgetown University Press, 2011), 65.

150. Gregory E. Kaebnick, *The Idea of Nature. Debates About Biotechnology and the Environment,* (Baltimore, MD: The Johns Hopkins University Press, 2011, 49–56.

151. Allen Buchanan, *Beyond Humanity?* (Oxford, UK: Oxford University Press, 2011, 118–119).

152. Buchanan, *Beyond Humanity,* 117.

153. *Genesis* 1:26-29.

154. Nigel M. de S. Cameron and Amy Michelle DeBaets, "Germline Gene Modification and the Human Condition of before God," in *Design and Destiny,* ed. Ronald Cole-Turner, (Cambridge, MA: The MIT Press, 2008): 96–98.

155. Walter Doerfler, "*Conditio Humana* as Viewed by a Geneticist," in *Theology, Disability and the New Genetics. Why Science Needs the Church,* edited by John Swinton and Brian Brock, (New York, NY: T&T Clark, 2007), 117–130.

156. Jonathan, Glover, *Choosing Children. Genes, Disability and Design*, (Oxford, UK: Clarendon Press, 2006), 88.
157. Glover, *Choosing Children. Genes, Disability and Design*, 89.
158. Glover, *Choosing Children. Genes, Disability and Design*. 90.
159. Glover, *Choosing Children*, 4–18.
160. Stephen Wilkinson, *Choosing Tomorrow's Children. The Ethics of Selective Reproduction*. (Oxford, UK: Oxford University Press, 2010), 63–75.
161. Christopher Newell, "'What's Wrong with You?' Disability and Genes as Ethics," in *Theology, Disability and the New Genetics. Why Science Needs the Church*, ed. John Swinton and Brian Brock. (New York, NY: T&T Clark, 2007), 50.
162. Newell, "'What's Wrong with You?' Disability and Genes as Ethics," 44–45.
163. Michigan State University, "The Unpopular Truth about Biases toward People with Disabilities," ScienceDaily. (July 28, 2019), www.sciencedaily.com/202907/90718112453.htm.
164. American Bar Association, "Implicit Biases & People with Disabilities," *ABA Commission on Disability Rights. Implicit Bias Guide*. January 7, 2019. https://www.american bar.org/groups/diversityrights/resources/implicit_biases.
165. American Bar Association, ABA Commission on Disability Rights, "Implicit Biases & People with Disabilities."
166. Martina Holder-Franz, "Life as Being in Relationship: Moving Beyond a Deficiency-orientated View of Human Life," in *Theology, Disability and the New Genetics. Why Science Needs the Church*, ed. by John Swinton and Brian Brock. (New York, NY: T&T Clark, 2007), 61.
167. Martina Holder-Franz, "Life as Being in Relationship: Moving Beyond a Deficiency-orientated View of Human Life," 57.
168. Michigan State University, "The Unpopular Truth about Biases toward People with Disabilities."
169. Martina Holder-Franz, "Life as Being in Relationship: Moving Beyond a Deficiency-oriented View of Human Life," 62.
170. Shane Clifton, *Crippled Justice. Disability. Virtue Ethics, and the Good Life*, 132.
171. Martina Holder-Franz, "Life as Being in Relationship: Moving Beyond a Deficiency-orientated View of Human Life," 64.
172. *Matthew 22:34–40*.
173. Matt Edmonds, *A Theological Diagnosis. A New Direction on Genetic Therapy, 'Disability' and the Ethics of Healing*, (London, UK: Jessica Kingsley Publishers, 2011), 29–42, 130.
174. Nancy Eiesland, *The Disabled God. Toward a Liberatory Theology of Disability*, (Nashville, TN: Abingdon Press, 1994), 40–41, 47.
175. Kathy Black, *A Healing Homiletic. Preaching and Disability*, (Nashville, TN: Abingdon Press, 1996), 34–42.
176. Eva Feder Kittay, "Equality, Dignity and Disability, 98.
177. Joel Michael Reynolds, "Three Things Clinicians Should Know About Disability," in *AMA Journal of Ethics*, (December 2018) vol. 20. no.12, E1183.
178. Reynolds, "Three Things Clinicians Should Know About Disability," E1183.
179. Jewell, *Disability Ethics. A Framework for Practitioners, Professionals and Policy Makers*, 164.
180. Lisa I. Iezzoni and Bonnie L. O'Day, *More than Ramps. A Guide to Improving Health Care Quality and Access for People with Disabilities*, (New York, NY: Oxford University Press. 2006), 18.
181. Jackie Leach Scully, *Disability Bioethics. Moral Bodies. Moral Difference*. (Lanham, MD: Rowman and Littlefield Publishers, Inc., 2008), 19.
182. Edmonds, *A Theological Diagnosis*, 43.
183. Emily Johnson, Letter from the Editor. "Disability, Medicine and Ethics," *American Medical Association Journal of Ethics* April 2016) vol 18. no. 4: 355–358.

184. Muscular Dystrophy Association, accessed May 2, 2020, https://www.mda.org/disease/becker-muscular-dystrophy/medical-management.
185. Anne Matthews, "Impact of Medical and Technological Advances on Survival Rates of People with Disabilities," Disability Services Commission, (May 2008), 6.
186. Matthews, "Impact of Medical and Technological Advances on Survival Rates of People with Disabilities," Disability Services Commission, 1.
187. Tobin Siebers, *Disability Theory*, (Ann Arbor, MI: University of Michigan Press, 2008), 25.
188. Siebers, *Disability Theory*, 9.
189. Michael Oliver, *Understanding Disability. From Theory to Practice*. 2nd edition. (New York, NY: Palgrave MacMillan, 2009), 44.
190. Alicia Ouellette, *Bioethics and Disability. Toward a Disability-Conscious Bioethics*. (New York, NY: Cambridge University Press, 2011), 319.
191. Institute of Medicine, *The Future of Disability in America*. (Washington, DC: The National Academies Press, 2007), 168.
192. Institute of Medicine, *The Future of Disability in America*, 169.
193. Ouellette, *Bioethics and Disability. Toward a Disability-Conscious Bioethics*, 320.
194. Siebers, *Disability Theory*, 3.
195. Black, *A Healing Homiletic*, 50–51.
196. Nancy J. Lane, "Healing Bodies and Victimisation of Persons: Issues of Faith-Healing for Persons with Disability," in *Disability Rag & Resource*, vol 14. (1993), 12.
197. Black, *A Healing Homiletic*, 51.
198. Glover, *Choosing Children*, 171–173, 175.
199. Stephen Wilkinson, *Choosing Tomorrow's Children. The Ethics of Selective Reproduction*, 162–163; Benjamin S. Wilfond, "Ethical and Policy Implications of Conducting Carrier Testing and Newborn Screening for the Same Condition," in *Ethics and Newborn Genetic Screening. New Technologies and Challenges*, ed. Mary Ann Baily and Thomas H. Murray. (Baltimore, MD: The Johns Hopkins University Press, 2009).300.
200. Barbara A. B. Patterson, "Redeemed Bodies: Fullness of Life," in *Human Disability and the Service of God. Reassessing Religious Practice*, ed. Nancy L. Eisland and Don E. Saliers. (Nashville, TN: Abingdon Press, 1998):124.
201. Celia Deanne-Drummond, *Genetics and Christian Ethics*, (New York, NY: Cambridge University Press, 2006): 1–2.
202. Deanne-Drummond, *Genetics and Christian Ethics*, 3.
203. Deanne-Drummond, *Genetics and Christian Ethics*, 8.
204. Amy Lauren Hall, "To Form a More Perfect Union: Mainline Protestantism and the Popularization of Eugenics," in *Theology, Disability and the New Genetics. Why Science Needs the Church*, ed. ohn Swinton and Brian Brock. (New York, NY: T&T Clark, 2007), 87.
205. Mary B. Mahowald, "Aren't We All Eugenicists Anyway?' in *Theology, Disability and the New Genetics. Why Science Needs the Church*, ed. John Swinton and Brian Brock. (New York, NY: T&T Clark, 2007), 96; *Buck v. Bell*, 274 U.S. 200 (1927).
206. Michael J. Sandel, *The Case Against Perfection in Ethics in the Age of Genetic Engineering*, (Cambridge, UK: The Belknap Press of Harvard University, 2007), 64–66; Matthew Edmonds, *A Theological Diagnosis*, 50–51.
207. Wilkinson, *Choosing Tomorrow's Children. The Ethics of Selective Reproduction*, 155–157.
208. Deanne-Drummond, *Genetics and Christian Ethics*, 73–74.
209. Mahowald, "Aren't We All Eugenicists Anyway?" 106.
210. Jeffrey P. Bishop, "The Broken Body and the Disabled Body: Reflections on Disability and the Objects of Medicine," in *Theology, Disability and the New Genetics. Why Science Needs the Church*, ed. John Swinton and Brian Brock (New York, NY: T&T Clark, 2007), 222–223.

211. Jeffrey P. Bishop, "The Broken and the Disabled Body: Reflections on Disability and the Objects of Medicine," 220.
212. David Wasserman, "Ethical Constraints on Allowing or Causing the Existence of People with Disabilities," in *Disability and Disadvantage*, ed. Kimberly Brownlee and Adam Cureton. (New York, NY: Oxford University Press, 2009), 319–320.
213. Wilkinson, *Choosing Tomorrow's Children. The Ethics of Selective Reproduction*, 2.
214. David Wasserman, "Ethical Constraints on Allowing or Causing the Existence of People with Disabilities, 325.
215. Wilkinson, *Choosing Tomorrow's Children. The Ethics of Selective Reproduction*, 174.
216. Wilkinson, *Choosing Tomorrow's Children, The Ethics of Selective Reproduction*, 61.
217. Wilkinson, *Choosing Tomorrow's Children, The Ethics of Selective Reproduction*, 129–141.
218. Deanne-Drummond, *Genetics and Christian Ethics*, 55.
219. Mary Ann Baily, "Fair Distribution of Newborn Screening Costs and Benefits," in *Ethics and Newborn Genetic Screening*, ed. Mary Ann Baily and Thomas H. Murray. (Baltimore, MD: The Johns Hopkins University Press, 2009), 30–38.
220. Jannine De Maes Cody, "An Advocate's Perspective on Newborn Screening Policy," In *Ethics and Newborn Genetic Screening. New Technologies, New Challenges*, ed. Mary Ann Baily and Thomas H. Murray. (Baltimore, MD: The Johns Hopkins University Press, 2009), 77, 79, 81–82.
221. Reynolds, "Three Things Clinicians Should Know About Disability," E1183.
222. Reynolds, "Three Things Clinicians Should Know About Disability," E1181.
223. Jacki Leach Scully, *Disability Bioethics. Moral Bodies, Moral Difference*, (Lanham, MD: Rowman & Littlefield Publishers, Inc., 2008), 9.
224. Scully, *Disability Bioethics. Moral Bodies, Moral Difference*, 23.
225. Scully, *Disability Bioethics. Moral Bodies, Moral Difference*, 9.
226. Scully, *Disability Bioethics. Moral Bodies, Moral Difference*, 11.
227. Scully, *Disability Bioethics. Moral Bodies, Moral Difference*, 11–12.
228. Hans S. Reinders, "Life's Goodness: On Disability, Genetics and 'Choice,'" in *Theology, Disability and the New Genetics. Why Science Needs the Church*, ed. by John Swinton and Brian Brock., 169, 171.
229. Reinders, "Life's Goodness: On Disability, Genetics and 'Choice,'" 173; H. Tristram Engelhardt, Jr., "A Traditional Christian Reflections on Reengineering Human Nature," in *Design and Destiny. Jewish and Christian Perspectives on Human Germline Modification*, ed. by Ronald Cole-Turner. (Cambridge, MA: The MIT Press, 2008), 85.
230. *Genesis 1:1–31*.
231. William E. May, William E. May, *Catholic Bioethics and the Gift of Human Life*, 3rd edition, (Huntington, IN: Our Sunday Visitor, Inc., 2013), 268.
232. Ronald Rolheiser, *Against an Infinite Horizon. The Finger of God in Our Everyday Lives*, (New York, NY: The Crossroad Publishing Company, 2001), 78–80.
233. Clifton, *Crippled Justice. Disability. Virtue Ethics, and the Good Life*, 121.
234. Clifton, *Crippled Justice. Disability. Virtue Ethics and the Good Life*, 121.
235. William Stillman, *Autism and the God Connection. Refining the Autistic Experience through Extraordinary Accounts of Spiritual Giftedness*, (Naperville, IL: Sourcebooks, Inc., 2006), 1–14.
236. Stillman, *Autism and the God Connection*, 63, 70–71.
237. Robert Song, "Fragility and Grace; Theology and Disability," in *Theology, Disability and the New Genetic*, edited by John Swinton and Robert Brock (New York, NY: T&T Clark, 2007), 242.
238. William E. May, *Catholic Bioethics and the Gift of Human Life*, 30.
239. William E. May, *Catholic Bioethics and the Gift of Human Life*, 31.
240. Eva Feder Kittay, "Equality, Dignity and Disability," 117.
241. Eva Feder Kittay, "The Ethics of Care, Dependence and Disability," 52.

242. Kittay, "Equality, Dignity and Disability,"116.
243. Kittay, "The Ethics of Care, Dependence and Disability," 54.
244. Catriona MacKenzie, Wendy Rogers, and Susan Dodds, "Introduction: What is Vulnerability and Why Does it Matter for Moral Theory?" 13.
245. Kittay, "The Ethics of Care, Dependence and Disability," 50.
246. Jackie Leach Scully, "Disability and Vulnerability: On Bodies, Dependence, and Power," In *Vulnerability. New Essays in Ethics and Feminist Philosophy*, ed. Catriona MacKenzie, Wendy Rogers, and Susan Dodds (New York, NY: Oxford University Press, 2014), 208.
247. Jewell, *Disability Ethics. A Framework for Practitioners, Professionals and Policy Makers*, 164.
248. Scully, *Disability Bioethics. Moral Bodies, Moral Difference*, 25.
249. Siebers, *Disability Theory*, 4.
250. Michael Oliver, *Understanding Disability. From Theory to Practice*, 44.
251. Oliver, *Understanding Disability. From Theory to Practice*, 45.
252. Oliver, *Understanding Disability. From Theory to Practice*, 47.
253. Wilkinson, *Choosing Tomorrow's Children*, 172.
254. U.S. Department of Health and Human Services, Office of Disease Prevention and Health Promotion. Disability and Health (2020) http://www.healthypeople.gov/2020/data-search.
255. U.S. Department of Health and Human Services, Office of Disease Prevention and Health Promotion. Disability and Health (2020).
256. Ouellette, *Bioethics and Disability. Toward a Disability-Conscious Bioethics*, (New York, NY: Cambridge University Press, 2011), 5, 320.
257. Alicia Ouellette, *Bioethics and Disability. Toward a Disability-Conscious Bioethics*, 332,339.
258. Reynolds, "Three Things Clinicians Should Know About Disability," E1184.
259. Institute of Medicine of the National Academies, *The Future of Disability in America*. (Washington, DC: The National Academies Press, 2007), 130.
260. Reynolds, "Three Things Clinicians Should Know About Disability, E1185.
261. Reynolds, "Three Things Clinicians Should Know About Disability, E1184.
262. Iezzoni and O'Day, *More than Ramps. A Guide to Improving Health Care Quality and Access for People with Disabilies*, 171.
263. Iezzoni and O'Day, *More than Ramps. A Guide to Improving Health Care Quality and Access for People with Disabilities*, 172.
264. Iezzoni and O'Day, *More than Ramps. A Guide to Improving Health Care Quality and Access for People with Disabilities*, 182.

6 Conclusion

The Essence of Care

To say that my mother wanted the life she enjoyed before the onset of her diseases is an understatement. Given a choice, I am certain she would have preferred living independently in her tidy home, enveloped in the warmth of lifelong friendships, and surrounded by the decades-old treasures she collected, rather than in her sanitized and safe assisted living suite. But, as her conditions worsened and decisions about her care became more complex, where she lived was not what mattered to her, nor was she concerned with her pathologies or prognoses. What was most important to her at that place on her life continuum was the same thing that mattered most throughout her adult life – knowing that her children were okay. It was that simple.

Her physician's respect for the intimacy of their relationship enabled him to pursue what was good for *her* alongside those things that were medically indicated, thus reflecting his moral commitment to her vulnerability. He acted from his soul which I am confident was in union with the mission of the integrated health system whose patients he cared for. Since the ethically accountable HCO is an interdependent construct, as its normative stakeholders, my sisters and I were dependent upon the quality of the interactions with my mother's formal care providers. Her physician understood the significance of his duty to respect this interdependency as he consciously brought all our voices together while he cared for her, and throughout the course of his relationship with her. By helping me to understand what mattered most to her, I was able to create an environment that allowed her to live out the remainder of her life strengthened by the fruits of those values. For my sisters and me, this view into my mother's world also enriched the privilege of caring for her without the self-doubt and guilt that often plagues informal family caregivers.

I began to visit with her every day. The most mundane of life's tasks were transformed into the most meaningful experiences. I learned things about my mother I would not otherwise have discovered. By completing her daily meal plans together, I realized that she liked to eat liver and onions; although frankly, I never understood why. While joining her for group activities, I learned that she hated playing bingo, but loved having her fingernails painted pink. While folding laundry together, I learned that she hated her compression socks, but loved sequined blouses. My mother learned things about me that I would not

DOI: 10.4324/9781003229957-6

have otherwise cared to share. She would listen and stare intently during stories about my workday, and then suddenly ask where I had purchased something I was wearing or carrying that she thought was new. Unfailingly she would ask if and what I had eaten that day. She developed a keen interest in my smartphone with its bells and clicks, asking why I played with it all the time and if she could have one, too. And, as I prepared to leave her at the end of every visit, she would ask if I was finished writing whatever it was that was taking up so much of my time.

The interdependent relationships that connect caring for, being cared about, and the consequences of ethical decisions represent the essence of healthcare and undergird stakeholder theory. The dependency of vulnerable stakeholders upon those connected set of relationships, and the moral agency of organizational leadership to understand those stakeholders' values is the cornerstone of ethical accountability in healthcare. In its simplest form, ethics is the pursuit of good. The good attributed to an organization is manifest through individual and institutional decisions and actions that are motivated by soul.

The good from these decisions is exhibited most vibrantly when an organization's actions consider or even yield to the interests and preferences of its communities of stakeholders. The diversity and vulnerability of stakeholder communities necessitates that ethically accountable leadership in healthcare understand stakeholder values and expectations, especially those that seek respect for human dignity, a flourishing life, and preservation of trust. To that end, not all healthcare interests concern physical well-being.

The secrets that a patient conveys to her physician throughout the course of their relationship create a sacrosanct duty of confidentiality that is the cornerstone of trust in that relationship. Trust in others enables intimacy and is needed most when a person surrenders some aspect of control to another. Surrendering control of ones' secrets increases vulnerability and fosters trust. The ethics of secrecy underscores the importance of secrecy in healthcare as a stakeholder interest.

The interdependency and value of connected relationships in healthcare makes it incumbent upon the ethically accountable HCO to create a culture of ethics that recognizes its moral duty as an accountable keeper of secrets. This includes creating an overall data strategy that recognizes stakeholder values and preferences and incorporates them into standard practices for ethical review of data. Data ethics as part of the HCO's ethical culture will help to ensure that its moral agents exercise their moral reasoning and judgments on behalf of its stakeholders in place of the void left by non-human algorithmic and machine learning decisions. They must do what machines cannot in recognition of the vulnerability and fragility of human dignity that is part of the human condition.

As a condition of human life, all of humankind is vulnerable; that is, susceptible to harm, by virtue of its dependent nature. Susceptibility to harm is relational in that power inequalities and dependency on others render some stakeholders more exposed than others. Vulnerability is also contextual in that certain social, economic, and cultural factors create and exacerbate risk of harm for certain stakeholder groups. Relational ethics recognizes the importance of these contexts and individual values in addressing vulnerability.

Those in positions of power and authority have special responsibilities to the vulnerable. As such, ethical accountability in healthcare includes an HCO's moral commitment to the most vulnerable and disempowered normative stakeholder communities it serves across the life continuum. This commitment to empower and enable human flourishing while respecting human dignity includes an obligation to mitigate threats and provide for unmet needs. Particularly compelling is the moral duty to empower children. Such empowerment includes understanding the values unique to children, the pathology of diseases, and disorders that affect them through clinical research. In addition to clinical research considerations, moral accountability to vulnerable pediatric populations includes the responsibility to understand and manage population health to understand the epidemiology of a particular population. In particular, the HCO has a moral obligation to mitigate and prevent the psychosocial and physiological effects of pediatric obesity, which is upheld as a critical public health threat.

Vulnerability is further amplified by aggravating influences such as biases, negative trends in public policy, societal and cultural pressures, and barriers to human flourishing within certain environments. Older adults and persons with disabilities represent vulnerable and often inaudible stakeholder communities whose dignity and ability to flourish are diminished by such influences. The healthcare setting can be particularly intimidating to vulnerable stakeholders. As such, the power, authority, and influence of the HCO underscore its moral duty and ethical accountability to positively impact the lives of these groups, and to improve their human condition and dignity.

My mother's physician understood that there is no universal standard for what it means to flourish. A flourishing life depends upon the unique differences, circumstances, and environments attributed to everyone. What it means to flourish in life is determined by the person who lives it according to their preferences and experiences. Barriers to human flourishing, are often the result of misperceptions and cultural assumptions of age, disability, normalcy, and preferences that foster intolerance or discriminatory practices. Moreover, removing barriers to flourishing is a matter of collaboration between the physician, the community of stakeholders, and patients. It enables each to direct their expertise and voices to the issues that matter most in the quest to improve the human condition – those complex variables that challenge human life across the life continuum.

Healthcare organizations are powerful stakeholders. Their interdependence with the communities of stakeholders they serve requires that they understand the values and experiences of constituents within those communities. To that end, applying a relational ethic of care emphasizing the relationship between the physician, the patient, and the care narrative will illuminate what matters most to patients. Adherence to the ethics of care model also brings additional factors such as social determinants into the care decisions, thereby embracing a communal rather than individualistic approach to care. The ethics of care model encourages the HCO and its professional moral agents to engage in effective advocacy to see themselves as in-relation with their patients, exercising empathy and compassion for their dignity.

Understanding what mattered most to my mother did not ensure that my sisters and I could escape the inevitable internal tensions, conflicts, and emotional chaos that too often accompany caring for an aging parent. We had our own set of value conflicts to resolve. Nevertheless, we found unity in our commitment to provide what mattered most to her, and that made all the difference.

My mother died almost two years to the day of that pivotal wellness exam. We could not stop or slow the progression of her diseases or temper the cruelty of her physical suffering. But, because we understood what mattered most to her – the opportunity for her to bear witness to *our* world, the one she helped to create – we made certain she flourished, and her remaining years were grace-filled for all of us. What she lost of her independence she gained through her dependence on us. And what I lost of my independence, I gained through my dependence on her. That is the essence of *care*.

Gathered around her bed, the three of us spent the overnight hours watching her sleep, listening to her breathe, and reliving whatever shared memories my sisters and I had, heard about, or tried to recall of her 85-year life. We laughed cathartically at her many "isms" and idiosyncrasies, and the indelible imprint her values left on us. In the early morning hours, my sisters left for their homes. I remained with her until she passed.

She thought we were okay. And we were.

Bibliography

Abrams, Martin. "The Origins of Personal Data and its Implication for Governance." Paper presented at the OECD Expert Roundtable Discussion in Paris, France: *Protecting Privacy in a Data-Driven Economy: Taking Stock of Current Thinking*. (March 21, 2014).

Abrams, Martin, John Abrams, Peter Cullen and Lynn Goldstein, "Artificial Intelligence, Ethics and Enhanced Data Stewardship." In *IEEE Security & Privacy*. Vol. 17 March–April 2019: 17–30. doi:10.1109/MSEC/2018.2888778.

Acuff, Katherine L. "Healthcare Ethics, Public Policy and Healthcare Organization." In *Managerial Ethics in Healthcare. A New Perspective*, edited by Gary J. Filerman, Ann E. Mills and Paul M. Schyve. Chicago: Health Administration Press. 2014: 223–241.

Adams, A.O. "Quality of Board Governance in Nonprofit Healthcare Organizations." In *The Internet Journal of Healthcare Administration*. 205 Vol 2. doi: 10.5580/251d http://archive.ispub.com/journal/the-internet-journal-of-healthcareadminstration/volume- 2.

Adams, Katie, "Google Deepens its Healthcare Presence: A Timeline of the Last Year," In *Becker's Hospital Review*, (June 23, 2021) accessed June 30, 2021, http://www.beckerhospitalreview.com/healthcare-information-technology/google-deepen.

Ahia, C. Emmanuel. *The Danger-to-Self-or-Others Exception to Confidentiality*, Lanham: University Press of America, Inc. 2012.

AHIP. *Access to Healthy Foods: Social Determinants of Health. Issue Brief*. (May 2018). http://www.ahip.org/access-to-healthy-foods-social-determinants-of-health.

Alalouch, Chaham, Peter A. Aspinall, and Harry Smith. "Design Criteria for Privacy-Sensitive Healthcare Buildings." In *ISCSIT International Journal of Engineering and Technology*. 8 (February 2016).

Albright, Jamie N., Cynthia D. Fair, and Christy Newman, "Psychosocial Considerations for Children and Adolescents with HIV." In *A Clinical Guide to Pediatric HIV. Bridging the Gaps Between Research and Practice*, edited by Tiffany Chenneville. Cham: Springer International Publishing AG. 2016: 73–94.

Alderson, Priscilla and Virginia Morrow. *The Ethics of Research with Children and Young People. A Practical Handbook*, Los Angeles: SAGE. 2011.

Alexander, Randell, *Research and Practices in Child Maltreatment and Prevention. Definitions of Abuse and Prevention*. Vol. i. St Louis: STM Learning, Inc. 2017.

Allen, Anita L. "The Duty to Protect Your Own Privacy." In *Privacy, Security and Accountability. Ethics, Law and Policy*, edited by Adam D. Moore. London: Rowman and Littlefield. 2016: 19–38.

Allen, Anita L. *Why Privacy Isn't Everything. Feminist Reflections on Personal Accountability*. Lanham: Rowman & Littlefield Publisher, Inc. 2003.

American Association on Intellectual and Developmental Disabilities. "Frequently Asked Questions on Intellectual Disability." 2019. http://www.aidd.org/intellectual-disability/definition/faqs-in-intellectual-disability.

American Bar Association. ABA Commission on Disability Rights. "Implicit Biases & People with Disabilities" January 7, 2019. http://www.americanbar.org/groups/diversityrights/resources/implicit_biases.

American Council on Aging, accessed December 30, 2019, http://www.MedicaidPlanningAssistance.org/medicaid-eligibility-pennsylvania.

American Council on Aging, "Medicaid and Home Health Care and Non-Medical In-Home Care." January 28, 2021. https://www.medicaidplanningassistance.org/in-home-care/.

Anna, George J. and Michael Groden. "The Nuremberg Code." In *The Oxford Textbook of Clinical Research Ethics*, edited by Ezekiel J. Emanuel, Christine Grady, Robert A. Crouch, Reider K. Lie, Franklin G. Miller, and David Wendler. Oxford: Oxford University Press, 2008: 136–140.

Arani, Shireen. *State Intervention in the Cases of Obesity-Related Medical Neglect*. 82 B.U.L. Rev. 875 (2002).

Armijo, Patrick. "State Says Details Hurt Girl." *Albuquerque Journal*. November 20, 2000: B1.

Arnason, Vilhajalmur, Hongwen Li, and Yali Cong. "Informed Consent." In *The SAGE Handbook of Health Care Ethics*, edited by Ruth Chadwick and Henk ten Have. Los Angeles: Sage Publications. 2011, 106–116.

Ashe, Marice, Dora Barilla, Eileen Borsi and Stephanie Cihon. "A Systems Thinking Approach to the Social Determinants of Health." In *Stakeholder Health. Insights from New Systems of Health*, edited by Teresa F. Cutts and James R. Cochrane. Winston-Salem: Stakeholder Health, 2016: 10–22.

Aukley, Dennis. "When the Patient-Physician Relationship is Broken." In AMA *Journal of Ethics* 10 (September 2008) 548–552.

Ayalon, L. and C. Tesch-Romer, eds. *Contemporary Perspectives on Ageism*. International Perspectives on Aging, Cham: Springer Open, 2018. https://doi.org/10.008/978-3-319-73820-8_13.

Bae, Jong-Myon. "Value-Based Medicine: Concepts and Application." In *Epidemiology and Health* 37, accessed September 6, 2017. http://www.dcx.doi.org/10.4178/ephi.e2014014.

Baily, Mary Ann. "Fair Distribution of Newborn Screening Costs and Benefits." In *Ethics and Newborn Genetic Screening*, edited by Mary Ann Baily and Thomas H. Murray. Baltimore: The Johns Hopkins University Press, 2009: 19–57.

Baily, Mary Ann and Thomas H. Murray, eds. *Ethics and Newborn Genetic Screening. New Technologies, New Challenges*, Baltimore: The Johns Hopkins University Press. 2009.

Bambauer, Derek E., "Uncrunched: Algorithms, Decision Making and Privacy," *Abstract* 2017.

Barnbaum, Deborah R. *The Ethics of Autism. Among Them, But Not of Them*. Bloomington: Indiana University Press. 2008.

Barocas, Solon and Helen Nissenbaum. "Big Data's End Run Around Anonymity and Consent." In *Privacy, Big Data and the Public Good*, edited by Julia Lane, Victoria Stodden, Stefan Bender and Helen Nissenbaum. New York: Cambridge University Press, 2014: 44–75.

Barondess, Jeremiah A., David E. Rodgers, and Kathleen N. Lohr, eds. In *Report of a Forum of the Council on Health Care Technology. Care of the Elderly Patient: Policy Issues and Research Opportunities*. Washington DC: National Academy Press, 1989.

Barry, Danielle and Nancy M. Petry. "Obesity and Psychiatric Disorders." In *Psychiatric Times*. December 5, 2009. http://www.psychiatricimes.com/anxiety/obesity-and-psychiatric- disorders.

Beauchamp, Tom L. "The Belmont Report." In *The Oxford Textbook of Clinical Research Ethics*, edited by Ezekiel J. Emanuel, Christine Grady, Robert A. Crouch, Reider K. Lie, Franklin G. Miller, and David Wendler. Oxford: Oxford University Press, 2008: 149–155.

Beauchamp, Tom L. and James F. Childress. *Principles of Biomedical Ethics*. 7th ed. New York: Oxford University Press, 2013.

Belasen, Alan T., Barry Eisenberg and John W. Hyppertz, *Mastering Leadership. A Vital Resource for Health Care Organizations*. Burlington: Jones and Bartlett Learning. 2016.

Beltran-Aroca, Cristina, Elroy Girela-Lopez, Eliseo Collazo-Chao, Manuel Monero-Perez-Barquero, and Maria C. Munoz-Viallanueva, "Confidentiality Breaches in Clinical Practice: What Happens in Hospitals," BMC Medical Ethics, 1–12. September, 2016. doi: 10.1186/s12910-016-0136-y.

Benefiel, Margaret. *Soul at Work. Spiritual Leadership in Organizations*. New York: Church Publishing, 2005.

Berg, Kristen L. and Michael E. Msall. "The Prevention of Maltreatment among Children with Disabilities Through Early Identification and Comprehensive Provision of Services." In *Research and Practices in Child Maltreatment and Prevention. Societal, Organizational, and International Approaches*. vol.ii. Randell Alexander. St. Louis: STM Learning, Inc. 2017: 261–282.

Bishop, Jeffrey P. "The Broken Body and the Disabled Body: Reflections on Disability and the Objects of Medicine." In *Theology, Disability and the New Genetics. Why Science Needs the Church*, edited by John Swinton and Brian Brock. New York: T&T Clark, 2007: 214–233.

Black, Henry Campbell. *Black's Law Dictionary*. 6th ed. St. Paul: West Publishing, 1990.

Black, Kathy. *A Healing Homiletic. Preaching and Disability*. Nashville: Abingdon Press, 1996.

Blacksher, Erika and Jonathan D.Moreno. "A History of Informed Consent in Clinical Research." In *The Oxford Textbook of Clinical Research Ethics*, edited by Ezekiel J. Emanuel, Christine Grady, Robert A. Crouch, Reider K. Lie, Franklin G. Miller, and David Wendler. Oxford: Oxford University Press, 2008: 591–605.

Bok, Sissela. *Secrets: On the Ethics of Concealment and Revelation*. New York: Vintage Books, 1989.

Brewis, Alexandra A., *Obesity. Cultural and Biocultural Perspectives*. Piscataway: Rutgers University Press. 2011.

Brossoie, Nancy. "Social Gerontology." In *Gerontology for the Health Care Professional*. 2nd edition. Edited by Regula H. Robnett and Walter C. Chop. Sudbury: Jones and Bartlett Publishers, 2010:19–51.

Brownlee, Kimberly and Adam Cureton, eds. In *Disability and Disadvantage*. Oxford: Oxford University Press, 2009.

Brug, Johannes, Saskia te Velde, Ilse DeBourdeaudhuij and Stef Kremers. "Evidence of the Influence of the Home and Family Environment," In *Preventing Childhood Obesity: Evidence, Policy and Practice*. Edited by Elizabeth Waters, et al. West Sussex: Blackwell Publishing, Ltd., 2010: 64–65.

Buchanan, Allen. *Beyond Humanity?* Oxford: Oxford University Press, 2011.

Burns, L.R., Cucciamani, Clement J., Aquino, W. "The Fall of the House of AHERF: The Allegheny System Debacle." *Health Affairs* (serial on the Internet 2000) 19 (1): 7–14. http://www.medscape.com/view_article/409812.

Burton, Brian K. and Craig P. Sunn. "Feminist Ethics as a Moral Grounding for Stakeholder Theory." *Business Ethics Quarterly* 6 no. 2 (1996): 133–147.

Buttarelli, Giovanni. "Towards a New Digital Ethics, Data, Dignity, and Technology." Paper presented at the EDPS. Brussels, Belgium. September 11, 2015.

Cafardi, Nicolas P. ed. *Voting and Holiness. Catholic Perspectives on Political Participation.* New York: Paulist Press, 2012.

Caine, Kelly and Rima Hanania. "Patients Want Granular Privacy Control over Health Information in Electronic Health Records." In *Journal of American Medical Information Association.* 20 (2013): 7–15.

Callahan, Daniel. *What Price Better Health? Hazards of the Research Imperative.* Los Angeles: The University of California Press. 2003.

Campbell, Kenneth and Kayhan Parisi. "A New Age of Patient Transparency: An Organizational Framework for Informed Consent." In *The Journal of Law, Medicine and Ethics.* 45 (2017): 60–65.

Caniano, D.A. "Ethical Issues in Pediatric Bariatric Surgery." In *Seminars in Pediatric Surgery.* August 2009, 18(3): 186–192. doi: 10.1053/j.sempedsurg.2009.04.009.

Capron, Alexander M. "Legal and Regulatory Standards of Informed Consent in Research." In *"The Oxford Textbook of Clinical Research Ethics,"* edited by Ezekiel J. Emanuel, Christine Grady, Robert A. Crouch, Reider K. Lie, Franklin G. Miller, and David Wendler. Oxford: Oxford University Press, 2008: 613–632.

Carlson, Licia. "Research Ethics and Intellectual Disability: Broadening the Debates." In *Yale Journal of Biology and Medicine.* 86 (2013): 303–314.

Catechism of the Catholic Church, 2nd ed., translated by the United States Conference of Catholic Bishops. Vatican City: Libreria Editrice Vaticana, 1994, 1997.

Catholic Health Association. *With Justice for All? The Ethics of Healthcare Rationing.* St. Louis: Catholic Health Association of the United States. 1991.

Chadwick, Ruth, Henk ten Have and Eric M. Meslin, eds. *The SAGE Handbook of Health Care Ethics: Core and Emerging Issues.* London: SAGE Publications Ltd. 2011.

Chadwick, Ruth, Mairi Levitt, and Darren Shickle. eds. *The Right to Know and the Right Not to Know.* Cambridge: Cambridge University Press. 2014.

Charles, Karol. *Aging in America. A Cautionary Tale of Wrongful Death in Elder Care.* Senior Care Publishing, LLC. 2018.

Chenneville, Tiffany. ed. *A Clinical Guide to Pediatric HIV. Bridging the Gaps between Research and Practice.* Cham: Springer International Publishing AG. 2016.

Chop, Walter C. "Demographic Trends of an Aging Society." In *Gerontology for the Health Care Professional.* 2nd edition. Edited by Regula H. Robnett and Walter C. Chop. Sudbury: Jones and Bartlett Publishers. 2010: 1–17.

Clifton, Shane. *Crippled Grace. Disability, Virtue Ethics and the Good Life.* Waco: Baylor University Press. 2018.

Cody, Jannine De Mars. "An Advocate's Perspective on Newborn Screening Policy." In *Ethics and Newborn Genetic Screening. New Technologies, New Challenges,* edited by Mary Ann Baily and Thomas H. Murray. Baltimore: The Johns Hopkins University Press, 2009: 89–105.

Cohen, I. Glenn, Holly Fernandez Lynch, Effy Vayena, and Urs Gasser, eds. *Big Data, Health Law, and Bioethics.* New York: Cambridge University Press. 2018.

Cohen, I. Glenn, "Overcoming the Downsides of Big Data." In *Big Data, Health Law, and Bioethics,* edited by I. Glenn Cohen, Holly Fernandez Lynch, Effy Vayena and Urs Gasser, New York: Cambridge University Press. 2018: 69–72.

Cole-Turner, Ronald. ed. *Design and Destiny. Jewish and Christian Perspectives on Human Germline Modification.* Cambridge: The MIT Press. 2008.

Cole-Turner, Ronald. ed. *Transhumanism and Transcendence. Christian Hope in an Age of Technological Enhancement*. Washington DC: Georgetown University Press. 2011.

Collie-Akers, Vicki L., and Stephen B. Fawcett. "Preventing Childhood Obesity through Collaborative Public Health Action in Communities." In *Handbook of Childhood and Adolescent Obesity*, edited by Elissa Jelalian and Ric G. Steele. New York: Springer. 2008: 351–368.

Collins, Pamela Y, Beverly Pringle, Charlee Alexander, Gary L. Darmstadt Jody Heymann, Gillian Huebner, et al. "Global services and support for children with developmental delays and disabilities: Bridging research and policy gaps." *PLoS Med* 14 (9): e1002392. https://doi.org/10.1371/journal.pmed. 1002393.

Cook, Michael. "Consent Language Can Be Too Complicated for Patients." In *BioEdge. Bioethics News from Around the World*. August 18, 2019. https://www.bioedge.org/bioethcis/consent-language-can-be-too-complicated-for-patients

Cottingham, John, Robert Stoothoff, Dugald Murdoch, trans. *The Philosophical Writings of Descartes*. Vol 2. New York: Cambridge University Press. 1984.

Cotton, Chris, David W. Crippen, Farhad Kapadia, Arthur Morgan, Hold N. Murray, and Gill Ross. *Ethics Roundtable Debate: Is a Physician-Patient Confidentiality Relationship Subservient a Greater Good?* http://ccforum.com/content/9/3/233.

Crawford, Patricia, Gail Woodward-Lopez, Suzanne Rauzon, Lorrene Ritchie, and May C. Wang. "The Role of Public Policy in Addressing the Pediatric Obesity Epidemic." In *Issue in Clinical Child Psychology: Handbook of Childhood and Adolescent Obesity*. Edited by Elissa Jelalian and Ric G. Steele. New York: Springer. 2008: 371–386.

Cribb, Alan. "Why Ethics? What Kind of Ethics for Public Health." In *Public Health Ethics and Practice*. Edited by Stephen Peckham and Alison Hann. Bristol: The Policy Press, 2010: 17–31.

Currey, Richard. "Ageism in Healthcare: Time for a Change." In *Aging Well* 1 no.1 (Winter 2008): 16–18.

Cuskelly, Monica. "Ethical Inclusion of Children with Disabilities in Research." In *Ethical Research with Children*, ed. Ann Farrell, Berkshire: Open University Press. 2005.

Cutts, Teresa F. and James R. Cochrane. eds. *Stakeholder Health. Insights form New Systems of Health*. Winston-Salem: Stakeholder Health. 2016.

Daly, Barbara J., Ashley Rosko, Shulin Zhang and Hilliard M. Lazarus. "The Devil is in the Details: Confidentiality Challenges in an Age of Genetics." *HEC Forum* 27:79–86. 2015.

Daniels, Norman. "Justice Between the Young and the Old: Rationing From an International Perspective," In *Choosing Who's to Live. Ethics and Aging*, ed. J.W. Walters, Chicago: University of Illinois Press. 1996: 24–46.

Daniels, Norman. *Just Health. Meeting Health Needs Fairly*. New York: Cambridge University Press. 2008.

Deanne-Drummond, Celia. *Genetics and Christian Ethics*. Cambridge: Cambridge University Press. 2006.

Decrew, Judith Wagner. *In Pursuit of Privacy, Law, Ethics and the Rise of Technology*. New York: Cornell University Press, 1997.

Degrazia, David and Tom L. Beauchamp. "Philosophy: Ethical Principles and Common Morality," In *Methods in Medical Ethics*, edited by Jeremy Sugarman and Daniel P. Sulmasy, Washington DC: Georgetown University Press. 2010: 37–53.

De S. Cameron, Nigel M. and Amy Michelle, DeBaets. "Germline Gene Modification and the Human Condition before God." In *Design and Destiny*. Edited by Ronald Cole-Turner, (Cambridge, MA: The MIT Press, 2008): 93–118.

Dheensa, Sandi, Angela Fenwick, and Anneke Lucassen. "Is this knowledge mine and nobody else's? I don't feel that. Patient views about consent, confidentiality and information – sharing in genetic medicine," In *Journal of Medical Ethics*. 42 (2016), 174–179.

Doerfler, Walter. "*Condition Humana* as Viewed by a Geneticist," In *Theology, Disability and the New Genetics*, edited by John Swinton and Brian Brock. New York: T&T Clarke, 2007: 117–131

Donabedian, Avedis. "Quality of Care and the Health Needs of the Elderly Patients." In *Report of a Forum of the Council on Health Care Technology. Care of the Elderly Patient: Policy Issues and Research Opportunities*, edited by J.A. Barondess, D.E Rodgers, and K.N. Lohr. Washington DC: National Academy Press. 1989: 3–13.

Downey, Shane J. *One Data. Achieving Business Outcomes through Data*. Lexington: Shane Downey. 2015.

Drake, Brett and Melissa Jonson-Reid. "Defining and Estimating Child Maltreatment." In *The ASPAC Handbook on Child Maltreatment*. 4th edition. Edited by J. Bart Klika and Jon R. Conte. Los Angeles: SAGE Publications, Inc. 2018. 14–33.

Dresser, Rebecca. "The Reasonable Person Standard for Research disclosure: A Reasonable Addition to the Common Rule." In *The Journal of Law, Medicine and Ethics*. 47 (2019): 194–202.

Dube, Karine, Laurie Sylia, Lynda Dee, Jeff Taylor, David Evans, Carl Dean Bruton, et al. "Research on HIV Cure: Mapping the Ethics Landscape." In *PloS Med* 14(12): e1002470 (2017). https://doi.org.org.10.1371/journal.pmed. 1002470.

DuBois, James M. *Ethics in Mental Health Research. Principles, Guidance, and Cases*. New York: Oxford University Press. 2008.

Duke University. "Prospect of Direct Benefit in Pediatric Clinical Trials." Discussion Guide presented in Washington, DC at the *Margolis Center for Health Policy* (March 29, 2019).

Dwork, Cynthia. "Differential Privacy: A Cryptographic Approach to Private Data Analysis," In *Privacy, Big Data and the Public Good*, edited by Julia Lane, Victoria Stodden, Stefan Bender and Helen Nissenbaum. New York: Cambridge University Press. 2014: 296–322.

Eden Alternative. *2019 Global Impact Statement*. http://www.edenalt.org

Eden Alternative. *Improving the Lives of Elders*. http://www.edenalt.org

Edmonds, Matt. *A Theological Diagnosis. A New Direction on Genetic Therapy, 'Disability' and the Ethics of Healing*. London: Jessica Kingsley Publishers. 2011.

eHealth Exchange Overview, http://sequoiaproject.org/ehealth-exchange/about/.

Eisland, Nancy L. *The Disabled God. Toward a Liberatory Theology of Disability*. Nashville: Abingdon Press. 1994.

Eisland, Nancy L. and Don E. Saliers. eds. *Human Disability and the Service of God. Reassessing Religious Practice*. Nashville: Abingdon Press. 1998.

Emanuel, Ezekiel J., Christine Grady. Robert A. Crouch, Reider K. Lie, Franklin G. Miller and David Wendler. Eds. *The Oxford Textbook of Clinical Research Ethics*. Oxford: Oxford University Press. 2008.

Engelhardt, H. Tristam, "A Traditional Christian Reflection on Reengineering Human Nature." In *Design and Destiny. Jewish and Christian Perspectives on Human Germline Modification*, edited by Ronald Cole-Turner. (Cambridge, MA: The MIT Press, 2008), 85.

Eubanks, Virginia. *Automating Inequality. How High-Tech Tools Profile, Police, and Punish the Poor*. New York: Picador. 2018.

Evans, Barbara J. "Barbarians at the Gate: Consumer-Driven Health Data Commons and the Transformation of Citizen Science," In *The American Journal of Law and Medicine*. 42 (2016).

Executive Office of the President, *Big Data: Seizing Opportunities and Preserving Values*. (May 2014).

Fagerberg, Ingegerd, and Gabriella Engstrom, "Care of the Old – A Matter of Ethics, Organization and Relationships." In *International Journal of Qualitative Studies of Health and Well-Being*. May 8, 2012.

Family Caregiver Alliance. National Center on Caregivin. "Caregiver Statistics Demographics," accessed December 28, 2019.https://www.caregiver.org.

Farrell, Ann. ed. *Ethical Research with Children*. Berkshire: Open University Press. 2005.

Farrell, David, Cathie Brady, and Barbara Frank. *Meeting the Leadership Challenge in Long-Term Care. What You Do Matters*. Baltimore: Health Professions Press, Inc. 2011.

Federal Trade Commission Act, Section 5. 15. U.S.C. §45 (n).

Federal Policy for the Protection of Human Subjects, 82 Federal Register 7149. Final Rule January 19, 2017.

Filerman, Gary L., Ann E. Mills, and Paul M. Schyve. eds. *Managerial Ethics in Healthcare. A New Perspective*. Chicago: Health Administration Press. 2014.

Fisher, Celia B. Miriam R. Arbeit, and Tiffany Chenneville, "Goodness-of-Fit Ethics for Practice and Research Involving Children and Adolescents with HIV," In *A Clinical Guide to Pediatric HIV*, edited by Tiffany Chenneville. Cham: Springer International Publishing AG. 2016: 229–258.

Fleischman, Alan R. and Laure K. Collagen. "Research with Children." In *The Oxford Textbook of Clinical Research Ethics*. Edited by Ezekiel J. Emanuel, Christine Grady, Robert A. Crouch, Reider K. Lie, Franklin G. Miller, and David Wendler. Oxford: Oxford University Press, 2008: 446–460.

Fontes, Lisa Aronson. "Child Maltreatment Services for Culturally Diverse Families," In *The APSAC Handbook on Child Maltreatment*. 4th edition. Edited by J. Bart Klika and Jon R. Conte. Los Angeles: SAGE Publications, Inc. 2018: 366–384.

Forcia, Mary Ann. "History of Medicine. Geriatric Medicine: History of a Young Specialty." In *American Medical Association Journal of Ethics*. 16(5), (May 2014).

Francis, Leslie P. "Understanding Autonomy in Light of Intellectual Disability." In *Disability and Disadvantage*. Edited by Kimberly Brownlee and Adam Cureton. Oxford: Oxford University Press, 2009: 200–215.

Franklin, Benjamin, *Poor Richard's Almamac*, 1735.

Freeman, R. Edward, Jeffrey S. Harrison, Andrew C. Wicks, Bidhan L. Parmar, and Simone DeColle. *Stakeholder Theory, the State of the Art*, New York: Cambridge University Press, 2010.

Freeman, R. Edward. *Strategic Management. A Stakeholder Approach*. New York: Cambridge University Press. 2010.

Friedman, Alexander, Emil Robbins and David Wendler. "Which Benefits of Research Participation Count as Direct?" in *Bioethics* 26(2) 2012: 60–67.

Friedman, Andrew L. and Samantha Miles. *Stakeholders: Theory and Practice*. New York: Oxford University Press, 2006. Reprinted 2009.

Fryar, Cheryl D., Margaret D. Carroll and Joseph Afful, "Prevalence of Overweight, Obesity and Severe Obesity Among Children and Adolescents Aged 2-19 Years: United States, 1963-1965 through 2017-2019." *NCHS Health eStats*. 2020.

Furton, Edward J., Peter J. Cataldo, and Albert S. Moraczewski. eds. *Catholic Health Care Ethics. A Manual for Practitioners*. Philadelphia: The National Catholic Bioethics Center. 2009.

Gallagher, David M. "The Common Good," In *Catholic Health Care Ethics. A Manual for Practitioners*, edited by Edward J. Furton, Peter J. Cataldo and Albert S. Moraczewski Philadelphia: The National Catholic Bioethics Center. 2009: 29–31

Gallagher, Michael. "The Intersection of Relational Autonomy and Narrative Ethics for the Patient Unwilling to Disclose Genetic Diagnosis Information." In *Life Sciences, Society and Policy*" A Springer Open Journal, 2014, accessed June 7, 2017. http://www.lsspjournal.com/content/10/1/7.

Ganguli-Mitra, Agomoni, and Nikola Biller-Andorno. "Vulnerability in Healthcare and Research Ethics." In *The SAGE Handbook of Health Care Ethics: Core and Emerging Issues*, edited by Ruth Chadwick, Henk ten Have, and Eric M. Meslin (London, UK: SAGE Publications, 2011: 239–250.

Gert, Bernard. *Common Morality. Deciding What to Do*. New York: Oxford University Press. 2007.

Gert, Bernard. *Bioethics. A Systematic Approach.* 2nd ed. New York: Oxford University Press. 2006.

Gillespie, Susan. "Epidemiology of Pediatric HIV Infection." In *A Clinical Guide to Pediatric HIV. Bridging the Gaps Between Research and Practice*, edited by Tiffany Chenneville, Cham: Springer International Publishing AG. 2016: 1–14.

Gillick, Muriel R. *Old & Sick in America. The Journey through the Health Care System*. Chapel Hill: University of North Carolina Press. 2017.

Gilligan, Carol. *In a Different Voice*. Cambridge: Harvard University Press. 1982.

Gilligan, Carol. *Joining the Resistance*. Cambridge: Polity Press. 2011.

Gilmartin, M.J. and R. E. Freeman. "Business Ethics and Healthcare: A Stakeholder Perspective," In *Healthcare Management Review* 27 (2) Spring 2002: 52–65.

Glover, Jonathan. *Choosing Children. Genes, Disability and Design*. Oxford: Clarendon Press, 2006.

Goldfarb, Ronald, *In Confidence. When to Protect Secrecy, and When to Require Disclosure*. New Haven: Yale University Press. 2009.

Gonyea, Judith G. "The Oldest Old and a Long-Lived Society. Challenges for Public Policy." In *The New Politics of Old Age Policy*, 2nd edition, edited by Robert B. Hudson, Baltimore: Johns Hopkins University Press, 2010: 83–207.

Goodpaster, Kenneth E. and John B. Matthews, Jr. "Can a Corporation have a Conscience?" In *Harvard Business Review* 163. January–February 1982.

Grant, Patricia and Peter McGhee, "Organizational Narcissism: A Case of Failed Corporate Governance?" In *The Heart of the Good Institution. Virtue Ethics as a Framework for Responsible Management*. Netherlands: Springer, 2013: 97–109.

Greene, Sheila and Diana Hogan. *Researching Children's Experience*. London: Sage Publications, 2012.

Groenhout, Ruth E. *Connected Lives. Human Nature and Ethics of Care*. Lanham: Rowman and Littlefield Publishers, Inc. 2004.

Guttman, Katherine, Michelle Shouldice, Alex V. Levin, *Ethical Issues in Child Abuse Research*. Cham: Springer Nature Switzerland, 2019.

Hall, Amy Lauren. "To From a More Perfect Union: Mainline Protestantism and the Popularization of Eugenics," in *Theology, Disability and the New Genetics, Why Science Needs the Church*, edited by John Swenton and Brian Brock. New York: T&T Clark, 2007), 96.

Harari, Yuval Noah. *Homo Deus. A Brief History of Tomorrow*. New York: Harper Collins Publishers, 2017.

Harari, Yuval Noah. "Yuval Noah Harari on Big Data, Google and the End of Free Will." (blog), *The Financial Times Ltd.*, accessed September 9, 2016, https://www.ft.com/content/50bb-4830-6a4c-11e6-ae5b-a7cc5dd5a28c?siteedition+intl.

Harris, Howard, Gayathri Wijesinghe, and Stephen McKenzie. eds. *The Heart of the Good Institution. Virtue Ethics as a Framework for Responsible Management.* Netherlands: Springer. 2013.

Harris, Jared D., Brian T. Moriarty and Andrew C. Wicks. *Public Trust in Business.* Cambridge: Cambridge University Press. 2014.

Harrison, Jeffrey S. and Steven M. Thompson. *Strategic Management of Healthcare Organizations. A Stakeholder Management Approach.* New York: Business Expert Press. 2015.

Hassink, Sandra G. *Pediatric Obesity. Prevention, Intervention, and Treatment Strategies for Primary Care.* 2nd edition. Elk Grove Village: American Academy of Pediatrics. 2014.

Healy, Michelle. "Price Tag for Childhood Obesity: $19,000 Per Kid," *USA today,* April 7, 2014. http://www.usatoday.com/story/news/nation/2014/04/07/childhood-obesity-costs/7298461.

Held, Virginia. *The Ethics of Care. Personal, Political and Global.* Oxford: Oxford University Press. 2006.

Henry, Linda Gambee, and James Douglas Henry. *Reclaiming Soul in Health Care. Practical Strategies for Revitalizing Providers of Care.* Chicago: Cambridge AHA Press. 1999.

HIPAA Privacy Rule. 45 C.FR. Parts 160 and 164.

Hoke, John B. *Parens Patriae: A Flawed Strategy for State-Initiated Obesity Litigation,* 54 Wm & Mary Law Rev. 1753, 1755 (2013)

Holder-Franz, Martina, "Life as Being in Relationship: Moving beyond a Deficiency-orientated View of Human Life." In *Theology, Disability and the New Genetics. Why Science Needs the Church,* edited by John Swinton and Brian Brock. New York: T&T Clark. 2007: 57– 66.

Holland, Stephen. *Public Health Ethics.* Cambridge: The Polity Press. 2007.

Holland, Stephen. "Public Health Ethics: What it is, and how to do it." In *Public Health Ethics and Practice,* edited by Stephen Peckham and Alison Hann. Bristol: The Policy Press. 2010: 33–48.

Holstein, Martha B, Jennifer A. Parks and Mark H. Waymack, *Ethics, Aging and Society: The Critical Turn.* New York: Springer Publishing Company. 2011.

Hudson, Robert B, ed. *The New Politics of Old Age Policy.* Baltimore: The Johns Hopkins University Press, 2010.

Husted, Jorgen. "Autonomy and a Right Not to Know." In *The Right to Know and the Right Not to Know,* edited by Ruth Chadwick, Mairi Levitt, and Darren Shickle. Cambridge: Cambridge University Press. 2014: 24–37.

Iezzoni, Lisa I. and Bonnie L. O'Day. *More than Ramps. A Guide to Improving Health Care Quality and Access for People with Disabilities.* New York: Oxford University Press, 2006.

Inness, Julie C. *Privacy, Intimacy and Isolation.* New York: Oxford University Press, 1992.

Institute for Clinical Research Education. "What does it mean to communicate effectively?" accessed July 28, 2017. http://www/icre.pitt.edu/mentoring/effective.html.

Institute for Healthcare Improvement. *Age Friendly Health Systems: Guide to Using the 4Ms in the Care of older Adults,* accessed July 2020.

Institute of Medicine. *Ethical Conduct of Clinical Research Involving Children.* Washington DC: The National Academies Press. 2004

Institute of Medicine. *Legal Strategies in Childhood Obesity Prevention Workshop Summary.* Washington DC: The National Academies Press. 2011.

Institute of Medicine. *The Future of Disability in America.* Washington DC: The National Academies Press. 2007.

Jaffee v. Redmond, 518 U.S. 1 (1996).

Jasanoff, Sheila. *The Ethics of Invention. Technology and the Human Future.* New York: W.W. Norton and Company, 2016.

Jecker, Nancy S. "Caring for the Disabled Elderly: The Economics and Ethics of Financing Long-Term Care." In *Choosing Who's to Live. Ethics and Aging,* edited by James W. Walters. Chicago: University of Illinois, 1996: 72–92.

Jelalian, Elissa and Ric G. Steele, ed. *Handbook of Childhood and Adolescent Obesity.* New York: Springer, 2008.

Jewell, Paul. *Disability Ethics: A Framework for Practitioners, Professionals and Policy Makers.* Chicago: Common Ground Publishing, 2010.

Joffe, Steven and Robert D. Truog. "Equipoise and Randomization." In *The Oxford Textbook of Clinical Research Ethics,* edited by Ezekiel J. Emanuel, Christine Grady, Robert A. Crouch, Reider K. Lie, Franklin G. Miller, and David Wendler. Oxford: Oxford University Press, 2008: 245–260.

Johns Hopkins Berman Institute of Bioethics. "Is the Nanny State Ethical When Policing Obesity?" *Science Daily,* March 19, 2014. www.sciencedaily.com/releases/2014/03/14031943738.htm.

Johnson, Craig E., *Organizational Ethics. A Practical Approach. Los Angeles,* SAGE Publications, Inc., 2016.

Johnson, Craig E., *Meeting the Ethical Challenges of Leadership. Casting Light or Shadow.* Los Angeles: SAGE Publications, Inc., 2018.

Johnson, Emily, "Disability, Medicine and Ethics," Letter from the Editor, In *American Medical Association Journal of Ethics.* 18(4). (April 2016): 355–358.

Johnson, Richard W. "The Strains and Drains of Long-Term Care." In *American Medical Association Journal of Ethics.* 10(6), (June 2008): 397–400.

Jones, James H. "The Tuskegee Syphilis Experiment." In *The Oxford Textbook of Clinical Research Ethics,* edited by Ezekiel J. Emanuel, Christine Grady, Robert A. Crouch, Reider K. Lie, Franklin G. Miller, and David Wendler. Oxford: Oxford University Press, 2008: 86–96.

Jonsen, Albert R. *The Birth of Bioethics.* New York: Oxford University Press, 1998.

Kaebnick, Gregory E. "Human Nature without Theory." In *the Ideal of Nature. Debates about Biotechnology and the Environment.* Maryland: The Johns Hopkins University Press, 2011: 49–70.

Kaebnick, Gregory E. ed. *The Ideal of Nature. Debates about Biotechnology and the Environment.* Maryland: The Johns Hopkins University Press, 2011.

Kelly, Anita. *The Psychology of Secrets.* New York: Plenum Publishers, 2002.

Keyserlingk, E., K. Glass, S. Kogan, and S. Gauthier, "Proposed Guidelines for the Participation of Persons with Dementia as Research Subjects." In *Perspectives in Biology and Medicine* 38 (1995): 319–361.

Khatibloo, Fatemeh. *The New Privacy: It's All about Context. Vision: The Customer Trust and Privacy Playbook.* Forrester Research Inc. (June 30, 2017):1–2.

Kilner, John F. "Why Now? The Growing Interest in Limiting the Lifesaving Health Care Resources Available to Elderly People." In *Choosing Who's to Live. Ethics and Aging,* edited by J.W. Walters. Chicago: University of Illinois Press. 1996: 120–157.

King, Nancy. "Defining and Describing Benefit Appropriately in Clinical Trials." In *The Journal of Law, Medicine and Ethics,* 2000, 28: 332–343.

King, Nancy M.P. "Key Information in the New Common Rule: Can It Save Research Consent." In *The Journal of Law, Medicine and Ethics* 47 (2019): 203–212.

Kittay, Eva Feder. "Equality, Dignity and Disability." In *Perspectives on Equality. The Second Seamus Heaney Lectures.* Edited by Mary Ann Lyons and Fionnuala Waldron. Dublin: The Liffey Press. 2005: 95–122.

Kittay, Eva Feder. "The Ethics of Care, Dependence, and Disability." In *Ratio Juris*. 24 (2011): 49–58.

Klebanow, Diana. "Everybody (Well Almost) Lies...to Their Doctor," In *USA Today Magazine* 142, issue 2826 (March 2014): 66–67.

Klika, J. Bark and Jon R. Conte, eds. *The APSAC Handbook on Child Maltreatment*. Los Angeles: SAGE Publications, Inc., 2018.

Konnoth, Craig. "Data Collection, EHRs and Poverty Determinations." In *The Journal of Law, Medicine & Ethics*. 46 (2018): 622–628.

Kopaczynski, Germain. "Selected Moral Principles. Totality and Integrity." In *Catholic Health Care Ethics. A Manual for Practitioners*. 2nd edition. Philadelphia: The National Catholic Bioethics Center. 2009: 13–15.

Kowalski, Robin Marie, Chad Alan Morgan, Elizabeth Whittaker, Brittany Zaremba, Laura Frazee, and Jessica Dean. "Will they or Won't They? Secret Telling in Interpersonal Interactions." In *The Journal of Social Psychology* 155 (2015): 86–90.

Kroll, Joshua A., Joanna Huey, Solon Barocas, Edward W. Felten, Joel R. Reidenberg, David G. Robinson, and Harlan Yu. "Accountable Algorithms." *165 Univ. of Penn. L. Rev.* 633. (2017): 633–705.

Krugman, Richard D. "The More We Learn, the Less We Know: A Brief History of the Field of Child Abuse and Neglect." In *The ASPAC Handbook on Child Maltreatment*. 4th edition. Edited by J. Bart Klika and Jon R. Conte. Los Angeles: SAGE Publications, Inc. 2018: 1–13.

Kutz, Christopher. *Complicity: Ethics and Law for a Collective Age*. New York: Cambridge University Press, 2000.

Lakoff, George, and Mark Johnson. *Metaphors We Live By*. Chicago: University of Chicago Press. 1980.

Landwehr, Carl. "Engineered Controls for Dealing with Big Data." In *Privacy, Big Data and the Public Good. Frameworks for Engagement*, edited by Julia Lane, Victoria Stodden, Stefan Bender, and Helen Nissenbaum, New York: Cambridge University Press. 2014: 211–233.

Lane, Julia, Victoria Stodden, Stefan Bender, and Helen Nissenbaum, eds. *Privacy, Big Data and the Public Good. Frameworks for Engagement*. New York: Cambridge University Press. 2014.

Lane, Nancy J., "Healing Bodies and Victimisation of Persons: Issues of Faith-Healing for Persons with Disabilities," In *Disability Rag & Resource* vol. 14 1993: 3–17

Lawrence, Mark and Boyd Swinburn. "The Role of Policy in Preventing Childhood Obesity." In *Preventing Childhood Obesity. Evidence, Policy and Practice*. Edited by Elizabeth Waters, Boyd Swindburn, Jacob Seidell, and Ricardo Uauy, West Sussex: Blackwell Publishing, Ltd., 2010: 203–211.

Leadbeater, Bonnie, Elizabeth Baniser, Cecila Benoit, Mikael Jansson, Anne Marshall, and Ted Riccken, eds. *Ethical Issues in Community-Based Research with Children and Youth*. Toronto: University of Toronto Press. 2003.

Lear, Jonathan. "Confidentiality as a Virtue." In *Confidentiality. Ethical Perspectives and Clinical Dilemmas*, edited by Charles Levin, Allannah Furlong and Mary Kay O'Neill, New York: The Analytic Press, Inc. 2012: 4–17.

Leeb, Rebecca. "Etiology and Risk and Protective Factors in the Context of Primary Prevention." In *Research and Practices in Child Maltreatment. Definitions of Abuse and Prevention*. Vol i. Edited by Randell Alexander St Louis: STM Learning, Inc. 2017.

Levin, Charles, Allanah Furlong, and Mary Kay O'Neill, eds. *Confidentiality. Ethical Perspectives and Clinical Dilemmas*. New York: The Analytic Press. 2012.

Levine, Robert J. "The Nature, Scope, and Justification of Clinical Research: What is Research? Who is a Subject." In *The Oxford Textbook of Clinical Research Ethics*, edited by Ezekiel J. Emanuel, Christine Grady, Robert A. Crouch, Reidar K. Lie, Franklin G. Miller, and David Wendler. Oxford: Oxford University Press, 2008: 211–221.

Levitsky, Sandra R. "Caregiving and the Construction of Political Claims for Long-Term Care Policy Reform." In *The New Politics of Old Age Policy*, edited by Robert B. Hudson. Baltimore: The Johns Hopkins University Press. 2010: 208–230.

Lewis, Connie S. "Childhood Obeisty: Physiological and Psychological Implications and Ethical Responsibilities." In *Online Journal of Health Ethics* 13 (1). http://dx/doi. org/10.18785/ojhe.1301.5.

Livingston, Gretchen. "More Than One-In-Ten U.S. Parents are Also Caring for an Adult." *FACTANK News in the Numbers.* November 18, 2018.

Lobstein, Tim, Louise A. Baur, and Rachel Jackson-Leach, "The Childhood Obesity Epidemic." In *Preventing Childhood Obesity: Evidence, Policy and Practice*, edited by Elizabeth Waters, et al. West Sussex: Blackwell Publishing, Ltd. 2010: 3–14.

Lock, Karen and Rebecca Hillier. "The Prevention of Childhood Obesity in Primary Care Settings: Evidence and Practice." In *Preventing Childhood Obesity: Evidence, Policy and Practice*, edited by Elizabeth Waters, et al. West Sussex: Blackwell, Ltd. 2010: 94–104.

Lohr, Steven. "IBM is Counting on Its Bet on Watson, and Paying Big Money for It." In *The New York Times.* (October 17, 2016): B1.

Lohr, Steven. "Watson's Life After Jeopardy!" In *The New York Times.* (July 18, 2021): BU.

Ludwick, Ruth and Mary Cipriano Silva. "Ethics: Ethical Challenges in the Care of Elderly Persons." *In Online Journal of Issues in Nursing.* 9 (December 9, 2003):1–6 www. nurseingworld.org/MainMenuCatoegories/ANAMarketplace/ANAPeriodicals/OJIN/TableofContents/Volume92004/No1Jan04/EthicalChallenges.aspx.

Lunshof, Jeantine and Ruth Chadwick. "Genomics, Inconvenient Truths and Accountability." In *The Right to Know and the Right Not to Know.* edited by Ruth Chadwick, Mairi Levitt and Darren Shickle, Cambridge: Cambridge University Press, 2014: 116–130.

Lynch, Holly Fernandez. *Conflicts of Conscience in Health Care. An Institutional Compromise.* Cambridge: The MIT Press. 2008.

Lyons, Mary Ann and Fionnuala Waldron, eds. *Perspective on Equality. The Second Seamus Heaney Lectures.* Dublin: the Liffey Press. 2005.

Maccoby, Michael. "Why People Follow the Leader: The Power of Transference." In *Harvard Business Review.* September 2004. https://hbr.org/2004/09/why-people-follow-the-leader- the-power-of-transference.

Mackenzie, Catriona, Wendy Rogers, and Susan Dodds, eds. *Vulnerability. New Essays in Ethics and Feminine Philosophy.* New York: Oxford University Press, 2014.

Mackenzie, Catriona, Wendy Rogers, and Susan Dodds. "What is Vulnerability and Why Does it Matter for Moral Theory?" In *Vulnerability. New Essays in Ethics and Feminine Philosophy*, edited by Catriona Mackenzie, Wendy Rogers, and Susan Dodds. New York: Oxford University Press, 2014:1–29.

Maehle, Andrea-Holger. *Contesting Medical Confidentiality, Origins of the Debate in the United States, Britain and Germany.* Chicago: University of Chicago Press, 2016.

Magill, Gerard. "A Moral Compass for Cooperation and Wrongdoing." In *Voting and Holiness. Catholic Perspectives on Political Participation*, edited by Nicolas P. Cafardi. New York: Paulist Press, 2012.

Mahowald, Mary B. "Aren't We All Eugenicists Anyway?" In *Theology, Disability and the New Genetics. Why Science Needs the Church*, edited by John Swinton and Brian Brock. New York: T&T Clark, 2007: 96–106.

Malhotra, Deepa. "Too Big to Trust? Managing Stakeholder Trust in Business in the Post-Bail- Out Economy." In *Public Trust in Business*, edited by Jared D. Harris, Brian T. Moriarty, and Andrew C. Wicks. Cambridge: Cambridge University Press, 2014: 51–85.

Mamlin, Burke W. and William Tierney, "The Promise of Information and Communication Technology in Healthcare: Extracting Value from the Chaos," In *The American Journal of Medical Sciences*, 351 (2016): 59–68.

Manderson, Lenore, Mark Davis, Chip Colwell, and Tanja Ahlin. "On Secrecy, Disclosure, the Public and the Private in Anthropology." *Current Anthropology* 56 (December 2015): supp. 12.

Mansell, Samuel F. *Capitalism, Corporations, and the Social Contract: A Critique of Stakeholder Theory*. Cambridge: Cambridge University Press, 2013.

Manson, Neil C. and Onora O'Neill. *Rethinking Informed Consent in Bioethics*. New York: Cambridge University Press, 2008.

Marcelin, Jasmine R., Dawd S. Siraj, Robert Victor, Shaila Kotadia, and Yvonne Maldonado, "The Impact of Unconscious Bias in Healthcare: How to Recognize It and Mitigate It." In *The Journal of Infectious Disease*. 220 Suppl. 2 (2019): S62–S73.

Marhefka, Stephanie L., DeAnne E. Turner, and Tiffany Chenneville, "HIV Disclosure in Pediatric Populations: Who, What, When to Tell, and then What?" In *A Clinical Guide to Pediatric HIV. Bridging the Gaps between Research and Practice*. Edited by Tiffany Chenneville. Cham: Springer International Publishing AG. 2016: 189–227.

Mark, Joshua J. "Protagoras of Abdera: Of All Things, Man is the Measure." In *Ancient History Encyclopedia*. Last modified January 18, 2012. https://www.ancient.eu/article/61/.

Marr, Bernard. "What is the Difference between Artificial Intelligence and Machine Learning?" Accessed June 29, 2017.https://www.Forbes.com/sites/bernardmarr/2016/12/06/what-is- the-difference-between-artificial-intelligence-and-machine-learning/2/#7/c53944f483d.

Matthews, Deb. "Protecting the Privacy of Patients: Quiet Death of Doctor-Patient Confidentiality," In *The Toronto Star*, February 13, 2014: A18.

Matthews, Anne. "Impact of Medical and Technological Advances on Survival Rates of People with Disabilities." Disability Services Commission. May 2008: 1–19.

Mavoa, Helen, Shirik Kumanyuha, and Andre Renzaho. "Socio-cultural Issues and Body Image." In *Preventing Childhood Obesity: Evidence, Policy and Practice*, edited by Elizabeth Waters, et al. West Sussex: Blackwell Publishing. Ltd. 2010: 138–146.

May, William E. *Catholic Bioethics and the Gift of Human Life*. Huntington: Our Sunday Visitor Publishing, 3rd ed. 2013.

McCarthy, Charles R. "The Origins and Policies that Govern Institutional Review Boards." In *the Oxford Textbook on Clinical Research Ethics*, edited by Ezekiel J. Emanuel, Christine Grady, Robert A. Crouch, Reidar K. Lie, Franklin G. Miller, David Wendler, Oxford: Oxford University Press. 2008. 541–551.

McDonough, Mary J. *Can a Health Care Market be Moral? A Catholic Vision*. Washington, DC: Georgetown University Press, 2007.

Menzel, Paul T., "The Justification and Implications of Age-Based Rationing." In *Choosing Who's to Live. Ethics and Aging*, edited by James W. Walters. Chicago: University of Illinois Press. 1996: 3–23.

Merriam-Webster Online, http://www.merriam-webster.com/dictionary/secret.

Metcalf, Jacob and Emily F. Keller and Dana Boyd. "Perspectives on Big Data, Ethics and Society." *The Council for Big Data, Ethics and Society.* (May 23, 2016).

Michigan State University. "The Unpopular Truth about Biases toward People with Disabilities." ScienceDaily. July 18, 2029. www.sciencedaily.com/2029/07/90718112453. htm.

Mills, Anne. "Ethics and the Healthcare Organization." In *Managerial Ethics in Healthcare. A New Perspective,* edited by. Gary J. Filerman, Gary Mills, E. and Paul M. Schyve. Chicago: Health Administration Press. 2014: 19–50.

Moore, Adam D. *Privacy Rights. Moral and Legal Foundations.* University Park: The Pennsylvania State University Press, 2010.

Moore, Adam D., ed. *Privacy, Security and Accountability. Ethics, Law and Policy.* London: Roman and Littlefield, 2016.

Moore, Geoff. "Re-imagining the Morality of Management: A Modern Virtue Ethics Approach." In *The Heart of the Good Institution. Virtue Ethics as a Framework for Responsible Management,* edited by Howard Harris, Gayathri Wijesinghe and Stephen McKenzie. 8-9 Netherlands: Springer, 2013: 7–34.

Moraczewski, Albert S. "The Human Person and the Church's Teaching." In *Catholic Health Care Ethics: A Manual for Practitioners,* edited by E. J. Furton, P.J. Cataldo, and A.S, Moraczewski Philadelphia: The National Catholic Bioethics Center, 2009.

Morreim, E. Haavi, *Balancing Act. The New Medcial Ethics of Medicine's New Economics.* Washington: Georgetown University Press, 1995.

Mosher, Paul W. and Jeffrey Berman, *Confidentiality and Its Discontents. Dilemmas of Privacy in Psychotherapy.* New York: Fordham University Press, 2015.

Moskop, John C., Catherine A. Marco, Gregory Luke Larkin, Joel M. Gelderman and Arthur R. Derse. "From Hippocrates to HIPAA: Privacy and Confidentiality in Emergency Medicine – Part I: Conceptual, Moral and Legal Foundations." In *Annals of Emergency Medicine* 43 no.1 (January 2005): 53–59.

Mukherjee, Siddhartha. *The Gene. An Intimate History.* New York: Simon and Schuster, Inc., 2016.

Mullin, Amy. "Children, Vulnerability, and Emotional Harm." In *Vulnerability. New Essays in Feminine Philosophy,* edited by Catriona MacKenzie, Wendy Rogers and Susan Dodds. New York: Oxford University Press, 2014: 266–287.

Muscular Dystrophy Association. May 2, 2020. https://www.mda.org/disease/ becker-muscular- dystrophy/medical-management.

National Commission for the Protection of Human Subjects of Biomedical and Behavioral Research. "The Belmont Report. Ethical Principles and Guidelines for the Protection of Human Subjects of Research." April 18, 1979.

National Research Council, *Understanding Child Abuse and Neglect.* Washington, D. C.: The National Academies Press, 1993: 324–342.

National Science Foundation, Solicitation 12–299: *Core Technologies for Advancing Big Data Science and Engineering (BIG DATA),* 2012, http://www.nsf.gov/publs/2012/ nsf12499/nsf12499.pdf.

Negriff, Sonya, editor. *Child Maltreatment, Research, Policy, and Practice. Contributions of Penelope K. Trickett.* Los Angeles: Springer, 2018.

Ndebele, Paul. "Research Ethics." In *The SAGE Handbook of Health Care Ethics: Core and Emerging Issues,* edited by Ruth Chadwick, Henk ten Have, and Eric M. Meslin, London: SAGE Publications, Inc. 2011: 306–325.

Newell, Christopher, "'What's Wrong with You?' Disability and Genes as Ethics." in *Theology, Disability and the New Genetics. Why Science Needs the Church.* edited by John Swinton and Brian Brock. New York: T&T Clark. 2007: 44–56.

Ninkovich, Jordan. *Epidemic: Obesity. Harassment. Bullying A Survivor's Story.* Lincoln: iUniverse, 2006, 7.

Noddings, Nel. *Caring: A Relational Approach to Ethics in Moral Education.* Berkeley: University of California Press. 2013.

Noddings, Nel. *The Maternal Factor. Two Paths to Morality.* Berkeley: University of California Press. 2010.

Noel-Miller, Claire. "Medicare Beneficiaries' Out-of-Pocket Spending for Health Care." In *Insight on the Issues.* AARP Public Policy. June 2020. https://doi.org/10.26419/ppi.00105.

Nuffield Council on Bioethics. *Public Health: Ethical Issues.* November 2007.

Oath and Law of Hippocrates (circa 400 B.C.) In *Harvard Classics* 38. Boston: P.F. Collier & Son, 1910, accessed November 23, 2017. http:www.cirp.org/library/ethics/Hippocrates/.

O'Brien, Ruth. *Crippled Justice. The History of Modern Disability Policy in the Workplace.* Chicago: The University of Chicago Press, 2001.

O'Brien, William J. *Character at Work. Building Prosperity through the Practice of Virtue.* Mahwah: Paulist Press, 2008.

OECD, *Obesity Update* 2017. http://www.oecd.org/healthy/obesity-update.htm.

O'Keefe, Katherine and Daragh O. Brien. *Ethical Data and Information Management. Concepts, Tools and Methods.* London: Kogan Page Limited, 2018.

O'Sullivan, Ann and Regula H. Robnett, "Living Options and the Continuum of Care." In *Gerontology for the Health Care Professional,* 2nd edition, edited by Regula H. Robnett and Walter C. Chop, Sudbury: Jones and Bartlett Publishers, 2010: 259–283.

Ohm, Paul. "Changing the Rules: General Principles for Data Use and Analysis." In *Privacy, Big Data and the Public Good,* edited by Julia Lane, Victoria Stodden, Stefan Bender, and Helen Nissenbaum, New York: Cambridge University Press, 2014.

Oliver, Michael. *Understanding Disability from Theory to Practice.* 2nd ed., New York: St. Martin's Press, 1996.

Oliver, Paul, *The Student's Guide to Research Ethics.* 2nd ed., Berkshire: McGraw Hill Education. Open University Press, 2010.

Orimo, Hajime, Hideki Ito, Takao Suzuki, Atsuchi Araki, Takayuki Hosoi, and Motoji Sawabe, "Reviewing the Definition of 'Elderly'." In Geriatrics and Gerontology International February 2006. doi: 10.1111/j-1447-0594-2006.00341.x.

Ouellette, Alicia. *Bioethics and Disability. Toward a Disability-Conscious Bioethics.* New York: Cambridge University Press. 2011.

Paddock, Catherine. "Obesity Linked to Type 2 Diabetes by an Absent Protein." *Medical News Today,* July 7, 2014. http://www.medicalnewstoday.com/articles/279129.php.

Parasidis, Efthimios. "The Future of Pharmacovigilance. Big Data and the False Claims Act." In *Big Data, Health Law and Bioethics,* edited by I. Glenn Cohen, Holly Fernandez Lynch, Effy Vayena and Urs Gasser, New York: Cambridge University Press, 2018: 73–84.

Parikh, Ravi B, Ziad Obermeyer, and David Westfall Bates, MD, "Making Predictive Analytic a Routine Part of Patient Care," in *Harvard Business Review* (April 21, 2016) accessed September 9, 2017.

Patterson, Barbara A.B., "Redeemed Bodies: Fullness of Life." In *Human Disability and the Service of God. Reassessing Religious Practice,* edited by Nancy L. Eisland and Don E. Saliers. Nashville: Abingdon Press, 1998: 123–143.

Pearson, Steven D., James E. Sabin and Ezekiel J. Emanuel. *No Margin, No Mission. Health Care Organizations and Quest for Ethical Excellence.* New York: Oxford Press, 2003.

Peckham, Stephen and Alison Hann, eds. *Public Health Ethics and Practice.* Bristol: The Policy Press, 2010.

Peckins, Melissa K., Sonya Negriff, Jonathan M. Reader, and Elizabeth J. Susman, "Perception of Maltreatment: Gender-Specific Mental Health Outcomes Associated with Maltreatment ad Most Upsetting Experience." In *Child Maltreatment, Research, Policy and Practice. Contributions of Penelope K. Trickett.* Los Angeles: Springer, 2018: 27–47.

Pelligrino, Edmund D. "Codes, Virtue, and Professionalism." In *Methods in Medical Ethics, 2nd edition,* edited by Jeremy Sugarman and Daniel P. Sulmasy. Washington, DC: Georgetown University Press, 2010: 91–107

Perryman, Mandy L. and Kara A. Sidoti. "Ethical Considerations in the Treatment of Obesity." In *Medicolegal and Bioethics* 5 (2015): 17–26.

Peters, Ted. "Progress and Provolution. Will Transhumanism Leave Sin Behind." In *Transhumanism and Transcendence. Christian Hope in the Age of Technological Enhancement,* edited by Ron Cole-Turner. Washington, DC: Georgetown University Press, 2011: 65–86.

Petronio, Sandra, Mark J. DiCorcia, and Ashley Duggan. "Navigating Ethics of Physician-Patient Confidentiality: A Communication Privacy Management Analysis," in *The Permanente Journal* 16(4), (December 2012):41–45.

Phillips, Robert. A. *Stakeholder Theory and Organizational Ethics.* San Francisco: Berrett-Koehler Publishers, Inc., 2003.

Pioneer Network. *Continuum of Person Directed Culture,* accessed February 19, 2019. https://www.pioneernetwork.netabout- us/overview/.

Plummer, Carol. "Cultural Considerations in Prevention of Child Abuse and Neglect." In *Research and Practices in Child Maltreatment and Prevention. Societal, Organizational, and International Approaches.* vol. ii. Randell Alexander. St. Louis: STM Learning, Inc. 2017: 283–299.

Pollack, Andrew. "A.M.A. Recognizes Obesity as a Disease." In *The New York Times.* (June 19, 2013): B1.

Pope, Thaddeus Mason. "Certified Patient Aids: Solving Persistent Problems with Informed Consent Law." In *The Journal of Law, Medicine and Ethics* 24 (2017): 12–40.

Porter, Joan P. and Greg Koski, "Regulations for the Protection of Humans in Research in the United States." In *The Oxford Textbook of Clinical Research Ethics.* Edited by Ezekiel J. Emanuel, Christine Grady. Robert A. Crouch, Reider K. Lie, Franklin G. Miller and David Wendler Oxford: Oxford University Press. 2008:156–167.

Post, Linda Farber, Jeffrey Bluestein and Nancy Neveloff Dubler. *Handbook for Health Care Ethics Committee.* Baltimore: The Johns Hopkins University Press, 2007.

Powell, Alvin. "Obesity? Diabetes? We've been set up." In *The Harvard Gazette.* (March 7, 2012): news.harvard.edu/gazette/story/2012/03/the-big-setup/.

Prainsack, Barbara. "DIY Genetics: The Right to Know Your Own Genome." In *The Right to Know and the Right Not to Know. Genetic Privacy and Responsibility.* 2nd edition, edited by Ruth Chadwick, Mairi Levitt and Darren Shickle. Cambridge: Cambridge University Press, 2014: 100–115.

Presidential Commission for the Study of Bioethical Issues. *Privacy and Progress in Whole Genome Sequencing.* October 2012.

Purves, Duncan, Ryan Jenkins, Bradley J. Strawser. "Autonomous Machines, Moral Judgement, and Acting for the Right Reasons." In *Ethical Theory Moral Practice* 18 (2015): 1–2.

Pyles, Robert L., "The American Psychoanalytic Association's Fight for Privacy." In *Confidentiality. Ethical Perspectives and Clinical Dilemmas*, edited by Charles Levin, Allannah Furlong, and Mary Kay O'Neill. New York: The Analytic Press, 2012: 252–264.

Rahill, Guitele J., Manisha Joshi, and Celia M. Lescano, "Cultural Considerations for Pediatric HIV Research and Practice." In *A Clinical Guide to Pediatric HIV. Bridging the Gaps Between Research and Practice*. Edited by Tiffany Chenneville. Cham: Springer International Press, 2016: 259–271.

Reinders, Hans S. "Life's Goodness: On Disability, Genetics and Choice." In *Theology, Disability and the New Genetics. Why Science Needs the Church*, edited by John Swinton and Brian Brock, New York: T&T Clark, 2007: 163–181.

Reis, Samuel, Aya Biderman, Revital Mitki, and Jeffrey M. Borkan. "Secrets in Primary Care: A Qualitative and Conceptual Model." In *Society of General Medicine* 22 (2007): 1246– 1253.

Reynolds, Joel Michael. "Three Things Clinicians Should Know About Disability." In *AMA Journal of Ethics* 20 (December 2018): E1181–1187.

Rhodes, Rosamond. "When is Participation in Research a Moral Duty?" In *The Journal of Law, Medicine and Ethics* 45 (2017): 318–326.

Rich, Carrie R., J. Knox Singleton, and Seema S. Wadhwa. "Introduction to Environmental and Sustainability Issues in Health Care Management." In *Managerial Ethics in Healthcare. A New Perspective*. Edited by Gary J.

Richard, Claude. "Therapeutic Privilege: Between the Ethics of Lying and the Practice of Truth." In *The Journal of Medical Ethics*. 36 no.6 (June 2010): 353–357.

Robinson, Walter M. and Brandon T. Unruh. "The Hepatitis Experiment at Willowbrook State School." In *The Oxford Textbook of Clinical Research Ethics*, edited by Ezekiel J. Emanuel, Christine Grady. Robert A. Crouch, Reider K. Lie, Franklin G. Miller and David Wendler Oxford: Oxford University Press. 2008; 80–85.

Robnett, Regula H. "The Cognitive and Psychological Changes Associated with Aging," In *Gerontology for the Health Care Professional*. 2nd edition, edited by Regula H. Robnett and Walter C. Chop. Sudbury: Jones and Bartlett Publishers, 2010: 115–153.

Robnett, Regula H. and Walter C. Chop. Eds. *Gerontology for the Health Care Professional*. 2nd edition. Sudbury: Jones and Bartlett Publishers, 2010.

Rodwin, Marc A. *Conflicts of Interest and the Future of Medicine. The United States, France and Japan*. New York: Oxford University Press, 2011.

Rogers, Wendy. "Vulnerability and Bioethics." In *Vulnerability. New Essays in Ethics and Feminine Philosophy*. edited by Catriona Mackenzie, Wendy Rogers and Susan Dodds. New York: Oxford University Press, 2014: 60–87.

Rolheiser, Ronald. *Against and Infinite Horizon. The Finger of God in our Everyday Lives*. New York: The Crossroad Publishing Company, 2001.

Rosen, George. *The History of Public Health*. Baltimore: Johns Hopkins University Press. 1993.

Rosenstein, Donald and Franklin G. Miller, "Research Involving Those at Risk for Impaired Decision-Making Capacity." In *The Oxford Textbook of Clinical Research Ethics*, edited by Ezekiel J. Emanuel, Christine Grady. Robert A. Crouch, Reider K. Lie, Franklin G. Miller and David Wendler Oxford: Oxford University Press. 2008: 437–445.

Ross, Alec. *Industries of the Future*. New York: Simon and Schuster, 2016.

Ross, Lainie Friedman. *Children in Medical Research. Access versus Protection*. New York: Oxford University Press. 2006.

Rothstein, Mark A. "The Effects of Health Information Technology on the Physician-Patient Relationship: The Hippocratic Bargain and Health Information Technology." In *The Journal of Law, Medicine and Ethics* 38 (Spring 2010): 7–13.

Rothstein, Mark A. and Meghan K. Tulbott. "Compelled Disclosures of Health Records: Updated Estimates." In *The Journal of Law, Medicine and Ethics* 45 (Spring 2017): 149–155.

Sabharwal, Sabhyta, Jason W. Mitchell, and Victoria Y. Fan, "Should There Be a Disclosure Mandate for Physicians Caring for Perinatally Infected Adolescents Who Don't Know There HIV Serostatus?" In *AMA Journal of Ethics* 20 (August 2019): E742–749.

Samuel, Julie, Bartha Maris Knoppers, and Denise Avard. "Medical Research Involving Children: A Review of International Policy Statements." In *The SAGE Handbook of Health Care Ethics: Core and Emerging Issues* edited by Ruth Chadwick, Henk ten Have and Erick M. Meslin. London: SAGE Publications Ltd. 2011: 261–277.

Sandel, Michael J. *The Case Against Perfection. Ethics in the Age of Genetic Engineering.* Cambridge: The Belknap Press of Harvard University Press. 2007.

Sargeant, Jonathon and Deborah Harcourt. *Doing Ethical Research with Children.* Maidenhead: McGraw Hill/Open University, 2012.

Sawicki, Nadia N. "Informed Consent as Societal Stewardship." In *The Journal of Law, Medicine and Ethics* 45 (Spring 2017): 40–41.

Scanlon, Valeria C., and Tina Sanders. *Essentials of Anatomy and Physiology.* 7th ed. Philadelphia: F.A. Davis Company. 2015.

Schick, Thomas A. "The Ethics of Keeping Corporate Secrets." In *Public Relations Strategist*, 4.2 (Summer 1998): 29–32.

Schmidt, Charles. "Pediatric Predicament." In *Scientific American* 317 (September 2017): 24–25.

Schneier, Bruce. *Data and Goliath. The Hidden Battles to Collect your Data and Control Your World.* New York: W.W. Norton Company, Inc. 2015.

Schroder-Butterfill, Elisabeth and Ruly Marianti, "A Framework for Understanding Old-Age Vulnerabilities." In *Ageing Society* 26(1) (January 2006): 9–35. https://doi: 10.1017/S0144686X05004423.

Scully, Jackie Leach. "Disability and Vulnerability: On Bodies, Dependence, and Power." In *Vulnerability. New Essays in Ethics and Feminist Philosophy.* Edited by Catriona MacKenzie, Wendy Rogers, and Susan Dodds. New York: Oxford University Press. 2014: 204–221.

Scully, Jackie Leach. *Disability Ethics. Moral Bodies, Moral Difference.* Lanham: Rowman and Littlefield Publishers, Inc. 2008.

Seegert, Liz. "U.S. Ranks Worse in Elder Care vs. Other Wealthy Nations." In *Association of Health Care Journalists. Center for Excellence in Health Care Journalism.* November 15, 2017, accessed December 26, 2019. https://healthjournalism.org.

Shanley, Agnes. "The Future of Pharma. Innovating in a Value-Based World." In *Pharmaceutical Technology.* May 2017, 16–23. PharmTech.com.

Shore, David A. *The Trust Crisis in Healthcare. Causes, Consequences and Cures.* New York: Oxford University Press, 2007.

Shrivastava, Saurabh Ram Bihar Lal, Prateek Saurabh Shrivastava, and Jegadeesh Ramasamy, "Health-care of Elderly: Derminants, Needs and Services." In *International Journal of Preventive Medicine,* 10 (October 3, 2013): 1224–1225.

Shuman, Daniel W. "Legal Boundaries on Conceptions of Privacy: Seeking Therapeutic Accord." In *Confidentiality. Ethical Perspectives and Clinical Dilemmas.* New York: The Analytical Press, Inc. 2012: 265–275.

Siebers, Tobin. *Disability Theory*. Ann Arbor: The University of Michigan Press. 2008.

Silve-Sanigorski, Andrea M., and Christina Economos. "Evidence of Multi-Setting Approaches for Obesity Prevention: Translation to Best Practices." In *Preventing Childhood Obesity: Evidence, Policy and Practice*. Edited by Elizabeth Waters, Boyd Swindburn, Jacob Seidel, and Ricardo Uauy. West Sussex: Blackwell Publishing, Ltd. 2010: 57–63.

Simborg, Donald W. "Promoting Electronic Health Record Adoption. Is it the Correct Focus?" In *Journal of American Informatics Association* 12 (2) (March-April 2008): 127–129.

Slepian, Michael L., Jinseok S. Chun, and Malia F. Mason. "The Experience of Secrecy." In *The Journal of Personality and Social Psychology* 113 (1) (July 2017): 1–33.

Smith II, George P. *The Elderly and Health Care Rationing*. 7 Pierce L. Rev. 171. (2009).

Solbakk, Jan Helge. "Vulnerability: A Futile or Useful Principle in Healthcare Ethics?" In *The SAGE Handbook of Health Care Ethics: Core and Emerging Issues*, edited by Ruth Chadwick, Henk ten Have, and Eric M. Meslin, London: SAGE Publications, Inc. 2011: 228–250.

Solove, Daniel J. *Privacy and Power: Computer Databases and Metaphors for Information Privacy*. 53 Stan. L. Rev. 1393. (2008).

Solove, Daniel J. *Understanding Privacy*. Cambridge: Harvard University Press. 2008.

Solove, Daniel J. and Paul M. Schwartz. *Information Privacy Law*. 6th edition. New York: Wolters Kluver. 2018.

Solove, Daniel J. and Paul M. Schwartz. *Privacy Law Fundamentals 2017*. Portsmouth: IAPP. 2017.

Song, Robert. "Fragility and Grace; Theology and Disability." In *Theology, Disability and the New Genetic*, edited by John Swinton and Robert Brock. New York: T&T Clark, 2007.

Span, Paula. "A Nursing Home that Feels, Well, Homey." In *The New York Times*. (December 26, 2017): D5.

Spencer, Edward M, Anne E. Mills, Mary V. Rorty and Patricia H. Werhane. *Organization Ethics in Health Care*. New York: Oxford University Press, 2000.

Staff, Rowena Lindsay. "What will Artificial Intelligence Look Like in 15 Years?" In *Christian Science Monitor*. September 6, 2016.

Stillman, William. *Autism and the God Connection. Redefining the Autistic Experience through Extraordinary Accounts of Spiritual Giftedness*. Naperville: Sourcebooks, Inc. 2006.

Stodden, Victoria. "Enabling Reproducibility in Big Data Research: Balancing Confidentiality and Scientific Transparency." In *Privacy, Big Data and the Public Good*, edited by Julia Lane, Victoria Stodden, Stefan Bender, and Helen Nissenbaum, New York: Cambridge University Press. 2014: 112–132.

Stoll, Clifford. BrainyQuote.com, Xplore, Inc. accessed April 30, 2017. http://brainyquote. com/quotes/quotes/c/ccliffordst212166.html,

Strandburg, Katherine J. "Monitoring, Datafication and Consent: Legal Approaches to Privacy in the Big Data Context." In *Privacy, Big Data and the Public Good. Frameworks for Engagement*. Edited by Julia Lane, Victoria Stodden, Stefan Bender, and Helen Nissenbaum, New York: Cambridge University Press. 2014: 5–43.

Sugarman, Jeremy and Daniel P. Sulmasy. *Methods in Medical Ethics*, 2nd edition. Washington, DC: Georgetown University Press, 2010.

Sulmasy, Daniel P. and Jeremy. "The Many Methods of Medical Ethics, (Or, Thirteen Ways of Looking at a Blackbird." In *Methods in Medical Ethics*, 2nd edition. Washington, DC: Georgetown University Press, 2010: 3–19.

Sundelson, David. "Outing the Victim: Breached Confidentiality in the Ethics Procedure," In *Confidentiality. Ethical Perspectives and Clinical Dilemmas*. Edited by Charles Levin, Allannah Furlong, and Mary Kay O'Neill. New York: The Analytic Press, 2012.

Susman, Elizabeth, J., Jennie G. Noll and Karen Appleyard Carmody. "The Contribution of Penelope K. Trickett to the Study of Child Maltreatment." In *Child Maltreatment, Research, Policy and Practice. Contributions of Penelope K. Trickett*. Edited by Sonya Negriff. Los Angeles: Springer. 2018: 1–9.

Swazey, Judith P. *Merger Games. The Medical College of Pennsylvania, Hahnemann University, and the Rise and Fall of the Allegheny Health Care System*. Philadelphia: Temple University Press. 2013.

Swinton, John and Brian Brock. eds. *Theology, Disability and the New Genetics. Why Science Needs the Church*. New York: T&T Clarke. 2007.

Tarasoff v. Regents of the University of California, 551 P.2d 333 (1976).

Teach, S.J., J.W. St. Germe, "The Indirect Effects of COVID-19 on Pediatric Research." *Pediatric Research* (2021). https:doi.org/10.1038/s41390-021-01563-x.

Tellis-Nayak, V. and Mary Tellis-Nayak. *Return of Compassion to Health Care*. New York: Page Publishing, Inc. 2016.

Ten Have, Marieke, Ines de Beaufort and Soren Holm. "No Country for Fat Children? Ethical Questions Concerning Community Community-Based Programs to Prevent Obesity." In *Preventing Childhood Obesity: Evidence, Policy and Practice*. Edited by Elizabeth Waters, et al. West Sussex: Blackwell Publishing, Ltd. 2010: 31–39.

Thorpe, Jane Hyatt, Elizabeth A. Gray and Lara Cartwright-Smith, "Show Us the Data: The Critical Role Health Information Plays in Health System Transformation," In *Journal of Law, Medicine and Ethics*, 44 (2016): 592–597.

Tomlinson, Craig. "The Early History of the Concept of Confidentiality in Psychoanalysis," In *Confidentiality. Ethical Perspectives and Clinical Dilemmas*, edited by Charles Levin, Allannah Furlong and Mary Kay O'Neill. New York: The Analytic Press, 2012: 139–149.

"Total Medical Spending from 1970-2018." https://www.statista.com.

Tricker, Bob, and Gretchen Tricker. *Business Ethics. A Stakeholder, Governance, and Risk Approach*. London: Routledge, 2014.

UNAIDS. *AIDS by the Numbers*. http://ww.unaids.org/sites/default/files/media (2019)

U.S. Food and Drug Administration, http://fda.gov/drugs/drug-information-consuerts/drug- research-and-children.

U.S. Department of Commerce Economics and Statistics Administration, United States Census Bureau. *Population*. Washington DC, June 25, 2018.

U.S. Department of Commerce Economics and Statistics Administration, United States Census Bureau. *Subjective Well-Being of Eldercare Providers: 2012-2013*. Washington DC, February 2018.

U.S. Department of Health and Human Services. Additional Protection for Children Involved as Subjects in Research. *Federal Register* 56 (June 18, 1991) Regulation at 45 CFR 46 Subpart D.

U.S. Department of Health and Human Services. Administration for Community Living. 2017 Profile of Older Americans. April 2018.

U.S. Department of Health and Human Services. Centers for Disease Control and Prevention. Data Statistics on Autism Spectrum Disorder. September 3, 2019.

U.S. Department of Health and Human Services. Centers for Disease Control and Prevention. Division of HIV/AIDS Prevention, National Center for HIV/AIDS. August 14, 2019.

U.S. Department of Health and Human Services. Centers for Disease Control and Prevention. "Estimated Prevalence of Children with Diagnosed Disabilities in the United states, 2014-2016." NCHS Data Brief No. 291. November 2017.

U.S. Department of Health and Human Services. Centers for Medicare and Medicaid Services. 42 CFR §§ 430-447. March 17, 2014.

U.S. Department of Health and Human Services. Child Welfare Information Gateway. Child Maltreatment 2019: Summary of Key Findings, Numbers and Trends. April 2021. https://www/childwelfare.gov/pubs/factsheets/canstats/.

U.S. Department of Health and Human Services, "Examining Oversight of the Privacy and Security of Health Data Collected by Entities Not Regulated by HIPAA." June 16, 2016.

U.S. Department of Health and Human Services. Office for Civil Rights. Regulation text. 45 CFR Parts 160, 162 and 164. December 28, 2000, as amended through March 26, 2013. Accessed June 17, 2017 http://www.hhs.gov/ocr/combinedreg-text.pdf.

U.S. Department of Health and Human Services, Office for Civil Rights, Summary of the HIPAA Privacy Rule. Accessed June 16. 2017 http://www.hhs.gov/ocr/privacysummary.org

U.S. Department of Health and Human Services. Office of Disease Prevention and Health Promotion. Disability and Health. Healthy People 2020. Accessed May 16, 2020. http://www.healthypeople.gov/2020/data-search.

U.S. Department of Health and Human Services. Office of the National Coordinator for Health Information Technology. 21st Century Cures Act: Interoperability, Information Blocking, and the ONC Health IT Certification Program, 45. C.F.R. Parts 170 and 171. May 1, 2020.

U.S. Equal Employment Opportunity Commission, "Resources for Human Development Settles EEOC Disability Suite for $125,000." April 10, 2012. http://www.eeoc.gov/eeoc/newsroom/release/4-10-12a.cfm.

Van Dongen, Els, and Sylvia Fainzang. "Lying, Misery and Illness: Towards a Medical Anthropology of the Lie." In *Anthropology and Medicine* 9 no.2 (2002): 85–95

Van Geel, Mitch, Paul Vedder and Jerry Tamilon, "Relationship between Peer Victimization, Cyberbullying and Suicide in Children and Adolescents. A Meta-Analysis." JAMA *Pediatrics* http://www.jamanetwork.com/journals/jamapediatrics/fullarticle/184020.

Vanlaere, Linus, and Chris Gastmans. "A Personalist Approach to Care Ethics." In *Nurse Ethics* 18 (2011): 161–173. doi:10.1177/0969733010388924.

Verizon. 2015 Protected Health Information Data Breach Report.

Verizon. 2017 Data Breach Investigation Report.

Volpe, Rebecca, Maria Baker, George F. Blackall, Gordon Kauffman, and Michael J. Green. "A Case of Deceptive Mastectomy." In *Narrative Inquiry in Bioethics* 3.2 (2013) 175–191.

Wallenhorst, John. "Ethics and Governance." In *Managerial Ethics in Healthcare. A New Perspective*, edited by Gary J. Filerman, Ann E. Mills, and Paul M. Shyve. Chicago: Health Administration Press, 2014: 51–77.

Walsh, Christine and Harriet MacMillan, "Conducting Research in Child Maltreatment: Problems and Prospects." In *Ethical Issues in Community-Based Research with Children and Youth*, edited by Bonne Leadbeater, Elizabeth Baniser, Celcila Benoit, Mikael Jansson, Anne Marshall, and Ted Riccken. Toronto: University of Toronto Press. 2006: 190–206.

Walters, James W., editor. *Choosing Who's to Live. Ethics and Aging*. Chicago: University of Illinois. 1996.

Warren, Jacob C. and K. Bryant Smalley. *Always the Fat Kid. The Truth About the Enduring Effects of Childhood Obesity.* New York: Palgrave Macmillan, 2013.

Warren. Samuel D. and Louis D. Brandeis. *The Right to Privacy.* 4 Harv. L. Rev, 193. (1890).

Wasserman, David. "Ethical Constraints on Allowing or Causing the Existence of People with Disabilities." In *Disability and Disadvantage*, edited by Kimberly Brownlee and Adam Cureton, Adam. Oxford: Oxford University Press. 2009: 319–351.

Wassom, Brian. *Augmented Reality Law, Privacy and Ethics. Law, Society and Emerging AR Technologies.* Waltham: Elsevier, Inc. 2015.

Waters, Elizabeth, et al. eds. *Preventing Childhood Obesity: Evidence Policy and Practice.* West Sussex: Blackwell Publishing, Ltd. 2010.

Weber, Leonard J., "The Healthcare Organization as an Employer: The Demands of Fairness and the Healthcare Organization," In *Managerial Ethics in Healthcare. A New Perspective*, edited by Gary J. Filerman, Ann E. Mills, and Paul M. Shyve. Chicago: Health Administration Press, 2014: 177–194.

Weindling, Paul J. "The Nazi Medical Experiments." In *The Oxford Textbook of Clinical Research Ethics*, edited by Ezekiel J. Emanuel, Christine Grady, Robert A.Crouch, Reider K. Lie, Franklin G. Miller, and David Wendler. Oxford: Oxford University Press, 2008: 18–30.

Weiss, Joseph W. *Business Ethics: A Stakeholder and Issues Management Approach. Cases, Principles and Practices.* 6th ed. San Francisco: Berrett-Koehler Publishers, Inc. 2014.

Werhane, Patricia H. "The Healthcare Organization, Business Ethics and Stakeholder Perspective." In *Managerial Ethics in Healthcare. A New Perspective*, edited by Gary J. Filerman, Ann E. Mills, and Paul M. Shyve. Chicago: Health Administration Press, 2014: 79–94.

Westin, Alan F. *Privacy and Freedom.* Portsmouth: IAPP, 2014.

Wiener, Lori, Claude Ann Mellins, Stephanie Marhefka, and Haven B. Battles. "Disclosure of HIV Diagnosis to Children: History, Current Research and Future Directions" In *The Journal of Developmental Behavioral Pediatrics.* 28 (2) (April 2007): 155–166.

Wilcox, Tracy. "Embedded Moral Agency: A MacIntyrean Perspective on the HR Professional's Dilemma." In *The Heart of the Good Institution. Virtue Ethics as a Framework for Responsible Management*, edited by Howard Harris, Gayathri Wijesinghe and Stephen McKenzie. 129-140. Netherlands: Springer. 2013: 129–140.

Wilfond, Benjamin S. "Ethical and Policy Implications of Conducting Carrier Testing and Newborn Screening for the Same Condition." In *Ethics and Newborn Genetic Screening. New Technologies, New Challenges*, edited by Mary Ann Baily and Thomas H. Murray. Baltimore: The Johns Hopkins University Press, 2009: 292–311.

Wilkinson, Stephen. *Choosing Tomorrow's Children. The Ethics of Selective Reproduction.* Oxford: Oxford University Press. 2010.

World Health Organization. *Ethics and Governance of Artificial Intelligence for Health.* WHO Guidance. Geneva 2021.

World Health Organization. *Obesity: Preventing and Managing the Global Epidemic.* Report of a WHO Consultation, Geneva 2000.

World Health Organization, *World Report on Disability.* Geneva: WHO Press, 2011.

Wu, Edieth Y. *McFat – Obesity, Parens Patriae, and the Children*, 20 Okla. City U.L. Rev. 569.

Wyman, Mary F., Sharon Shioviz-Ezra, and Jurgen Bengal, "Ageism in the Health Care System: Providers, Patients and Systems." In *Contemporary Perspectives on Ageism.* Edited by L. Ayalon, and C. Tesch-Romer. International Perspectives on Aging, Cham: Springer Open, 2018.

Yan, Eric G. and Kerim M. Munir. "Regulatory and Ethical Principles in Research Involving Children and Individuals with Developmental Disabilities." In *Ethics Behav.* 14(1) (2004): 31-49.

Yarborough, Mark. "Why There is No Obligation to Participate in Clinical Research." In *The Journal of Law, Medicine and Ethics* 45 (2017): 327–332.

Zametikin, Alan, Alanna Jacobs, and Jessica Parrish, "Treatment of Children and Adolescents with Obesity and Comorbid Psychiatric Conditions." In *Issues in Clinical Childhood Psychology. Handbook of Childhood Adolescent Obesity.* Edited by Elissa Jelalian and Ric G. Steele. New York, NY: Springer, 2008: 425–443.

Zeller, Meg and Avan C. Modi. "Psychosocial Factors Related to Obesity in Children and Adolescents." In *Issues in Clinical Childhood Psychology. Handbook of Childhood and Adolescent Obesity.* Edited by Elissa Jelalian and Ric G. Steele, New York, NY: Springer, 2008: 25–42.

Zimmerman, Sheryl, Barbara J. Bowers, Lauren W. Cohen, David C. Grabowski, Susan Horn, Peter, Kemper. "New Evidence on the Green House Model of Nursing Home Care: Synthesis of Findings and Implications for Policy, Practice and Research." In *Health Service Research.* 51 (S1) (February 2016): 475–496.

Zwaigenbaum, Lonnie, Margaret L. Bauman, Roula Choueiri, Connie Kasari, Alice Carter, Doreen Granpeesheh. "Early Intervention for Children with Autism Spectrum Disorder Under 3 Years of Age: Recommendations for Practice and Research." In *Pediatrics* 136 (2015): S60–S81.

Index

Solove, Daniel 32, 47, 49, 61
Sorrell, William: Vermont attorney
general 108
stakeholder: communities 2–3, 20, 25–26,
113–114, 173–174; definition of 22;
derivative 22–23, 59, 63, 139; ethical
accountability to 5, 74; external 19;
internal 75; norms 25, 61, 65; third-
party 32, 45
stakeholder theory: doctrine of fair
contracts 24; ethics of care 21, 23, 26;
fairness 9, 23–24, 26; feminine/feminist
theory 23, 61; individual 11; moral
classification of 22; normative 9, 21–23;
social contract 23–26; stewardship
9, 24–26; value opportunities in
healthcare 3, 23; *see also* Freeman, R.
Edward; moral duty; organizational;
Phillips, Robert; stakeholder
stereotyping 130; research 76
Stevens, John Paul 41
stewardship: and human flourishing 156;
information management 25; *see also*
principles; Roman Catholic tradition;
stakeholder theory
Stillman, William 157
Stoll, Clifford 56
Strawser, Bradley J. 59

*Tarasoff v. Regents of the University of
California* 43, 64; duty to warn 64
technology: and healthcare/medicine 11,
32–33, 35, 49–53, 57–58, 60, 131–132,
151–152, 160; and the human condition
146; and privacy attitudes 49, 59; digital
64; genetic 153–154; interoperable 52;
intrusive 59; *see also* information and
communication technology (ICTs)
Tellis-Nayak, Mary 128, 143
Tellis-Nayak, V. 128, 143
Thomas, Bill, MD 144–145
transparency 15, 42, 52, 61; and trust 34,
63
truth/truth-telling: as a moral imperative
35; autonomy 39, 46; right to be told
46; withholding of 36; *see also* genetic;
moral dilemma; secrecy/secrets
trust: and discernment 14, as a human
value 33; in healthcare 4, 173, in
leadership 16, moral decision-making 20;
patient trust 63, *see also* confidentiality;
organizational; secrecy/secrets
Turner, Deanne E. 91
Tuskegee Syphilis Experiment 79

Type I diabetes *see* cure;
obesity
Type II diabetes *see* obesity

U.S. Department of Health and Human
Services 50–51, 61, 81
U.S. Institute of Medicine 112

value: based decisions 5, 12–13; conflicts/
dissonance 2, 4–6, 11, 13, 38, 59–60, 62,
65, 106; diversity of 23; organizational
15, 61; personal 11, 91, 114; *see also*
confidentiality; privacy; stakeholder theory
Verizon 54
virtue: and policymaking 141, and Roman
Catholic tradition 13–14; human 13;
moral soul 13; of care 128, of leadership
4, 14, 16, 20; virtuous character 10, 13;
see also common morality
vulnerable/vulnerability: accountability
to 5, 74, 78, 114, 128, 174; across the
life continuum 5; and autonomy 89;
and older persons 127; and the human
condition 77, 161–162, 173–174; as a condition of humanity/human life 74, 77;
contextual 5, 77, 89, 91, 128; contingent
77, 89, 91, 100; deferential 89; definition
of 77; effects of authority on 78, 88;
effects of biases on 127; institutional 89;
moral duty to 77, 94, 158, 174; ontological condition 77; pediatric 88; stakeholders 24, 127; universal 77; *see also*
informed consent; moral duty

Warren Jacob C. 98
Warren, Samuel D. 59, 62
Wasserman, David 154
Waymack, Mark H. 139–140
Weber, Leonard J. 139
Wendler, David 87
Westin, Alan 32, 47, 62
Wilkinson, Stephen 152–154, 159
Willowbrook State School 80, 82
Wilson, Mary Ellen: establish civil and
criminal penalties for maltreatment of
children 92
what matters most 1–2, 6, 10, 40, 62, 82,
140–142, 159, 174
World Health Organization (WHO):
Consultation on Obesity report 98;
disability 6, 128, 151 160; ethics of arti-
ficial intelligence 60; good health 41

Yarborough, Mark 83